CONVEX FIGURES

CONVEX FIGURES

I. M. Yaglom and V. G. Boltyanskiĭ

(LIBRARY OF THE MATHEMATICAL CIRCLE-VOLUME 4)

Translated by

PAUL J. KELLY and LEWIS F. WALTON

UNIVERSITY OF CALIFORNIA, SANTA BARBARA

HOLT, RINEHART AND WINSTON New York

И. М. Яглом и В. Г. Болтянский
Выпуклые фигуры
Библиотека математического кружка
Выпуск 4
Государственное издательство
Технико-теоретической литературы
Москва 1951 Ленинград

Translation copyright © 1961 by Holt, Rinehart and Winston, Inc.
Library of Congress Catalog Card Number: 61-7266
2102655
Printed in the United States of America

Dedicated to the memory of an outstanding scholar

L. G. Šnirel'man
(1905-1935)

Foreword to the American Edition

Plane Euclidean geometry introduces the student to deductive reasoning; if he is gifted, it awakens his geometric intuition, one of the sources of mathematical inspiration; and it gives him a sense of historical continuity, because the subject has come down to us from Euclid almost unaltered.

Lately all these merits of plane geometry have been challenged. There are mathematicians who would substitute subjects like elementary group and point set theory for geometry. Are these fields, as far as they can be taught in high school, really as important as the properties of triangles and circles, and are they not exceedingly dull compared with the wealth of ideas accessible to the student in Euclidean geometry? Geometric intuition as a way to mathematical creation is now not infrequently held in low esteem because modern mathematics is believed to be too intricate or sophisticated for direct intuition. Further, historical continuity is considered of minor importance in view of the usefulness of such modern concepts as group theory. It seems highly presumptuous to project our present valuations into the future and to interrupt on this basis a tradition of more than two thousand years. If every, or every second, generation were to take this attitude in the future, the resulting chaos would be inconceivable.

To be sure, few serious mathematicians, if any, would subscribe to these opinions in the strong formulations given here, but an unmistakable tendency in this direction exists. There is no better way of refuting these opinions than to present the public with a book that proves the vitality of plane geometry in a modern setting, strongly uses intuition to arrive at nontrivial results (less trivial in particular than the essentially tautotological arguments of elementary group or set theory), and nevertheless shares with Euclidean geometry its accessibility to intelligent high school students, beginning college students, and high school teachers.

It may be doubted whether such a book can be written, but with *Convex Figures*, Yaglom and Boltyanskiĭ have established the feasibility. They deal with the plane case of the quite active field of convex bodies; their reasoning is predominantly intuitive and provides an introduction to very powerful modern methods of proof, such as continuity arguments, maximum and minimum principles, and applications of Helly's Theorem.

By studying *Convex Figures* a high school teacher will greatly increase his insight and, if the expression is permissible, his pride in Euclidean geometry, while an undergraduate who is a prospective research mathematician will obtain excellent training of his intuition. When he meets the inescapable graduate student who looks down condescendingly on plane geometry, he can easily confound him with a series of nontrivial and appealing facts for whose proof abstract algebra, say, provides no help at all. The mathematically interested undergraduate who does not plan to pursue mathematics beyond his A.B. degree will derive lots of fun from a course or seminar based on the book, and even many mature mathematicians will enjoy perusing it.

However, the book does not fit any pattern familiar in the United States. The translators, Professors Paul J. Kelly and Lewis F. Walton, therefore thought that *Convex Figures* needed to be introduced to the public. It gives me great pleasure to do the honors, because I am convinced that the reader will not be disappointed.

Herbert Busemann

About the American Edition:

In 1956 a German translation of *Convex Figures* was produced and edited by H. Grell, K. Maruhn, and W. Rinow in consultation with the Russian authors. Some supplemental material was added along with additional German references.

The present edition includes these changes and further supplemental text, problems, solutions, and diagrams sent to the translators by the authors. The translators have also added a short note about similitudes, since these are not ordinarily a part of the high school curriculum.

Paul J. Kelly
Lewis F. Walton

Authors' Preface

This book is devoted to certain problems from the theory of convex bodies (see pages 3 and 7 for the definition of a convex body). The theory of convex bodies, which was developed at the end of the last century, is today a science that is rich in general methods and important special results. It is still being intensively investigated.[†] The number of printed scientific articles and books concerned with this subject is so great that the theory of convex bodies occupies a place as an independent mathematical discipline among the other branches of mathematical science in the tables of contents of the modern mathematical reviewing journals in which all mathematical publications are mentioned. This popularity of the theory of convex bodies is related first of all to its importance for geometry, but is also due to the significant applications which it has found in other fields of mathematics (algebra, number theory, etc.) as well as in the natural sciences (for example, mathematical crystallography). The importance of the theory of convex bodies has especially increased since the recent outstanding works of the Leningrad mathematician, A. D. Aleksandrov, who has made this theory the basis of a new development in a very important branch of modern geometry—differential geometry.[§]

The above facts completely justify the publication of popular books on the theory of convex bodies. There is, however, a further circumstance which makes these books especially useful. The theory of convex bodies is the only field of modern mathematics that at no place in its development makes essential use of so-called "higher mathematics." The methods of this theory are especially beautiful and inspired, though far from simple, and yet as a rule are entirely elementary and can be explained to students in the upper classes of high school. This popularity of the theory of convex bodies is related to the fact that the theory is typically "geometric," for, in contrast to other fields of modern geometry, it uses no analytic apparatus and is based directly

[†] A good but rather out-of-date survey of this theory is provided by the work of T. Bonnesen and W. Fenchel entitled, *Theorie der Konvexen Körper* (Theory of Convex Bodies), Ergebnisse der Mathematik und ihrer Grenzgebiete *3*, Berlin, 1934, pp. 1-172.

[§] A. D. Aleksandrov: *Die innere Geometrie der konvexen Flächen* (The interior geometry of convex surfaces). Akademie-Verlag, Berlin, 1955.

vii

on elementary geometric concepts. A good illustration of what has been said is given by the recent book of A. D. Aleksandrov, *Convex Polyhedra*, Moscow-Leningrad, 1950. This monograph is, to be sure, not a popular book designed for a large group of readers; it is, however, in essential parts understandable to advanced students of higher classes. There is a popular book in Russian on the theory of convex bodies which is intended for pupils of advanced classes, for university students in early semesters in mathematics, and for teachers colleges. This is the book of L. A. Lyusternik, *Convex Bodies*, Moscow-Leningrad, 1941. Hence, a special justification is needed for the appearance of a further book on the theory of convex bodies designed for the same group of readers.

Our book takes the form of a collection of exercises with solutions, which distinguishes it markedly from the book of L. A. Lyusternik. It appears in the series *Library of the Mathematical Circle*, and although it differs considerably from the previous books of this series, its basic principles agree with those of its predecessors. The principles have to do first of all with the orientation toward independent, creative work by the reader and are not concerned with passive absorption of the material presented. It is our opinion that, despite the usefulness of reading popular scientific literature, a real inclination toward mathematics can only be developed by independent thinking about mathematical problems. The presentation of the elements of the theory of convex bodies in the form of exercises appears to us particularly appropriate since, thanks to the small amount of knowledge necessary for independent scientific work in this field, such work can begin here relatively early. One of our objectives in writing this book was to provide the essential practice for creative work in the field of the theory of convex bodies.

The choice of the form of a collection of exercises determined also to a high degree the content of the book. In assembling the material we directed our attention chiefly to methods and not to results. Many of the theorems presented in the book are of no great importance in the theory of convex bodies. This fact strikes one especially if one compares this book with the book of L. A. Lyusternik, previously mentioned, which contains the really important facts of this theory. However, it was our goal to illuminate in our book the chief methods of the theory of convex bodies by the use of examples, even if these examples are not particularly essential. In order to contrast various methods appropriately, we often give several proofs for the same theorem.

We have sought to choose exercises which are noteworthy in their formulation and which will appear to the reader as interesting questions. This also explains the emphasis (disproportionate to their scientific value) which this book gives to various definitions of the "center" of an arbitrary convex figure and to the estimation of the "degree of centralness" of convex figures (more exactly one should say the "degree of central symmetry"); see Exercises 2-6b, 2-6c, 2-7a, 3-7, 3-8, 3-10, 6-3. It explains further the detailed exploration of Jung's Theorem regarding the smallest circumcircle of all figures of a given diameter and the attention given to similar theorems (see Exercises 2-4, 2-5, 2-7b, 3-5, 3-9a, 6-1, 6-2) and to curves of constant width and related curves (Sections 7 and 8).

Our attempt to achieve the highest degree of perspicuity is related to the fact that the exercises of the book deal essentially with two-dimensional problems. As a rule the theorems cited in the book about convex figures in the plane can be applied without change in statements and proofs to the case of convex bodies in space, or else, on the other hand, such a transfer causes extreme difficulties. In some cases the corresponding facts for three-dimensional space are presented at the end of the paragraph in the form of a reference and, indeed, without proof. In this connection the contents of this book almost never go beyond the contents of the book by L. A. Lyusternik previously referred to, which is in the main devoted to "three-dimensional" problems. In our book, the theory of convex polyhedra, which represents the most important and most interesting part of the theory of convex bodies, remains completely untouched. This theory is extensively treated in the books by L. A. Lyusternik and A. D. Aleksandrov mentioned above and also in the last chapters of *Exercise Collection in Geometry* by B. N. Delone and O. K. Žitomirskiĭ (Moscow-Leningrad, 1950) and in the cycle of exercises, *Theory of Polyhedra*, in the third part of the book by D. O. Šklyarskiĭ *et al.*, *Selected Exercises and Theorems of Elementary Mathematics*, which has appeared as Volume 3 of the *Library of the Mathematical Circle*.

This book has been written for pupils of the higher classes in secondary schools and for students in the first semester of universities, as well as for all those who love mathematics. It can be used for study in mathematical work groups in secondary schools as well as universities. The presentation assumes nothing beyond high school mathematics, and the largest part of the book can be understood with the background acquired by the eighth grade in a secondary school. Moreover, we have striven in presenting the material to present even an inexperienced reader with as few difficulties as possible, although at some places, in the interest of ready comprehension, we were forced to give up complete rigor. We believe that all necessary steps toward precision can be carried out independently by any student in the middle semester in mathematics at a university or teachers college. To make this work easier, we introduce at the end of the book the rigorous definition of the concept of a plane figure as used in this book (see Appendix II on page 108; the reading of this appendix is, however, not at all necessary for the understandng of the book). We hope that the scholars among our readers will forgive us for certain statements which may shock a person acquainted with analysis.

Before reading the book, it is advisable to read through carefully the instructions for using it. The manuscript was tried out in the work of the proseminars for first-year students at the Moscow State University, under the direction of the first author and in the work of a section of the mathematical students' circle[†] at Moscow State University, under the supervision of the other author. Some of the problems arose in a problem-solving contest which was held for students in earlier semesters at Moscow and Leningrad Universities. Other problems arose in the Mathematical Olympiads in the Moscow schools. In all cases, the problems were completely accessible.

In this book some theorems are quoted which we have not found in the literature. In addition, there is a large number of new proofs of well-known theorems.

Sections 2, 3, 5, and 6 originated with I. M. Yaglom; Section 4 and the appendices were written by V. G. Boltyanskiĭ, Sections 1, 7, and 8 were produced by both authors jointly. The final editing of the common text was carried out jointly by both authors.

In preparing the book we constantly consulted A. M. Yaglom, whose advice concerning the presentation of various places in the book was carefully considered. The first half of the manuscript was carefully examined by L. I. Golovina-Kopeĭkina. Her rigorous criticisms have contributed to the improvement of the book. Numerous comments were given us by A. D. Aleksandrov and his students I. YA. Bokeľman, YU. A. Volkov, and YU. G. Rešetnyak. Many defects of exposition in the text and inaccuracies in the figures were removed on the initiative of the editor of the book, A. Z. Ryvkin. We regard it as our pleasant duty to express our sincere thanks to all these persons.

Moscow,   I. M. Yaglom
March 1951   V. G. Boltyanskiĭ

† The mathematical students' circle at Moscow University owes its existence to L. G. Sňirel'man, to whom this book is dedicated.

CONTENTS

Suggestions for Using This Book

This book consists of two parts. In the first part, 121 exercises on convex figures are stated, together with the definitions and basic theory necessary for understanding the problems. The second part presents the solutions of these exercises.

The contents of the book are divided into eight sections which are somewhat independent. Moreover, the book has also two special appendices. Each section begins with a brief introduction in fine print in which are listed the numbers of those exercises in the previous sections that can be used in solving the problems of the section about to be studied.

Just as in most other collections of exercises, it is possible here, in one section or another, to solve the exercises in any order that suits the taste of the reader, since the solutions of only relatively few exercises depend on previous ones of the same section. However, it appears to us to be most desirable to solve the exercises in the order in which they are presented (leaving out those in whose solution the reader is unsuccessful). In presenting the exercises in each section we have striven to arrange them so that they represent a certain complete unit. Also, in each section as a rule the easier examples precede the more difficult ones. At certain places in the book there are so-called "auxiliary exercises," which are designed to make it easier for the reader to solve the more difficult exercises that immediately follow.

In this book, the more difficult material, for whose grasp a greater familiarity with mathematical processes is necessary, appears in fine print. We advise beginners to omit such material on a first reading (including the two appendices, which are intended particularly for students in universities or teachers colleges). Likewise, all footnote references to Appendix I are to be disregarded by beginners. For the rest there is nothing in the entire contents of the book which requires of the reader more knowledge than is contained in the secondary school curriculum. Thus, even the text in fine print can be understood by a beginner if he manifests the necessary persistence.

Each section contains explanatory text and figures. Before a reader becomes occupied with an exercise, he should become completely familiar with the preceding textual explanation. The exercises are on the average rather difficult, and to solve them will require much time.

One should read the solution in the book only after the exercise has been solved independently, so that the solution found by the reader may be compared with that in the text, or when repeated efforts to obtain a solution have been unsuccessful.

If the reader decides not to return to a given section, he should still read the remaining unsolved exercises in that section in order to obtain an insight into the contents of the section as a whole. Of course, one can alternate working on the exercises in one section with working on those in another.

Those exercises which seemed to the authors particularly difficult have been especially designated. Difficult exercises are starred and the most difficult ones are marked with two asterisks. This designation of the more difficult exercises is to be taken with the reservation that it is no absolute criterion, since no exact measure of the degree of difficulty of an exercise exists. (As is well known, unsolved problems always appear difficult, while problems that have been solved seem easy.)

The present book need not be used entirely as an exercise collection. Thus one can read the solution immediately after reading the statement of an exercise. Although this procedure does not accord with the basic idea of the book, nevertheless it can be valuable, since the book presents a succession of interesting problems from the theory of convex curves. For such a purpose, Sections 5 and 7 are recommended (less so the more difficult Section 6).

The reading of the book should begin with Section 1, which contains all concepts necessary for the material that follows. This section is of an introductory character; hence one need not linger over it. After Section 1, one can continue with Sections 2, 5, or 7. So that the reader may better appreciate the most interesting exercises of Section 3 (Exercises 3-5, 3-7, 3-9a, and 3-10), we recommend the reading of Section 3 after Section 2. Likewise, it is advisable to read Section 6 (the apparently most difficult one in the book) after Section 5, and Section 8 after Section 7. Finally, Section 4 is an auxiliary one; it is best to read it after studying Sections 6 or 8 so that one can immediately apply the material of Section 4 to theorems having richer content. In addition, one should study parts of Section 4 before attempting the exercises in other sections in which the concepts of Section 4 are used.

It seems to us that Sections 7 and 8 are best suited to awaken the interest of the reader because of the elegance of the definitions and the unified formulation of an entire sequence of theorems. As regards the importance of the concepts, one should mention those in Section 5 first and next those in Section 6. The easiest section of the book is obviously Section 2.

At many places in our presentation we have stated certain open questions. Most of them are probably extremely difficult; however, it may happen that some of them will be solved by readers of this book.

In the introductions to certain sections, some supplementary references are given which may be interesting and useful. After the reader has worked through the present book, we recommend that he undertake the reading of the books *Convex Bodies* by L. A. Lyusternik and *Convex Polyhedra* by A. D. Aleksandrov, which are mentioned in the Preface. We refer the German reader to E. Steinitz, *Vorlesungen über die Theorie der Polyeder*, Berlin 1934, or to W. Blaschke, *Kreis und Kugel*, Berlin 1956. Also of interest is the book by L. Fejes-Tóth, *Lagerungen in der Ebene, auf der Kugel und im Raum,*Berlin 1953, which is closely related to the theory of convex figures. However, the last two books assume a knowledge of higher mathematics.[†]

[†] Translators' note. The book of H. Hadwiger *Vorlesungen über Inhalt, Oberfläche und Isoperimetrie* (Springer-Verlag, Berlin-Göttingen-Heidelberg, 1958) is also of interest. It covers from an advanced viewpoint many of the topics of the present book.

EXERCISES

GENERAL PROPERTIES
OF CONVEX FIGURES

This section is of an introductory character; it contains the basic definitions that are used in the book and simple exercises to illustrate these definitions. These exercises may seem boring or too simple to the reader, but they serve as preparation for the discussion of the much more interesting exercises in the following sections. It is not essential that these exercises be solved, but one should read over the text in order to become acquainted with the definition of convex figures, convex curves, and the notion of the supporting line of a convex figure (these concepts are used in Sections 2 through 8) and further with the definitions of regular points and corner points of a convex figure (these are used in Sections 4, 7, and 8), and with the length of a convex curve and the area of a convex figure (used in Sections 4 through 8). Finally, the solutions of the exercises can be read at once if this section is regarded as "theory" which precedes the exercises of the remaining sections.

A plane figure is called *convex* if it wholly contains the line segment that joins any two points of the figure. Thus, in Diagram 1 Figures a, b, and c are convex, but not Figure d. A circle and a triangle are convex

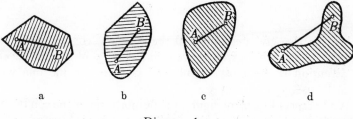

a   b   c   d

Diagram 1

figures; a quadrilateral can be either convex or nonconvex, according as the diagonals intersect inside or outside the quadrilateral (Diagram 2).

By the *intersection* of two (or more) figures we understand the figure composed of all points lying in both (or if more figures are involved, in *all*) figures.

1-1. Prove that the intersection of two or more convex figures is also a convex figure.

1-2. Show that every convex polygon is the intersection of a finite number of half-planes (see Diagram 3).

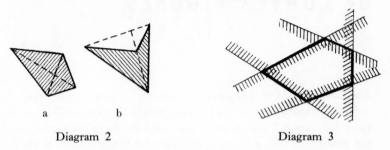

Diagram 2   Diagram 3

A figure is called *bounded* if it lies entirely within some fixed circle. Thus, every parallelogram, every triangle, and likewise all the figures shown in Diagram 1, are bounded.

In the exercises of this section, we shall always permit the figures to be unbounded if nothing is said to the contrary. In the following sections, however, we shall usually tacitly assume that all plane figures are bounded.

In Diagram 4 some unbounded figures are shown. Among them are the Figures a (half-plane), b (strip), c (angle), and d (general convex figure).

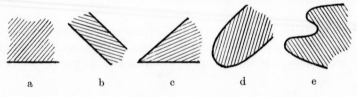

Diagram 4

We can also give definitions of the concept "convex figure" which are different from that given above (see pages 7 and 12); however, this first definition is the most useful, and is therefore the one we shall ordinarily use.

With respect to a plane figure, the points of the plane can be divided into three classes: interior points, exterior points, and boundary points.

A point of a figure is called an *interior* point if it is the center of a circle (with sufficiently small radius) which belongs entirely to the figure. Interior points are, for example, the points A and A' in Diagram 5.

A point is called an *exterior* point with respect to a figure if it is the center of a circle containing no point of the figure. The point B in Diagram 5 is an example of an exterior point with respect to a figure.

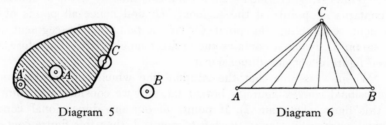

Diagram 5   Diagram 6

Finally, a point is called a *boundary* point of a figure if every circle about the point always contains both interior and exterior points.[†] The point C in Diagram 5 is an example of a boundary point. The boundary points form a line, a curve, or a polygonal path. This curve is called the boundary of the figure. If a plane curve is the boundary of a convex figure, then it is called a *convex curve*, or in case it is a succession of connected line segments, it is called a *convex polygon*.[§]

In what follows, we shall designate all interior points and all boundary points of a figure as "points belonging to the figure," or, more briefly, as "points of the figure." In all cases in which nothing else is said we shall assume in speaking of plane figures that these figures consist not only of boundary points but also of interior points (that is, they are not lines).

We shall frequently have occasion to speak of one figure being *contained in* or *enclosed by* a second figure, meaning that *every point of the first figure is also a point of the second figure*. If no point of the first is a boundary point of the second, the first figure is contained in the *interior* of the second.

We now consider one-dimensional convex figures, that is, lines having the property that the segment AB joining any two points A and B of such a line belongs entirely to it.[¶]

† All such points are sometimes called the "frontier" of the figure while those points of the frontier which belong to the figure form its "boundary." Since, however, closed figures exclusively will be considered (see above) the two concepts coincide.

§ Thus both the plane figure as well as the boundary curve are called "convex polygon." To avoid confusing terms we shall occasionally speak of the boundary of the polygon (although this boundary itself is likewise called a *convex polygon*).

¶ One-dimensional convex figures can be characterized as convex figures in which all points are boundary points.

While two-dimensional (plane) convex figures can be extremely varied (see, for example, Figures a, b, c in Diagram 1 and Figures a, b, c, d in Diagram 4), *the set of one-dimensional convex figures consists wholly of straight line segments, rays, and straight lines.*

In the first place, it is easy to see that all points of a one-dimensional convex figure must be on a straight line. If a convex figure contains three points A, B, C which are not collinear, then by virtue of convexity it contains all points of the segment AB and hence all points of all segments connecting the point C with a point of the segment AB (Diagram 6), hence it contains the entire triangle ABC. Therefore, the given figure is not one-dimensional.

We now assume that the straight line which contains our one-dimensional convex figure is horizontal, and we consider any point A of this figure (Diagram 7). If points of our one-dimensional convex figure lie arbitrarily far to the left of point A, then this figure contains the entire left half-line whose end point is the point A (since the figure must contain all joins of any two arbitrary points of the figure).

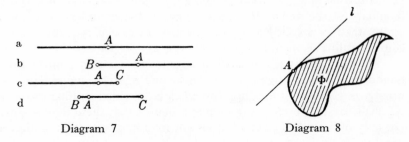

Diagram 7   Diagram 8

If, however, the points of the figure situated to the left of A are such that their distances from A are bounded, then our figure must obviously contain the join of A with the point B of the figure lying furthest to the left. The figure cannot, however, contain any point lying to the left of B. In particular the point B can coincide with the point A (that is, A itself can be the left endpoint of the figure). In like manner, the points of the figure to the right of A yield either a half-line or a definite segment AC. Summarizing all possible cases, we may conclude that our figure is either the entire line (Diagram 7 a), a half-line (Diagram 7 b, c), a segment (Diagram 7 d), or a point. We shall designate points as zero-dimensional convex figures.

Especially important in the further development of the theory is the fact that bounded one-dimensional convex figures are necessarily *segments*.

In what follows we shall always assume, unless the contrary is stated, that a convex figure is *two-dimensional*.

1-3. Prove:

(a) If A and B are interior points of a convex figure Φ, then all points of the segment AB are interior points of Φ.

(b) If A is an interior point and B a boundary point of a convex figure Φ, then all points of segment AB except B are interior points of Φ.

(c) If A and B are boundary points of a convex figure Φ, either all points of the segment AB are boundary points of Φ or all the points of segment AB except points A and B themselves are interior points.

1-4. Prove that every line passing through an interior point of a convex figure cuts the boundary of the figure in at most two points. If the convex figure is bounded, then every line passing through an inner point of the figure cuts the boundary of the figure in exactly two points.

1-5. (Converse of Exercise 1-4) If every line passing through an arbitrary interior point of a bounded figure cuts the boundary in two points, then the figure is convex.

Using Exercises 1-4 and 1-5 we can establish a new definition of a bounded convex figure: *A bounded figure is called convex if every line passing through an arbitrary interior point of this figure cuts the boundary in two points.*

Let Φ be any plane figure. A line l is called a supporting line of Φ if it passes through at least one boundary point of Φ and if the entire figure Φ lies on one side of l (Diagram 8). For example, a line which passes through a vertex of a triangle and is parallel to the opposite side (Diagram 9 a) or which contains a side of a triangle (Diagram 9 b) is a

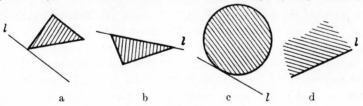

a　　　　b　　　　c　　　d

Diagram 9

supporting line of the triangle. Every line which contains a side of a convex polygon is a supporting line of the polygon (*cf.* Exercise 1-2). A tangent to a circle is a supporting line of the region bounded by the circumference of the circle (Diagram 9 c). A supporting line may have a single point (see, for example, Diagram 9 a, c) or an entire segment (Diagram 9 b) in common with a bounded convex figure. If the convex figure is unbounded, the entire supporting line may belong to the figure (Diagram 9 d).

We can also define a supporting line of a convex figure Φ as a line which contains boundary points but no interior points of the figure. It is at once clear that a supporting line cannot contain an interior point A of the figure; otherwise we could find on both sides of the supporting line points of Φ lying inside some circle about A (Diagram 10). On the other hand, if a line l contains no interior points of the figure Φ, then the entire figure must lie on one side of l. Indeed, let A be any interior point of Φ; if some point B (interior point or boundary point) of the

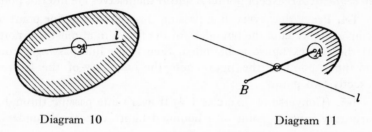

Diagram 10   Diagram 11

figure were on the other side of l, then the point A and also the intersection point of l with the segment AB (Diagram 11) would both be interior points of Φ (cf. Exercises 1-3 a, b).

In each direction there can be drawn exactly two parallel supporting lines to a bounded convex figure.

To prove this, we draw through each point of the bounded convex figure Φ a line parallel to the given direction (Diagram 12). All these lines cut an arbitrary perpendicular to the given direction in a one-dimensional convex figure (if A and B are any two points of intersection of the set of parallel lines with a line perpendicular to them, and if C is any point of the segment AB, then C must also belong to this intersection, as we can readily see from Diagram 12 by use of the convexity of Φ). As a result, in view of what was said on pages 4 and 6, this intersection must be a segment on the line (the boundedness of the intersection follows from the boundedness of the figure Φ), and the set of all lines parallel to the given direction and passing through the points of Φ must form a strip. The extreme (boundary) lines l_1 and l_2 of this strip are the two supporting lines parallel to the given direction.

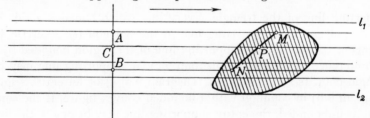

Diagram 12

1-6. Prove that two parallel supporting lines that are a maximum distance apart each contains a single boundary point of the figure, and that the line segment joining these two boundary points is perpendicular to the two supporting lines (Diagram 13).

1-7. Prove that the greatest distance between two points of a convex figure is identical with the greatest distance between parallel supporting lines.

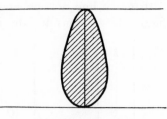

Diagram 13

The maximum distance between points of a plane figure Φ is called the diameter of the figure.[†] From Exercise 1-7 it follows that one can also define the diameter of a convex figure as the *maximun distance between parallel supporting lines of this figure.* (Compare this with the definition of the width of a convex figure, page 18.)

1-8. If A and B are two points of a convex figure Φ whose distance apart d has a maximum value, then the lines through the points A and B and perpendicular to AB are supporting lines of Φ.

A set of rays that emanate from a point O is called convex if, for each pair of distinct, noncollinear rays in the set, those rays which emanate from O and which lie in the smaller angle formed by the pair also belong to the set. (We speak of a convex bundle of rays.)

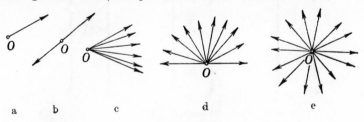

a   b   c   d   e

Diagram 14

If we choose any ray a of a convex bundle of rays and consider all rays lying on one side of the ray a, then all rays lying on the other side of a, we can easily prove the following with the help of the argument on pages 6 and 7: *A convex bundle of rays is either a ray, a pair of rays forming a line, an angle (less than 180°), a half-plane, or the entire plane (Diagram 14).*

[†] *Cf.* Appendix I, Exercise 5 (page 106).

This theorem can also be obtained as a consequence of the theorem about one-dimensional convex figures. Indeed, it follows directly from the definition of a convex bundle that the intersection of such a bundle with every line not passing through the point O produces a convex figure. If we consider the intersection of the convex bundle of rays

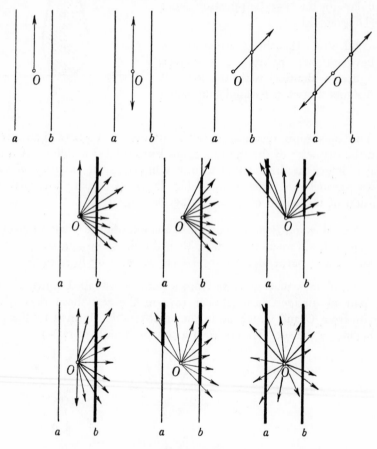

Diagram 15

with two parallel lines situated so that O is between them, and if we note that each of these intersections can be empty or can be a single point, a segment, a ray, or the entire line, it becomes clear at once that a convex bundle of rays can have only one of the above mentioned forms; all possible cases are represented in Diagram 15.

Let Φ be a convex figure and let O be a boundary point of Φ. We draw rays from the point O outward which join it with every point (interior point or boundary point) of Φ (Diagram 16, page 11) and obtain a convex bundle of rays. If, indeed, OA and OB are two rays of the bundle

(A and B are points of Φ), then all rays lying in the acute angle AOB cut the segment AB, which consists entirely of points of the figure, and are therefore contained in our bundle.

The bundle of rays obtained in this way cannot be a single ray nor a pair of rays forming an angle of 180°, since we assume that the

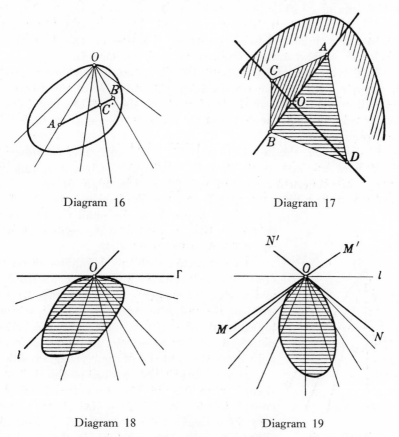

Diagram 16   Diagram 17

Diagram 18   Diagram 19

figure is not one-dimensional. Furthermore, it is easy to show that this bundle of rays cannot fill the entire plane. If, indeed, the rays did fill the plane, then we could choose from among them two pairs of rays, OA and OB, and OC and OD, so that the rays of each pair would be continuations of one another (that is, they would form an angle of 180°) and so that A, B, C, D would be points of the convex figure Φ that lies on these rays (Diagram 17). Then Φ would contain the entire triangle ABC since it would contain the points A, B, C (cf. Diagram 6, page 6); it would contain the convex quadrilateral $ABCD$ of which the point O is an interior point. Hence, in this case the point O could not be a boundary point of the figure Φ.

The bundle of rays being considered therefore forms either a half-plane or an angle less than 180°. In the first case (Diagram 18), the point O is called a *regular point* of the convex curve K which bounds the figure Φ. The line Γ which bounds the half-plane is a supporting line of the figure Φ (all points of Φ lie on rays of our bundle and therefore on one side of Γ). The line Γ is the only supporting line of Φ at the point O, since on both sides of every other line l through O there lie rays of our bundle and hence points of Φ (Diagram 18). The line Γ is called *the tangent* to the convex curve K at the point O.

In the second case (Diagram 19) the point O is called a *corner* (or *singular point*) of the convex boundary curve K of the figure Φ. Here, all points of Φ lie in the interior of the angle MON; hence every line l passing through the vertex of the angle MON', adjacent to MON, is a supporting line of Φ.

In particular, the rays OM and ON, which are called *semitangents* (or *one-sided tangents*), at the point O of the convex curve bounding the figure Φ are supporting lines of the figure. The angle $MON = \alpha$ is called the *interior angle* (or simply *angle*) of the convex curve K, or of the convex figure Φ, at the point O. The angle $MON' = 180° - \alpha$ is called the *exterior angle* of the curve K or of the figure Φ.

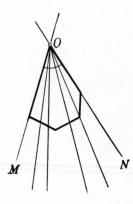

Diagram 20

In accordance with this definition, all points of a convex polygon except the vertices are regular; and indeed the tangents at these points are the sides of the polygon. The vertices of a convex polygon are its singular points, and the corner points, in the sense of our definition, coincide with the vertices of the polygon (Diagram 20).

If we consider the two cases—the case of a regular point and the case of a corner point of a convex curve—we conclude that *through every point of a convex curve there passes at least one supporting line*. The converse of this assertion forms the content of Exercise 1-9.

1-9. If through every boundary point of a bounded figure there passes at least one supporting line, then the figure is convex.

In this fashion we obtain still another definition of a bounded convex figure: *A bounded figure is called* convex *if through each of its boundary points there passes at least one supporting line*.

Let Φ be any bounded convex figure and let K be its boundary. We specify on the curve K a definite *sense of orientation*, for example, the counterclockwise sense. Moving on the curve in this direction leaves the figure always to the left (Diagram 21). In agreement with this, we also specify directions on the supporting lines of the figure, and indeed we shall select the direction of a supporting line l of Φ so that Φ is situated to the left of the line l (Diagram 22). In this case two parallel supporting lines l_1 and l_2 of Φ have opposite directions. In this

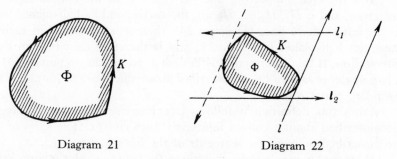

<table>
<tr><td>Diagram 21</td><td>Diagram 22</td></tr>
</table>

way a unique supporting line in the plane corresponds to every direction (indicated by an arrow) and has the given direction (Diagram 22). If K is a polygon, then this definition of orientation permits us to speak of the *directions* of the sides of the polygon.

We say that n boundary points $A, B, C, ..., P$ of a figure Φ are *arranged in cyclic order* if, when the boundary curve K of the figure Φ is traversed counterclockwise, these points appear in the given order (Diagram 23).

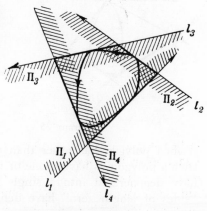

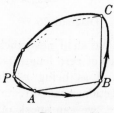

<table>
<tr><td>Diagram 23</td><td>Diagram 24</td></tr>
</table>

If the points $A, B, C, ..., P$ of the curve K are arranged cyclically, then the polygon $ABC ... P$ is said to be *inscribed* in the curve K.

1-10. Prove that every polygon inscribed in a bounded convex curve is convex.

1-11. (Converse of Exercise 1-10). Prove that if every set of n points of a bounded curve K comprises the vertices of a convex polygon, then the curve is convex.

1-12. Prove that if a bounded convex curve has only a finite number of corner points, then the sum of the exterior angles of all corner points is at most 360°. If the sum of all exterior angles is exactly 360°, then the curve is a convex polygon.

If n directed supporting lines l_1, l_2, ..., l_n of the convex figure Φ are given, and if Π_1, Π_2, ..., Π_n are the corresponding half-planes lying to the left of these lines (Diagram 24), then Φ is contained in each of these left half-planes (see page 13) and is therefore contained in their intersection. If this intersection is bounded, and is thus a polygon, then this polygon is said to be *circumscribed* about the figure Φ (or about the boundary curve K).

From this definition it follows (see Exercise 1-1) that a polygon circumscribed about a convex figure is always convex. The sides of the circumscribed polygon are segments of the lines l_1, l_2, ..., l_n.

However, it can happen that three (or more) of the n supporting lines pass through one and the same boundary point of Φ (which in this case is certainly a corner point; Diagram 25). Here the circum-

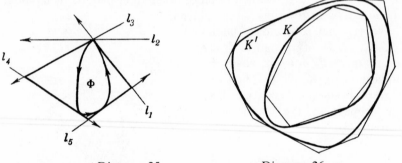

Diagram 25   Diagram 26

scribed polygon has fewer than n sides. We shall nevertheless regard such a polygon as having one or more sides of zero length (sides which have degenerated into a single point) and as being n-sided. These "sides of length zero" have definite directions: the directions of the corresponding supporting lines. Therefore, we can speak of n *interior angles* or n *exterior angles* of the circumscribed polygon, regardless of whether or not it has sides of length zero.

By the *length* of a bounded convex curve K and the *area* of the figure Φ of which K is a boundary, we mean the limiting value of the perimeters, or (in the latter case) of the areas, of the polygons inscribed in Φ whose sides become indefinitely small. As an alternative, we may use the circumscribed polygons whose exterior angles become indefinitely small.[†]

[†] The existence of the length of a convex curve and of the area of a convex figure are easily established with the aid of certain theorems of the theory of limits.

every chord passing through it); in daily life we often say, however, that a fountain is situated "in the very center" of a square, or that a certain person resides "in the very center" of a city, even when the square or the city has no center in the exact sense. Exercises 2-6 and 2-7a can be regarded as explanations of the assertion that a point O lies in the "center" of a certain figure Φ. Additional exercises of a similar nature will be introduced later (*cf.* Exercises 3-7 and 3-8).

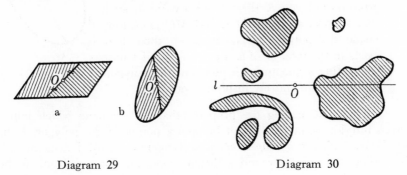

Diagram 29   Diagram 30

2-6. (a) Let n points A_1, A_2, ..., A_n be given in the plane. Prove that a point O exists in the plane such that on each side of any line l through the point O there are at least $n/3$ of the given points (including points lying on the line l itself).

(b) Let a bounded curve K of length L be given in the plane (K may consist of separated pieces; Diagram 30). Prove that there is a point O of the plane such that each line through the point O divides the curve K in two parts, each having a length of not less than $L/3$.

(c) Let Φ be a plane bounded figure (which may possibly consist of separated pieces; Diagram 30) with area S. Prove that there is a point O in the plane such that every line through O divides the figure into two parts, each having an area of not less than $S/3$.

If Φ is a *convex* figure, the estimate in Exercise 2-6 c can be improved significantly. In fact, we can show that within every bounded convex figure Φ there exists a point O such that every line through O divides the figure Φ into two parts, each having an area of not less than $\frac{4}{9}$ of the area of Φ (see Exercise 3-10). It would be interesting to find a corresponding improvement of the estimate of Exercise 2-6 b when K is a convex curve.

2-7.* (a) Prove that inside every bounded convex figure Φ there exists a point O such that every chord AB of Φ which passes through O is divided into two segments AO and BO, each of whose length is not less than $\frac{1}{3}$ the length of the segment AB (Diagram 31).

(b) Derive from the assertion of Exercise 2-7 a a new proof of Blaschke's Theorem (see Exercise 2-5).

2-8.** M. A. Krasnosel'skiĭ's Theorem. Prove that if for every three points A, B, C of an arbitrary polygon K there exists a point M such that all three segments MA, MB, MC lie entirely inside the polygon (Diagram 32 a), then there exists in the interior of K a point O all of whose connecting segments with points of the polygon K likewise lie entirely inside the polygon.

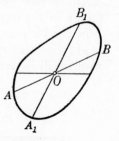

Diagram 31

Polygons K having the property that all segments which join a given interior point O with all boundary points of the polygon K lie in K are called *star-shaped polygons* (Diagram 32 b). Krasnosel'skiĭ's Theorem is a necessary and sufficient condition for a polygon to be star shaped.

This theorem can be visualized as follows. Imagine a painting gallery consisting of several rooms connected with one another whose

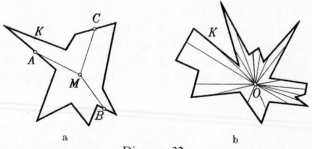

Diagram 32

walls are completely hung with pictures. Krasnosel'skiĭ's Theorem states that if for each three paintings of the gallery there is a point from which all three can be seen, then there exists a point from which *all* the paintings of the gallery can be seen.

2-9. In the plane, n parallel line segments are given. Prove that if for each three of them there exists a line that intersects the three line segments, then there also exists a line that intersects all the line segments.

Exercise 2-9 finds an interesting application in the theory of the approximation of functions. We shall say that the line $y = kx + b$

approximates the function $y = f(x)$ on the interval from $x = p$ to $x = q$ with exactness up to ϵ if for $p \leq x \leq q$ the absolute value of the difference $f(x) - (kx + b)$ does not exceed $\epsilon \geq 0$ (Diagram 33). Moreover, we shall say that the line $y = kx + b$ approximates the function $y = f(x)$ at the points x_1, x_2, ..., x_n with exactness up to $\epsilon \geq 0$ if the absolute value of the difference $f(x) - (kx + b)$ does not exceed the number ϵ when $x = x_1$, x_2, ..., x_n. From Exercise 2-9 it is easy to see that if for each three points of the interval $p \leq x \leq q$ there exists a line which approximates the function $y = f(x)$ with exactness up to ϵ at these three points, then there exists a line approximating the function to the given degree of accuracy on the entire interval $p \leq x \leq q$.

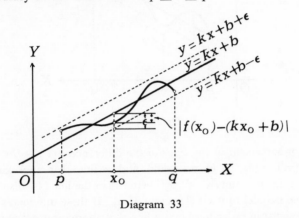

Diagram 33

This result allows us to draw certain conclusions about the behavior of the line having the "best form" of approximation to the function $y = f(x)$ on the interval $p \leq x \leq q$. Let us designate by ϵ_0 the *smallest* of the numbers $\epsilon \geq 0$ for which there exists a line approximating the function $y = f(x)$ on the interval $p \leq x \leq q$ with exactness up to ϵ. The line $y = kx + b$ which approximates the function $y = f(x)$ exactly up to ϵ_0 on the segment $p \leq x \leq q$ is also called the *best approximation* to the function $y = f(x)$ on this interval. From what was said above, it may be concluded that if the line l with equation $y = kx + b$ is the best approximation to the function $y = f(x)$, *then for any nonnegative ϵ smaller than ϵ_0* three points x', x'', x''' can be found such that no line approximates $f(x)$ in these points exactly up to ϵ; that is, *there exist three* points x', x'', x''' such that *no line approximates $f(x)$ in these points better than the line l* (which approximates $f(x)$ exactly up to ϵ_0). It follows from this, for $p \leq x' < x'' < x''' \leq q$, that

$$|f(x') - (kx' + b)| = |f(x'') - (kx'' + b)| = |f(x''') - (kx''' + b)| = \epsilon_0, \quad \text{✳}$$

where the signs of the differences $f(x') - (kx' + b)$, $f(x'') - (kx'' + b)$ and $f(x''') - (kx''' + b)$ *alternate*; that is, the first and last of these differences have the same sign and the middle difference has the opposite one (Diagram 34). Indeed, if the relation $*$ were not satisfied, for example, if

$$|f(x') - (kx' + b)| = |f(x'') - (kx'' + b)| = \epsilon_0,$$
$$|f(x''') - (kx''' + b)| < \epsilon_0,$$

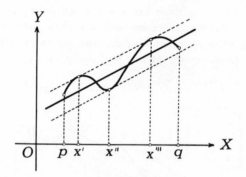

Diagram 34

then for agreement of the signs of the differences $f(x') - (kx' + b)$ and $f(x'') - (kx'' + b)$ we could find a line that approximates $y = f(x)$ in the points x', x'', x''' better than the line l by displacing this line parallel to itself (Diagram 35 a). If these differences have unlike signs, in order to obtain a line that approximates $f(x)$ in the points x', x'', x''' better than l it is sufficient to rotate l around the point with abscissa $(x' + x'')/2$ (Diagram 35 b). It is still simpler to show that two or all three of the differences $|f(x) - (kx + b)|$ for $x = x'$, x'', x''' cannot be less than ϵ_0. Analogously, it can also be shown that the signs of the differences $f(x') - (kx' + b)$, $f(x'') - (kx'' + b)$, $f(x''') - (kx''' + b)$ alternate.

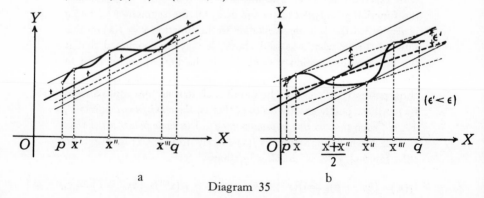

a

b

Diagram 35

These considerations may also assist in estimating the quantity ϵ_0 (which indicates how well the function $y = f(x)$ can be approximated by a straight line) and in finding the best approximation $y = kx + b$. Obviously, in order to find one line $y = kx + b$ which gives the best approximation to the function $y = f(x)$ for the three given points x', x'', x''' (where $p \leq x' < x'' < x''' \leq q$), it suffices to solve the following system of three equations of the first degree in three unknowns k, b, ϵ:

$$\begin{aligned} f(x') &= kx' + b + \epsilon & & & x'k + b + \epsilon &= f(x') \\ f(x'') &= kx'' + b - \epsilon & \text{ or } & & x''k + b - \epsilon &= f(x'') \\ f(x''') &= kx''' + b + \epsilon & & & x'''k + b + \epsilon &= f(x'''). \end{aligned}$$

(Here ϵ may be positive or negative.) It is easy to find ϵ from this system; the absolute value of this number (for an arbitrary choice of the points x', x'', x''') gives the value of the quantity ϵ_0: $\epsilon_0 \geq |\epsilon|$. The same number ϵ_0 coincides with the greatest value which the quantity $|\epsilon|$ may assume under all possible choices of the three points x', x'', x'''; if we succeed in finding the three points corresponding to the greatest value of $|\epsilon|$, then the coefficients k and b determine the line of best approximation to the function $y = f(x)$, which also follows from the above system.

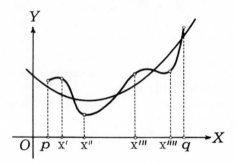

Diagram 36

Analogously we can obtain even more general results relating to the approximation of a function by *polynomials of arbitrary degree*; these results were first obtained in an entirely different manner by the noted Russian mathematican of the second half of the nineteenth century, P. L. Tschebyscheff. Thus, for example, in order to find a parabola $y = ax^2 + bx + c$ that best approximates the function $y = f(x)$ on the interval $p \leq x \leq q$, it is necessary to seek the parabolas which best approximate this function at all possible *quadruples* of points of the interval. Therefore, if the parabola $y = ax^2 + bx + c$ is the "best approximation" of the function

$y = f(x)$ (that is, if $|f(x) - (ax^2 + bx + c)| \leq \epsilon_o$ for $p \leq x \leq q$ and if there is no parabola $y = a_1x^2 + b_1x + c_1$ such that $|f(x) - (a_1x^2 + b_1x + c_1)| < \epsilon_o$ for $p \leq x \leq q$), then four points x', x'', x''', and x'''' of the interval $(p \leq x' < x'' < x''' < x'''' \leq q)$ can be found such that the difference $f(x) - (ax^2 + bx + c)$ for $x = x'$, x'', x''', x'''' is equal in absolute value to ϵ_o, and the signs of these differences alternate (Diagram 36; *cf.* the remark at the end of the solution of Exercise 2-9).

In the following exercises two new proofs of Helly's Theorem are sketched which are different from the solutions of Exercises 2-1 and 2-2. Exercise 2-10 shows how we can easily prove Helly's Theorem in the special case where all the convex figures are convex polygons. The truth of Helly's Theorem for convex polygons makes this theorem obvious for arbitrary convex figures. In fact, if a polygon is inscribed in (or a polygon is circumscribed about) each of the given convex figures so that it approximates the figure closely enough (Diagram 37), then these polygons intersect or not according as the figures themselves intersect or not. A rigorous proof of the general theorem of Helly from the analogous theorem for polygons offers, however, certain difficulties.

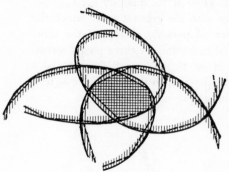

Diagram 37

The proof to which Exercises 2-11 to 2-13 are devoted is somewhat more complicated than our first proof; however, it can be more readily generalized to prove Helly's Theorem for convex bodies in space (see Exercise 2-14).

2-10. If among n half-planes each three have a common point, prove that all n half-planes have a common point (Helly's Theorem for half-planes).

(b) Derive from the assertion of Exercise 2-10 a the conclusion that n convex polygons possess a common point when each three of the n (not necessarily bounded) polygons have a common point (Helly's Theorem for polygons).

2-11. If each pair of n segments of a line have a common point, prove that all n segments possess a common point.

2-12. (Auxiliary exercise.) If two bounded convex figures Φ_1 and Φ_2 of the plane do not intersect, then there exists a line l such that Φ_1 and Φ_2 lie on different sides of l.

2-13. Using the results of Exercises 2-11 and 2-12, prove that four bounded convex figures of the plane possess a common point if each three of them have a common point.

From the assertion of Exercise 2-13, Helly's Theorem for bounded convex figures follows without difficulty (see the solution of Exercise 2-2).

We give here three proofs of Helly's Theorem, based on completely different ideas. Many other proofs of this theorem are now known. Recently a very interesting one was presented by M. A. Krasnosel'skiĭ, author of the theorem that forms the basis of Exercise 2-8.[†]

2-14. Helly's Theorem in space. Let n convex bounded bodies be given, each four of which have a common point. Prove that all n bodies possess a common point.

In addition the following is true: if infinitely many bounded convex bodies are given in space, each four of which have a common point, then all of these bodies possess a common point.

2-15. Formulate and prove theorems for three-dimensional space which are analogous to the theorems of plane geometry contained in Exercises 2-4 to 2-7 a.

[†] See M. A. Krasnosel'skiĭ: *On a proof of Helly's Theorem on sets of convex bodies with common points,* Trudy fiz.-mat. fakulteta Voronezskogo gosudarstvennogo Universiteta, 38, 1954, pages 19-20. We shall indicate briefly the nature of this proof. It is sufficient to prove the assertion of Exercise 2-1. Let Φ_1, Φ_2, Φ_3, Φ_4, ... be the convex figures under consideration; assume that they do not intersect. Denote by A_{123} any point belonging to the figures Φ_1, Φ_2, Φ_3; choose the points A_{124}, A_{134}, A_{234} analogously. Let T be a triangular pyramid (in space) such that its vertices are projected into the points A_{123}, A_{134}, A_{234}. By $\bar{\Phi}_1$ we denote the set of all those points of the pyramid T which are projected into points of the figure Φ_1; $\bar{\Phi}_2$, $\bar{\Phi}_3$, $\bar{\Phi}_4$ are defined analogously. The face of the pyramid T whose vertices are projected into points of index 1 (that is, into the points A_{123}, A_{124}, A_{134}) is denoted by Γ_1; the faces Γ_2, Γ_3, Γ_4 are defined similarly. It is easy to see that the set $\bar{\Phi}_i$, $i = 1, 2, 3, 4$, contains every vertex of Γ_i, but does not contain the vertex of the pyramid which lies opposite to the given face. In addition, the sets $\bar{\Phi}_1$, $\bar{\Phi}_2$, $\bar{\Phi}_3$, $\bar{\Phi}_4$ together cover the entire pyramid (because the projection of T coincides with the projection of the boundaries of the pyramid and each of the faces of T is completely projected into one of the figures Φ_i). Thus it follows that the fields $\bar{\Phi}_i$, $i = 1, 2, 3, 4$, have a common point. This fact is proved geometrically in any course in combinatorial topology under the name "Sperner's Lemma." The projection of this common point of the sets $\bar{\Phi}_i$ must belong to all the figures Φ_i, contrary to the assumption that these figures do not intersect. This is a contradiction and proves the assertion of Exercise 2-1.

The assertion of Exercise 2-11 can be called "Helly's Theorem for the line"; in Exercises 2-2 and 2-14 Helly's Theorem for the plane and for space are formulated. If we combine these exercises, we obtain a general theorem which includes all three cases. We shall call the line *one-dimensional*, the plane *two-dimensional*, and the entire space *three-dimensional*. Then the following theorem holds: *if in an n-dimensional space (n = 1, 2, 3) a certain number of bounded convex bodies are given, each n + 1 of which have a common point, then all these bodies have a common point.*

In mathematics and in physics the concept of n-dimensional space for $n > 3$ plays an extremely important role. Helly's Theorem is also correct for general, n-dimensional spaces in the formulations given above. All three proofs of this theorem (see Exercises 2-1, 2-2, 2-10, and 2-11 to 2-13) can be transferred to the n-dimensional case.[†]

[†] See the article of E. Helly, "Über die Menge konvexer Körper mit gemeinsamen Punkten" (On the set of convex bodies with common points). *Jahresberichte der Deutschen Mathematiker-Vereinigung*, v. 32, 1923, pages 175-176; see also the article by J. Radon, "Mengen konvexer Körper, die einen gemeinsamen Punkt enthalten" (Sets of convex bodies which have a common point). *Annals of Mathematics*, vol. 83, 1921, pages 113-115.

3

A PROPERTY OF
CONTINUOUS FUNCTIONS

This section occupies a special place in this book. It acquaints the reader with the extremely important concepts of *function* and *continuity*. The quite simple and easily visualized property of continuous functions considered here makes it possible to prove a whole series of by no means obvious geometric theorems (*cf.* for example, Exercises 3-5, 3-7, 3-10, and 3-11) which could otherwise be proved only in a very complicated fashion, or not at all. Regarding the concepts to which this section is devoted, the reader is advised to consult R. Courant and H. Robbins: *What Is Mathematics?*, Chapter VI.[†]

The reader who finds this section too difficult may omit it without impairing his understanding of the succeeding sections, except in the case of the solutions of Exercises 7-12 and 8-12, where Exercises 3-4 a and b are used respectively. Exercise 3-12 contains a new proof of Helly's Theorem, to which the preceding section was devoted.

All the figures considered in this section are to be regarded as bounded.

A variable y is called a *function*[§] of a variable x if to each value of x there corresponds a well-determined value of y. Thus the perimeter of a circle is a function of the radius; the sine of an angle is a function of the angle, the temperature at a given place is a function of the time. A suitable means of depicting a function is the graphic representation of the function (its curve).

[†] New York, Oxford University Press, 1941.

[§] In mathematics, functions are usually designated by f, F, ϕ, etc. For example, $y = f(x)$.

A function $y = f(x)$ is called *continuous* if its graphic representation is a connected curve. Thus, for example, the functions $y = 2x + 1$ (Diagram 38 a), $y = x^2 - 2$ (Diagram 38 b), $y = \sin x$ (Diagram 38 c), and also the functions shown in Diagrams 38 d and 38 e are continuous;

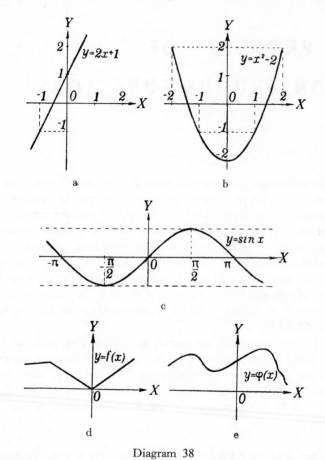

Diagram 38

the functions shown in Diagrams 39 are not. We can also give a definition of continuity without reference to the visual properties of the graph. Let x_0 be any value of the variable x and let x_1 be a value of some variable near x_0. The function f is continuous if, when x_1 approaches x_0, the absolute value of the difference $f(x_1) - f(x_0)$ can be made arbitrarily small.[†]

[†] Exact formulation: a function $y = f(x)$ is called *continuous at the point* $x = x_0$ if for each (arbitrarily small) positive number ϵ there exists a number δ such that $|f(x_1) - f(x_0)| < \epsilon$ whenever $|x_1 - x_0| < \delta$. The function $y = f(x)$ is called *continuous over the interval* (a, b) if it is continuous at each point of this interval.

Obviously the functions shown in Diagram 39 have points at which the functions are not continuous. In the neighborhood of these points, the values of the functions manifest "jumps"; hence the differences $f(x_1) - f(x_0)$ cannot be made arbitrarily small.

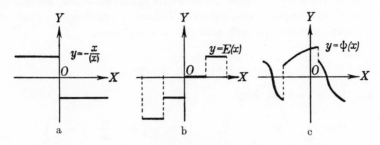

Diagram 39

All continuous functions have the following property:

If a function $f(x)$ which is continuous over the interval $a \leq x \leq b$ assumes for $x = a$ the value A and for $x = b$ the value B, then for each value M between A and B there is at least one place in the interval between $x = a$ and $x = b$ at which the function has the value M.

Geometrically this theorem is quite obvious. It states that a continuous curve, which is the graph of a function $y = f(x)$ and which passes through two points $P(x = a, y = A)$, $Q(x = b, y = B)$ lying on

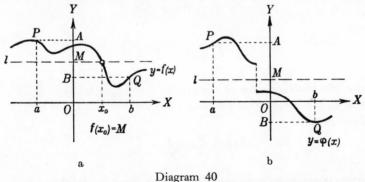

Diagram 40

different sides of a line l parallel to the x axis at distance M from that axis, must necessarily intersect the line l (Diagram 40 a).[†] Discontinuous functions need not have this property (Diagram 40 b).

[†] A rigorous proof of this theorem can be found in R. Courant and H. Robbins, *What Is Mathematics*, or in any textbook on advanced calculus.

This property of continuous functions is very important despite its apparent triviality, since it enables us to prove a whole series of theorems that are at first glance far from obvious.

As an example, we prove here the following assertion: *Every cubic equation* (equation of degree 3) *with real coefficients has at least one real root.* In this respect, cubic equations behave "more decently" than quadratic equations, which need not have real roots.

Let

$$ax^3 + bx^2 + cx + d = 0,$$

or, what is the same thing,

$$x^3 + px^2 + qx + r = 0, \qquad \left(p = \frac{b}{a},\ q = \frac{c}{a},\ r = \frac{d}{a}\right),$$

be our cubic equation. We investigate the function

$$y = x^3 + px^2 + qx + r,$$

or written differently,

$$y = x^3 \left(1 + \frac{p}{x} + \frac{q}{x^2} + \frac{r}{x^3}\right).$$

This function is continuous. Obviously one has

$$\left|\frac{p}{x}\right| < \frac{1}{3}, \qquad \left|\frac{q}{x^2}\right| < \frac{1}{3}, \qquad \left|\frac{r}{x^3}\right| < \frac{1}{3};$$

$$\left|\frac{p}{x} + \frac{q}{x^2} + \frac{r}{x^3}\right| < 1$$

and

$$1 + \frac{p}{x} + \frac{q}{x^2} + \frac{r}{x^3} > 0$$

when the absolute value of x is greater than $|3p|$, $\sqrt{|3q|}$, $\sqrt[3]{|3r|}$ (that is, it is greater than the largest of these numbers). The sign of the expression

$$x^3 \left(1 + \frac{p}{x} + \frac{q}{x^2} + \frac{r}{x^3}\right)$$

agrees therefore with the sign of x^3; that is, for x greater than $|3p|$, $\sqrt{|3q|}$, $\sqrt[3]{|3r|}$, y is positive, and for x smaller than $-|3p|$, $-\sqrt{|3q|}$, $-\sqrt[3]{|3r|}$, y is negative. Therefore, because of the continuity of the function $y = f(x)$, it is possible to find a value x_0 such that

$$f(x_0) = x_0^3 + px_0^2 + qx_0 + r = 0$$

holds. Hence there exists at least one real root of our equation.

The assertions in the exercises of the present section are consequences of the property of continuous functions formulated above.

3-1. Given a figure Φ (not necsesarily convex; it can, in fact, consist of several separate pieces) and any line l_0, prove the existence of a line parallel to l_0 which divides the figure Φ into two figures of equal area (Diagram 41).

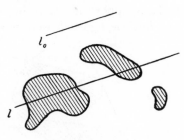

Diagram 41

3-2. (a) Let two convex figures Φ_1 and Φ_2 be given in the plane. Prove the existence of a line l which simultaneously divides the two figures Φ_1 and Φ_2 in half (Diagram 42 a).

(b) Given a convex figure Φ in the plane, prove that there exist two lines l and l^* perpendicular to each other which divide the figure Φ into four parts of equal size (Diagram 42 b).

3-3. Prove that a square can be circumscribed about every convex figure.

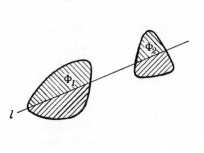

a

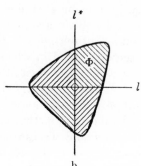

b

Diagram 42

It follows from Exercise 3-3 that we can circumscribe a square about every (not necessarily convex) figure Ψ (Diagram 43).

To prove this assertion, we draw all possible supporting lines of a nonconvex figure Ψ (Diagram 44 a) and investigate the intersection of all the half-planes, determined by these lines, in which the figure is contained. By Exercise 1-1 (which remains valid even for infinitely many convex bodies) this intersection is a convex figure; we denote it by Φ. The convex figure Φ is easily shown to be

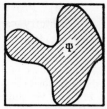

Diagram 43

the least convex figure which contains Ψ. It is called the *convex hull* of the figure Ψ.[†]

It is at once obvious that each supporting line of the convex figure Φ is also a supporting line of the nonconvex figure Ψ. Indeed, if a supporting line l of the figure Φ were not a supporting line of Ψ (Diagram 44 b),

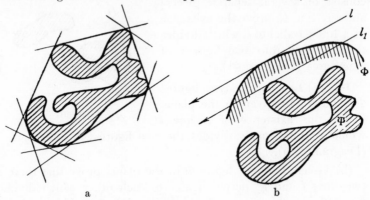

a   b

Diagram 44

then by moving l parallel to itself until it touched the boundary of Ψ we would obtain a supporting line l_1 of the figure Ψ. According to the definition of the figure Φ, l_1 would lie entirely in the half-plane bounded by the line l_1 and in which Ψ lies; hence the line l could not be a supporting line of Φ since it would lie in the other half-plane.

It follows that every square which is circumscribed about the convex figure Φ must also be circumscribed about the nonconvex figure Ψ.

By means of methods analogous to those used in solving the exercises of this section, we can show that a square can be inscribed in every convex curve. L. G. Šnirel'man proved in 1929 that a square can be inscribed in every plane closed curve; that is, on every closed curve one can find four points that are the vertices of a square (Diagram 45). The proof of this general theorem, however, is very difficult.[§]

   3-4. (a) Prove that an equiangular hexagon with two equal opposite sides can be circumscribed about every convex curve.

   (b)* Prove that an equiangular hexagon having an axis of symmetry can be circumscribed about every convex curve (Diagram 46).

   [†] The convex hull of a figure Ψ can be conceived of as the figure formed by a thin stretched rubber band (or rubber sheet in three dimensions) which encloses Ψ.
   [§] *Cf.* L. G. Šnirel'man: "O nekotoryh geometriçeskih svoistvah zamknutyh krivyh" (On some geometric properties of closed curves). Uspehi mat. nauk, vol. X, 1944, pages 34-44.

3-5.* Prove that every plane figure of diameter 1 (see page 9) can be inscribed in a regular hexagon of side length $1/\sqrt{3}$. Since each such regular hexagon can be inscribed in a circle of radius $1/\sqrt{3}$, this exercise strengthens Jung's Theorem considerably (see Exercise 2-4).

3-6.* (a) Given a convex curve K and any line l in the plane, prove that three chords[†] $A'B'$, $A''B''$, A_0B_0 of the curve K can be found which are parallel to the line l, and which have the property that the chord A_0B_0 is equidistant from the chords $A'B'$ and $A''B''$, and $A'B' = A''B'' = A_0B_0/2$.

(b) Prove that a hexagon can be inscribed in every convex curve so that any two opposite sides of the hexagon are parallel to each other and to the diagonal joining the vertices not lying on these sides.

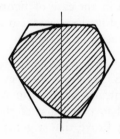

Diagram 45   Diagram 46

3-7.* (a) S. S. Kovner's theorem. Prove that in each convex figure Φ we can construct a centrally symmetric convex figure whose area is greater than or equal to $\frac{2}{3}$ the area of the figure Φ.

(b) Prove that it is impossible to construct within a general triangle a centrally symmetric figure whose area is greater than $\frac{2}{3}$ the area of the triangle.

Kovner's Theorem can be regarded as an estimate of the "degree of centralness" of a convex figure (analogous to the theorems of Exercises 2-6 a, 2-6 b, and 2-7 a or to Exercise 6-3). The center O of a centrally symmetric figure Φ can be defined as a point in which the figure can be symmetrically reflected (that is, if one replaces each point A of the figure by the point A', which is symmetric to A with respect to O, the figure is transformed into itself; Diagram 47 a).

[†] Every line segment whose end points belong to a convex curve is called a *chord* of the convex curve (if the curve has a linear segment, then every subsegment of this segment is a chord of the curve).

Not every convex figure Φ possesses a point with this property. However, Kovner's Theorem asserts that in the interior of every convex figure a point O exists such that the area of the intersection of the figure Φ and the figure Φ', obtained by reflecting Φ symmetrically with respect to O, is greater than or equal to $\frac{2}{3}$ the area of the figure Φ. Such a point is the center of symmetry of the centrally symmetric figure that is contained in Φ and has an area greater than or equal to $\frac{2}{3}$ the area of Φ.

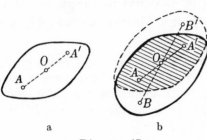

a　　　　　　b

Diagram 47

Obviously this figure, which is transformed into itself by symmetric reflection in O, lies in the intersection of Φ and Φ' (Diagram 47 b). In this way, Kovner's Theorem shows how the word "center" can be used even in the case of figures having no center of symmetry (*cf.* the text preceding Exercises 2-6 and 2-7).

Exercise 3-8 is simple, yet offers an interesting contrast to Exercise 3-7.

3-8. (a) Prove that every convex figure Φ can be contained in a centrally symmetric convex figure whose area is less than or equal to twice that of the figure Φ.

(b) Prove that a general triangle cannot be contained in a centrally symmetric convex figure whose area is less than twice that of the triangle.

Like Exercise 3-7, Exercise 3-8 may be regarded as an approximation for the "degree of centralness" of a convex figure.

We call attention to the fact that among the various methods of defining the "degree of centralness" of a convex figure (*cf.* Exercises 3-7, 3-8, 3-10; Exercise 2-7 or Exercise 6-3) a triangle always proves to be the "least centered."

To conclude this section, we introduce some exercises that are connected with the notion of the center of gravity of a convex figure. This concept actually belongs to mechanics rather than to geometry. The center of gravity of a body is the point of application of the force of gravity which acts upon the body (that is, it is the point of application of the resultant of all gravitational forces that act upon the individual elements of the body).

In geometry we designate as the center of gravity (centroid) of a (plane) figure Φ the point at which the center of gravity of a homogeneous sheet in the shape of the figure Φ is located. (We can imagine that the center of gravity of the sheet is a point M having the property that if M is used as a point of vertical support, then the sheet will be in equilibrium. See Diagram 48).

The center of gravity of a convex figure can be defined in a purely geometric fashion without the use of any physical considerations. As is well known, the center of gravity of a triangle coincides with the point of intersection of its medians.[†]

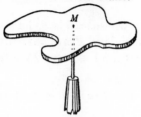

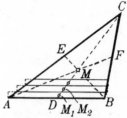

Diagram 48   Diagram 49

If the figure Φ consists of two parts, a part Φ_1 with area S_1 and a part Φ_2 with area S_2, then the center of gravity M of Φ lies on the line segment joining the center of gravity M_1 of the figure Φ_1 to the center of gravity M_2 of the figure Φ_2 and divides this segment in the ratio $MM_1 : MM_2 = S_2 : S_1$ (Diagram 50).

This theorem (which states the most important property of the center of gravity and which is used in the solution of the following exercises) allows us to determine the center of gravity of any polygon by subdividing it into triangles and finding the center of gravity of each triangle (Diagram 51).[§]

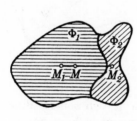

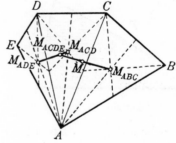

Diagram 50   Diagram 51

[†] Consider a triangle ABC consisting of rectangular strips lying parallel to the side AB (Diagram 49). Since the center of gravity of each strip is at its midpoint and therefore lies on the median CD, we may assert that the center of gravity of the entire triangle must also lie on the median CD. Similarly it follows that the center of gravity must also be on the other medians BE and AF and therefore coincides with their point of intersection.

[§] It can be shown that the center of gravity thus determined does not depend on the way in which the polygon is subdivided into triangles (obviously this subdivision is not unique).

The center of gravity of any convex figure can be defined as the limit point of the centers of gravity of inscribed polygons whose sides become arbitrarily small (or as the limit point of the centers of gravity of circumscribed polygons whose exterior angles become arbitrarily small).

3-9. (a) Prove that the center of gravity of a convex figure Φ of width 1 (see page 15) has a distance of at least $\frac{1}{3}$ from each supporting line of the figure Φ.

(b) Let a convex figure Φ be given whose area is S; let a segment AB of length 1 form part of its boundary. Prove that the center of gravity of the figure Φ has a distance of at most $2S/3$ from the line AB.

Blaschke's Theorem formulated in Exercise 2-5 is an immediate consequence of Exercise 3-9 a.

3-10.* Winternitz's Theorem. A convex figure is divided into two parts by a line l that passes through its center of gravity. Prove that the ratio of the areas of the two parts always lies between the bounds 4/5 and 5/4.

It follows from the Winternitz' Theorem that in each convex figure Φ there exists a point M (the center of gravity) such that any line through M divides Φ into two areas S_1 and S_2 whose ratio satisfies the bounds $4/5 \leq S_1/S_2 \leq 5/4$. It is easy to see that there is no point O inside a triangle for which the ratio of the partial areas (into which the triangle is subdivided by lines through O) can be enclosed within

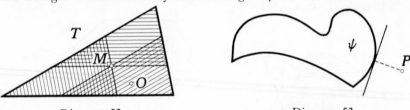

Diagram 52   Diagram 53

narrower bounds; for in a triangle T with area S, each point O different from the center of gravity M is in the interior of at least one of the three triangles of area $4S/9$ which is cut out from T by a line which passes through the point M parallel to a side of the triangle (see Diagram 52). Hence the area of one of the three triangles, which is cut out from the triangle T by a line which goes through O parallel to a side of T, is less than $4S/9$.

It is instructive to compare the result of this exercise with the theorem given in Exercise 2-6 c: for each (not necessarily convex) figure Ψ, a point O exists such that the ratio of the subareas S_1 and S_2 of Ψ into which Ψ is subdivided by an arbitrary line through O, lies between the bounds $1/2 \leq S_1/S_2 \leq 2/1$. (There are nonconvex figures Ψ for which no point O can be found such that the ratio of the parts into which Ψ is divided by an arbitrary line through O lies within narrower bounds; see the solution of Exercise 2-6.)

Let Ψ be any figure in the plane and let P be a point not belonging to this figure. *The distance from the point P to the figure Ψ* is, of course, the distance from P to the point of the figure Ψ which is nearest to P (Diagram 53). Notice that there may be several (Diagram 54 a) or even infinitely many (Diagram 54 b) points of the figure Ψ which are nearest to P.

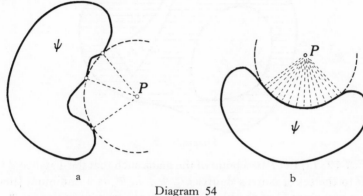

a   b

Diagram 54

3-11. (a) Prove that if Φ is a convex figure, then for any point P not in Φ there exists exactly one point of Φ which is nearest to P.

(b) Conversely, if the figure Ψ is bounded by a simple, closed curve L so that for every point P not in Ψ there exists exactly one point of the figure Ψ which is nearest to P, then the figure Ψ is convex.

Note that in the hypothesis of Exercise 3-11 b, the boundary of Ψ need not be a simple closed curve: if the figure Ψ contains "holes," then inside each of these holes it is possible to find a point P (not belonging to the figure Ψ) for which the nearest point of the figure Ψ is not unique (Diagram 55). Hence we have the following general *Theorem of Bunt-Motzkin*: a figure Ψ is convex if, and only if, for any point P not belonging to Ψ there is exactly one point of Ψ nearest to P.

This theorem gives a new definition of convex figures.†

Finally, we show how the introduction of this concept may be

---

† Those readers who are acquainted with the non-Euclidean geometry of Lobačevskiĭ may be interested in the fact that in this geometry the Bunt-Motzkin Theorem does not hold. For example, if M is the exterior of a limit circle and N is the interior of a circle whose center lies on the limit circle, then the intersection Ψ of the figures M and N is obviously not convex (Diagram 56), but for each point P which is exterior to Ψ there is a unique point of Ψ which is nearest to P.

employed to prove Helly's Theorem about the intersection of convex figures with common points (see Exercise 2-2). Suppose we are given n convex figures $\Phi_1, \Phi_2, ..., \Phi_n$. *The distance from a point P to the set of figures $\Phi_1, \Phi_2, ..., \Phi_n$ is by definition the greatest of the distances from P to the individual figures* $\Phi_1, \Phi_2, ..., \Phi_n$. Denoting this distance by d, we can then prove that for at least one of the figures $\Phi_1, \Phi_2, ..., \Phi_n$ the point of that figure nearest to P is at a distance d from P.

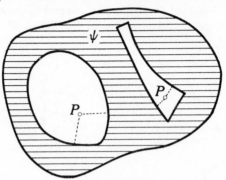

Diagram 55

3-12. (a) Let P be a point of the plane such that the distance d from P to the set of convex figures $\Phi_1, \Phi_2, ..., \Phi_n$ is a minimum (that is, for any point Q of the plane, the distance from Q to the set $\Phi_1, \Phi_2, \Phi_3, ..., \Phi_n$ is not less than d). Prove that either there are three of the given figures Φ_i, Φ_j, Φ_k, for which the points A_i, A_j, A_k nearest to P are at a distance d from P and form a triangle containing the point P within itself, or else there are two figures Φ_i, Φ_j for which the points A_i, A_j, nearest to P and distance d from it, are the ends of a segment containing the point P.

(b) Obtain from the theorem in Exercise 3-12 a a new proof of Helly's Theorem.

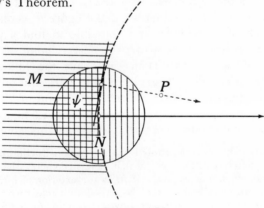

Diagram 56

4

THE ADDITION OF CONVEX
FIGURES AND CURVES

This section has certain unusual features. The addition of convex figures and curves is defined. This addition has many of the same properties as the addition of numbers, but it also has some properties not at all like those of ordinary addition. The distance between two convex curves is defined, and this concept has many of the properties of the usual notion of distance (*cf.* for example, 4-15). At first this definition may seem complicated and unnatural. Later, however, it will often be found useful in problems concerning convex curves. The concept of the distance between curves makes possible a natural definition of the limit of a sequence of convex curves.

Because of the unfamiliar material, this section may appear difficult or of little interest to the reader. If so, he may omit it without hesitation. If this is done, however, we recommend that he also omit 6-9 through 6-11, Exercises 7-15 through 7-18, and Exercises 8-13, 8-14, and 8-21, as well as the parts of Sections 7 and 8 in fine print. In case the reader is interested only in the applications of the exercises in this section, it is not necessary to solve the exercises but only to look at the solutions. For this purpose he can omit Exercises 4-12 through 4-14, 4-17, and 4-18, of which no further use will be made.

An interesting extension of the material of this section is the theory of linear systems of convex figures, which occupies an important place in the modern theory of convex bodies. This theory is discussed in Chapter V of the book by L. A. Lyusternik, *Convex Bodies*, referred to in the Introduction (page viii), and also in the third part of the book by W. Blaschke referred to on page xv.[†]

[†] These books assume that the reader is familiar with the mathematics taught in the first year of the university curriculum.

The well-known parallelogram law for the addition of vectors (forces, velocities, etc.) makes it possible to define the "sum" of points in the plane. We begin with this definition, which is basic for the subsequent developments.

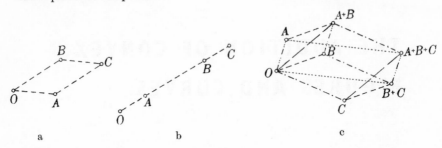

Diagram 57

We choose a certain point O of the plane as origin. If A and B are any two points of the plane, then we designate the vertex C of the parallelogram $OACB$ as the *sum* of the points A and B and we write $C = A + B$ (Diagram 57 a). If the points A and B are collinear with the origin O, then the figure $OACB$ (segment AC is parallel and equal to segment OB) is a degenerate parallelogram (Diagram 57 b).

From this definition it follows immediately that

$$A + B = B + A, \qquad (A + B) + C = A + (B + C)$$

(Diagram 57 c; the final sum is denoted by $A + B + C$) and

$$A + O = A.$$

Now let Φ_1 and Φ_2 be two bounded[†] plane convex figures with convex boundary curves K_1 and K_2; moreover let any point of the plane be taken as the origin O. We consider all possible sums $A_1 + A_2$ where A_1 and A_2 are (interior or boundary) points of Φ_1 and Φ_2, respectively. The set of points $A_1 + A_2$ constitutes a plane figure Φ (Diagram 58), which we call the sum of the figures Φ_1 and Φ_2 and denote by $\Phi_1 + \Phi_2$. If the figures Φ_1 and Φ_2 consist of single points, then $\Phi_1 + \Phi_2$ is the sum of these points; that is, the addition of convex figures represents a generalization of the addition of points. We call the boundary of the figure $\Phi_1 + \Phi_2$ the *sum of the curves K_1 and K_2* and denote it by $K_1 + K_2$. We call attention to the fact that the sum $K_1 + K_2$ does *not* coincide with the geometrical locus of all sums $A_1 + A_2$ where A_1 is a point of the curve K_1 and A_2 is a point of the curve K_2 (the locus of the points $A_1 + A_2$ is a plane figure and not a curve; *cf.* for example

---

† Since we shall consider only *bounded* convex figures and curves in this section, we shall omit the word "bounded" henceforth.

Exercise 4-1). A definition of the sum of convex curves which does not depend on the concept of the addition of figures is given in Exercise 4-5.

The sum of convex figures or curves is also a convex figure or convex curve (Exercise 4-2).

It follows at once from the properties of the addition of points that

$$\Phi_1 + \Phi_2 = \Phi_2 + \Phi_1,$$
$$(\Phi_1 + \Phi_2) + \Phi_3 = \Phi_1 + (\Phi_2 + \Phi_3)$$
(Diagram 59; the final sum is denoted by $\Phi_1 + \Phi_2 + \Phi_3$).

$$K_1 + K_2 = K_2 + K_1,$$
$$(K_1 + K_2) + K_3 = K_1 + (K_2 + K_3)$$
(Diagram 59; this sum is denoted by $K_1 + K_2 + K_3$).

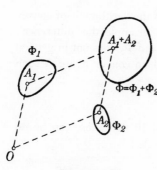

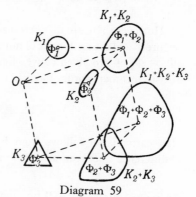

Diagram 58   Diagram 59

Proceeding from the concept of the sum of figures (or curves), it is natural to define multiplication of convex figures (or curves) by integers. Indeed, we can set

$$\Phi + \Phi = 2\Phi,$$
$$\Phi + \Phi + \Phi = 3\Phi,$$
and in general
$$\underbrace{\Phi + \Phi + \ldots + \Phi}_{m \text{ times}} = m\Phi.$$

$$K + K = 2K,$$
$$K + K + K = 3K,$$
and in general
$$\underbrace{K + K \ldots + K}_{m \text{ times}} = mK.$$

Moreover the figure $\frac{1}{n}\Phi$ (the curve $\frac{1}{n}K$) is defined as the figure (or curve) such that

$$n\left(\frac{1}{n}\Phi\right) = \Phi.$$

$$n\left(\frac{1}{n}K\right) = K.$$

Thus multiplication of convex figures (or curves) by rational numbers is defined:

$$\frac{m}{n}\Phi = m\left(\frac{1}{n}\Phi\right).$$

$$\frac{m}{n}K = m\left(\frac{1}{n}K\right).$$

Finally the concept of multiplication of convex figures (or curves) by any real number is defined. By the product $\alpha\Phi$ (or αK) where α is irrational, we understand the limit of the figures $a\Phi$ (or aK) when the rational number a approaches α (a rigorous definition of the limit of sequences of convex figures and convex curves will be introduced later in this section; see page 50).[†]

It is easy to see that addition and multiplication of convex figures (curves) by numbers are subject to the same rules that apply to these operations on numbers; that is,

$$\alpha(\Phi_1 + \Phi_2) = \alpha\Phi_1 + \alpha\Phi_2, \qquad \alpha(K_1 + K_2) = \alpha K_1 + \alpha K_2,$$
$$(\alpha + \beta)\Phi = \alpha\Phi + \beta\Phi, \qquad (\alpha + \beta)K = \alpha K + \beta K.$$

However there are distinctions between the "arithmetic of convex figures" and the arithmetic of numbers. For example, the "difference" $\Phi_1 - \Phi_2$ of two given convex figures Φ_1 and Φ_2 does not in general exist. In other words, there is in general no convex figure Φ such that

$$\Phi_2 + \Phi = \Phi_1.$$

(In particular it follows from Exercise 4-10 that there can be no "difference" between a triangle and a circle.)

In what follows, it will be useful to have a geometric description of the addition of convex figures. We assume that the point O is joined to the figure Φ_2 (the case is even simpler when the point O lies inside the figure Φ_2). We consider a fixed point A_1 of the figure Φ_1; then all possible sums of the form $A_1 + A_2$, in which A_2 ranges over all points of Φ_2, constitute a figure which is congruent to Φ_2 and which is obtained from Φ_2 by a parallel displacement in which O is carried into A_1. We denote this figure by $A_1 + \Phi_2$ (Diagram 60 a). The set of all the figures $A_1 + \Phi_2$, in which A_1 ranges over all points of the figure Φ_1, forms a

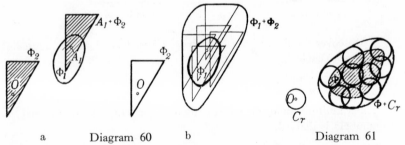

a   Diagram 60   b   Diagram 61

[†] It is easy to prove that $\alpha\Phi$ (or αK) is a figure (or curve) similar to the figure Φ (or to the curve K) with center of similitude (see translator's note, p. 111) at the point O and with ratio of similarity α. However we shall not use this fact in what follows.

figure which equals the sum $\Phi_1 + \Phi_2$ (Diagram 60 b). *In particular, the sum of a figure Φ and a circle C_r of radius r whose center is at O constitutes a figure that consists of the set of all circles of radius r about points of the figure Φ* (Diagram 61).

4-1. If Φ_1 and Φ_2 are two nonparallel segments, prove that the sum $\Phi_1 + \Phi_2$ is a parallelogram. If, however, Φ_1 and Φ_2 are parallel segments, then $\Phi_1 + \Phi_2$ is a segment parallel to Φ_1 and Φ_2 whose length is the sum of the lengths of Φ_1 and Φ_2.

4-2. Prove that the sum of convex figures is also convex (or, what is the same thing, that the sum of convex curves is convex).

4-3. If the convex curve K_1 is entirely enclosed by the convex curve L_1 and if the convex curve K_2 is entirely enclosed by the convex curve L_2, prove that the curve $K_1 + K_2$ is entirely enclosed by the curve $L_1 + L_2$ (Diagram 62).

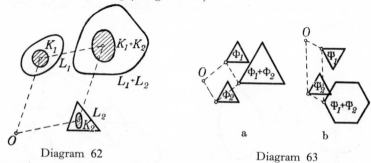

Diagram 62   Diagram 63

Geometry studies properties of figures that are independent of their position in the plane. However, the definition of the sum of convex figures (convex curves) does depend upon the location of the summands and also upon the choice of an origin. This circumstance is undoubtedly a serious defect in the definition. The following exercise shows, however, that the situation is better than it appears to be at first.

4-4. Prove that the form of the sum figure $\Phi_1 + \Phi_2$ (the form of the sum curve $K_1 + K_2$) remains invariant under change of origin and parallel displacement of the summands. Under these circumstances the sum undergoes only a parallel displacement.

Thus the form of the sum figure (sum curve) of two figures (curves) does not depend upon the choice of an origin and is not changed by parallel displacement of the summands. A rotation of the summands can, however, change the sum essentially: in Diagram 63 a the sum of two congruent triangles is represented; in Diagram 63 b the sum of the same triangles is shown after one of them has been rotated through an angle of 180°.

We note that the form of the sum curve of a curve K and of a circle O_r of radius r is completely independent of the position of the summands in the plane (see Exercise 4-16 and the related text). This fact is due to the circumstance that a simultaneous rotation of both summands K_1 and K_2 through the same angle obviously only results in a rotation of the sum $K_1 + K_2$ through the same angle. Hence the sum $K + O_r$ does not change under rotation of the curve K through and angle, but is turned through the same angle.

Now let K_1 and K_2 be two convex curves with counterclockwise orientation (Diagram 64). Let l_1 and l_2 be parallel and similarly oriented supporting lines of the curves K_1 and K_2 respectively (see page 13, especially Diagram 22). Let A_1 and A_2 be the contact points of l_1 and l_2 with K_1 and K_2 respectively (or any contact point if the supporting line has an entire segment in common with the curve). We then say that the points A_1 and A_2 are corresponding points of the curves K_1 and K_2. To each point of one curve there is at least one corresponding point on the other curve.

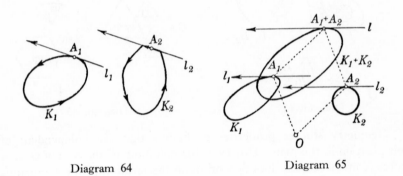

Diagram 64   Diagram 65

4-5. * (Another definition of the sum of convex curves.) Let K_1 and K_2 be two convex curves. Prove that if A_1 and A_2 are corresponding points of the curves K_1 and K_2, then the curve $K_1 + K_2$ is the locus of all points $A_1 + A_2$, where the point $A_1 + A_2$ of the curve $K_1 + K_2$ corresponds to the points A_1 and A_2 of the curves K_1 and K_2. The curve $K_1 + K_2$ possesses, therefore, a supporting line through the point $A_1 + A_2$ which is parallel to the supporting lines of the curves K_1 and K_2 through the points A_1 and A_2 (Diagram 65).

4-6. Let K be any convex polygon with perimeter L and area S; let O_r be a circle of radius r. Prove that the length of the curve $K + O_r$ is $L + 2\pi r$ and that the area of the figure bounded by this curve is $S + Lr + \pi r^2$.

Let $\overline{K}$ be a polygon inscribed in any convex curve K (Diagram 66).

4-11. Prove that the width h of the curve $K_1 + K_2$ in any given direction is equal to the sum of the widths h_1 and h_2 of the curves K_1 and K_2 in the same direction.

4-12.* Prove that every convex polygon can be represented as the sum of triangles and segments.

4-13. Prove that every convex quadrilateral can be uniquely represented as the sum of two triangles (or a triangle and a segment, or two segments). However, there are pentagons which can be represented in several ways as sums of triangles.

Let K be any convex curve and consider the set of all circles of radius r whose centers are on K. The points of the plane which are covered by at least one of these circles form a certain figure (a "strip" or "ring") which includes the curve K and which we shall call the *r-neighborhood* of the convex curve K (Diagram 69). This figure is bounded either by two curves, an inner and an outer one (Diagram 69 a), or by only one curve (Diagram 69 b).

From the definition of the sum of a convex curve and a circle given before (*cf.* Diagram 61 and the related text) it follows that the outer of the two curves that bound the r-neighborhood is the sum $K + O_r$ of the curve K and the circle O_r of radius r and center at the origin. From this it follows that this curve is always convex (*cf.* Exercise 4-2).

4-14. If there exists an inner boundary curve of the r-neighborhood of a convex curve K, then it is also a convex curve.

Diagram 70

Let K_1 and K_2 be two convex curves and let r be a number such that the curve K_2 is contained entirely within the r-neighborhood of the curve K_1, and yet for each $r' < r$, K_2 does not lie entirely within the r'-neighborhood of K_1. The number r is called the distance of the curve K_2 from the curve K_1 (Diagram 70).[†]

[†] Since the concept of the distance of a curve K_2 from a curve K_1 is very important, we shall explain its meaning from another point of view. By the distance from a point A to a curve K_1 we mean the distance from A to the point of K_1

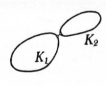

a   b   c

Diagram 71

the difference of their radii (Diagram 72 a, b; circles, their distance from each other equals If, for example, K_1 and K_2 are two concentric in Diagram 72 a the $(r_1 - r_2)$-neighborhood of the circle K_1 is shaded; in Diagram 72 b, the $(r_1 - r_2)$-neighborhood of the circle K_2 is shaded). However, the distance of the curve K_2 from the curve K_1 is not always equal to the distance of the curve K_1 from the

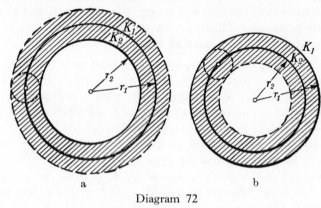

a   b

Diagram 72

curve K_2. If, for example, T_1 and T_2 are two equilateral triangles with parallel sides and a common center, then the distance of the inner triangle from the outer equals the distance between the parallel sides of the triangles (Diagram 73 a), but the distance of the outer triangle from the inner one is, however, equal to the distance between the corresponding vertices of the triangles (Diagram 73 b).

---

which is nearest to A (Diagram 71 a); we see at once that this definition and the one given above are the same in the case where K_2 consists of a single point (namely A). The distance of the curve K_2 from the curve K_1 is the distance from K_1 of the point of K_2 furthest from K_1 (Diagram 71 b). In other words, to define the distance of the curve K_2 from the curve K_1 we form all possible distances between points A_2 and A_1, where A_2 is a point of K_2 and A_1 is a point of K_1. For each fixed point A_2 one seeks the minimum of all of these distances: this minimum is the distance between A_2 and K_1. Then the *maximum* of all minima is sought, where A_2 runs over all points of the curve K_2; this maximum is then the distance between K_2 and K_1. This definition is quite complicated in its structure, but it proves to be practical in many problems, and it plays a significant role in modern mathematics.

The complexity of the definition of distance for two curves can be attributed to the natural demand that a small distance between curves shall imply that the curves be near each other throughout their entire extent.

In this sense the obvious definition of the distance between the curves K_1 and K_2 as the shortest distance between any point of K_1 and any point of K_2 is unsatisfactory: two curves can have points situated close together and yet be widely separated from each other (Diagram 71 c).

The greater of the two distances, that of the curve K_1 from the curve K_2 or of K_2 from K_1, is designated as the *distance between the curves K_1 and K_2.* In the case of equilateral triangles considered above (Diagram 73), the distance between the triangles equals the distance between their corresponding vertices.

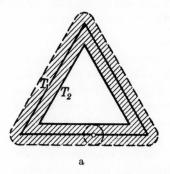
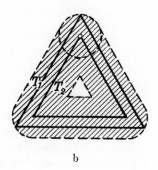

a   b

Diagram 73

It follows from the definition of the distance between two curves K_1 and K_2 and from the fact that the outer boundary curve of the r-neighborhood of the curve K coincides with the curve $K + O_r$, that if the distance between the convex curves K_1 and K_2 is r, then the curve K_1 lies inside the curve $K_2 + O_r$, and K_2 lies inside the curve $K_1 + O_r$.[†]

4-15. Let A, B, and C be three convex curves. We denote the distance between the curves A and B by $\overline{AB}$, the distance between the curves B and C by $\overline{BC}$, and that between the curves A and C by $\overline{AC}$. Prove the inequalities

$$\overline{AB} + \overline{BC} \geq \overline{AC}, \quad \overline{AC} + \overline{BC} \geq \overline{AB}, \quad \text{and} \quad \overline{AB} + \overline{AC} \geq \overline{BC}.$$

The inequalities in Exercise 4-15 are called triangle inequalities. They are so named because they affirm that the "length" of each side of a "triangle" does not exceed the sum of the "lengths" of the other two sides, where we regard the curves A, B, C as "points" of a certain "space" (the "space of the convex curves"), and, in fact, as vertices of a certain "triangle" ABC. The distance between two curves which we have defined is regarded as the "distance" between these "points"

[†] It is easy to see that the distance between two convex curves K_1 and K_2 is the smallest number r such that the curve K_1 lies within the curve $K_2 + O_r$ and the curve K_2 lies within the curve $K_1 + O_r$.

in the "curve space" or as the "length" of the side of the "triangle."†

4-16. Let K_1 and K_2 be two convex curves whose distance apart is not greater than r. Prove that the difference of the lengths of these curves is not greater than $2\pi r$ and the difference of the areas of the figures bounded by them does not exceed the value $Lr + \pi r^2$, where L is the greater of the lengths of the two curves.

We say that a *sequence of convex curves K_1, K_2, ..., K_n, ... has a convex curve K as limit* if the distance between the curve K and K_n approaches zero as $n \to \infty$.§ For example, a sequence of polygons M_1, M_2, ..., M_n, ..., that are inscribed in a curve K, and whose sides approach zero, has the curve K as limit; likewise a sequence of polygons that are circumscribed about the curve K, and whose exterior angles approach zero, has the curve K as limit. According to Exercise 4-16, the difference between the lengths of convex curves approaches zero when the distance between the curves approaches zero; moreover the difference of the areas bounded by these curves tends to zero. Thus it follows that if a sequence of convex curves K_1, K_2, ..., K_n, ... has a convex curve K as limit curve, then the length of the curve K is the limit of the lengths of the curves K_n; likewise the area of the region bounded by the curve K is the limit of the areas of the regions bounded by the curves K_n.

4-17.** Prove that if a sequence of circles has a limit curve, then this limit curve is a circle or a point.

4-18.** Prove that if a sequence of triangles has a limit, then this limit is a triangle, a segment, or a point.

---

† In modern mathematics, various kinds of "spaces" play an important role (such as our "space of convex curves"). Between the points of such a space a "distance" is defined which satisfies the triangle inequality. Such spaces are called "metric spaces."

§ Or in other words, for each $\epsilon > 0$, there exists an N such that for $n > N$ the distance between the curves K and K_n is less than ϵ.

5

THE ISOPERIMETRIC PROBLEM

The present section is devoted to a well-known problem which plays an important role in many branches of mathematics and physics. This is the so-called isoperimetric problem (that is, the determination of figures with the same perimeter). This section contains twelve exercises, the first five of which (Exercises 5-1 through 5-5) are geometric exercises about maxima and minima and have no necessary connection with convex figures. However, these exercises constitute a natural introduction to the isoperimetric problem, and knowledge of some of them is necessary for a solution of the isoperimetric problem. Exercises 5-6 through 5-8 refer directly to the isoperimetric problem. This problem is itself the subject of Exercise 5-8. Exercises 5-9 through 5-12 are consequences of Exercise 5-8.[†]

The isoperimetric problem can be formulated as follows: *Among all plane figures of perimeter 1, find the figure with the greatest area.*[§]

Although in this formulation the words "convex figure" do not appear, nevertheless it is natural to include them in the present book. In fact, Diagram 74 easily shows that the solution of the isoperimetric problem can only be a convex figure, since for each nonconvex figure Ψ of perimeter 1, a figure $\overline{\Psi}$ can be found with a smaller perimeter but

---

[†] A good supplement to the material of this section is the elementary book by D. A. Kryžanovskiĭ, *Izoperimetry*, Moscow-Leningrad, 1938. See also G. Polya, *Mathematics and Plausible Reasoning*, Princeton University Press, 1954, Vol. 1, Ch. X, and the first two chapters of W. Blaschke, *Circle and Sphere*, referred to above on page 15 and in the Bibliography.

[§] By the perimeter of a plane figure we understand the length of its boundary curve.

a greater area;† hence we can also find a figure with perimeter 1 with greater area than Ψ (this property is possessed by the figure of perimeter 1 which is similar to the figure $\overline{\Psi}$). Hence in order to solve the isoperimetric problem it is sufficient to find a plane convex figure of perimeter 1 and maximum area.

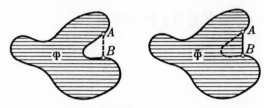

Diagram 74

Since the area of a plane figure and the square of its perimeter vary in the same ratio under a similitude,§ we need not require that the perimeter of the figure be 1. Hence we shall reformulate the problem as follows: *Among all plane figures to find the figure the ratio of whose area to the square of its perimeter is a maximum.* From this it is easy to see that the solution of the problem posed gives at once an answer to the further problem: *To find a closed plane curve of minimum perimeter enclosing a figure of area* 1.¶

   5-1. (a) Prove that of all triangles with two given sides, the triangle in which the sides are mutually perpendicular has the greatest area.

   (b) Prove that if two triangles are incongruent but have equal bases and equal angles opposite the equal bases, then the greater area and the greater perimeter belong to that triangle in which the difference of the base angles (or what is the same thing, the difference of the other two sides) is the smaller; of all triangles with given base and given angle opposite the given base, the isosceles triangle has the greatest area and the greatest perimeter.

   (c) Prove that of all parallelograms with a given acute angle and given perimeter, the rhombus has the greatest area.

   (d) Prove that of two incongruent triangles with equal bases and perimeters, the triangle for which the difference of the base

---

   † It follows from Section 3, Diagram 44a (page 32) that *for each nonconvex figure* Ψ, *a convex figure* Φ *can be found with smaller perimeter and greater area* (*cf.* the text relating to Diagram 44a).

   § See Translators' Note, page 111.

   ¶ If for a figure Φ the ratio of its area to the square of the perimeter is maximum, then the ratio of the square of the perimeter to the area is minimum; hence among all figures of area 1 there is a figure similar to Φ with minimum perimeter.

angles (or what is the same thing, the difference of the other two sides) is least has the greatest area; among all triangles with given base and perimeter the isosceles triangle has the greatest area.

(e) Prove that of all trapezoids with given base and given perimeter, the isosceles trapezoid has the greatest area.

5-2. (a) Prove that among all triangles of equal perimeter, the equilateral triangle has the greatest area.

(b) Prove that among all quadrilaterals with given perimeter, the square has the greatest area.

5-3. (a) Prove that among all n-sided polygons inscribed in a given circle, the regular n-sided polygon has the greatest area.

(b) Prove that among all n-sided polygons inscribed in a circle, the regular n-sided polygon has the greatest perimeter.

5-4.* Prove that among all convex quadrilaterals with given side lengths, the one with greatest area can be inscribed in a circle.

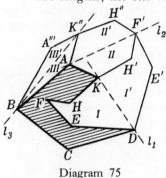

Diagram 75

For each nonconvex polygon, a convex polygon with the same perimeter can be determined which has a greater area (*cf.*, for example, Diagram 75 in which the broken line *DEFHK* has been reflected in the line l_1, then the broken line *AKH'F'* has been reflected in the line l_2, and finally *K"AB* has been reflected in the line l_3). Thus it follows that in the hypothesis of Exercise 5-4, the word "convex" can be deleted. Likewise in Exercises 5-9 and 5-10 we can speak of arbitrary polygons rather than only of convex polygons.

5-5.** (a) Prove that among all convex quadrilaterals with given angles and perimeter, that one in which a circle can be inscribed has the largest area.[†]

(b) Prove that among all convex n-sided polygons with given angles and perimeter, that one in which a circle can be inscribed has the greatest area.

Like Exercise 5-5 b, Exercise 5-4 can also be generalized (*cf.* Exercise 5-9).[§]

[†] In Exercises 5-5a and b we not only assume that the angles of the polygon in question are known, but also the order in which they occur when the boundary of the polygon is traversed. The requirement that the quadrilateral (or polygon) be convex implies that none of the angles (assumed known) is greater than 180°.

[§] The analogy between Exercises 5-4 and 5-5a is not accidental, but has deeper reasons; unfortunately we cannot treat this equation in more detail within the scope of this book.

5-6. If a chord of a convex figure Φ bisects the perimeter but divides the area in two unequal parts, prove that there is a figure $\overline{\Phi}$ with the same perimeter as Φ but a larger area.

5-7. Using the results of Exercises 5-6 and 5-1 a, prove that for each convex figure Φ which is not a circle there exists a figure $\overline{\Phi}$ with the same perimeter but greater area.

The isoperimetric problem (to which the present section is devoted) consists in finding a convex figure Φ of unit perimeter and maximum area. In Exercise 5-7 it is asserted that this figure must be a circle. Apparently this completely solves the isoperimetric problem: among all convex (and hence in general—among *all*) plane figures with unit perimeter, the circle of radius $r = 1/2\pi$ has the greatest area (since $2\pi r = 1$; all other plane figures of equal perimeter have a smaller area than that of this circle (which equals $\pi(1/2\pi)^2 = 1/4\pi = 0.078...$). Although this result is correct (*cf.* Exercise 5-8), we may not draw this conclusion as yet. Exercise 5-7 suggests the solution of the isoperimetric problem, but does not provide it.

That we may not regard the arguments of Exercise 5-7 as a solution of the isoperimetric problem is most easily explained by a comparison of Exercise 5-7 with the following very simple theorem: By squaring each whole number different from 1 we obtain a new whole number $\bar{n} = n^2$ greater than n. This assertion can be formulated by analogy with Exercise 5-7 as follows: If an integer n is different from 1, then there exists an integer $\bar{n}$ greater than n. From this fact we cannot, however, conclude that 1 is the largest integer. Obviously one can refute any person who wishes to assert such nonsense by observing that the statement that no integer different from 1 is the greatest does not prove anything since, in fact, a largest integer does not exist. If, however, we assert that from Exercise 5-7 it follows that the circle of radius $1/2\pi$ has among all (convex) figures the greatest area, then we must be prepared for the following mischievous question: "But how do you know that there is any figure at all with maximum area?" To this question Exercise 5-7 gives no answer.

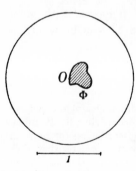

Diagram 76

Our example about integers is essentially different, however, from the problem that occupies us here. Among the integers we can find numbers as large as we please (in mathematics this fact is usually expressed by the statement that the set of integers is unbounded); from this it follows at once that there is no largest integer. In contrast, the areas of all figures with unit perimeter are bounded, for any of these figures can obviously be enclosed in a circle of radius 1 (Diagram 76) hence the area of each figure is less than the area π of this circle. The Swiss geometer Jakob Steiner, who was the first to show (in five different ways) that only the circle can be considered as a solution to the isoperimetric problem, assumed that from the boundedness of the areas of figures of perimeter 1, the existence of a figure with maximum area follows. However even this argument is open to objection. Consider for example all positive fractions with numerator 1:

$$\tfrac{1}{1} = 1, \tfrac{1}{2}, \tfrac{1}{3}, \tfrac{1}{4}, \dots .$$

The set of these fractions is bounded above (except for 1 they are all proper fractions less than 1); it is also bounded below (all these fractions are positive and thus greater than 0). Nevertheless, the fact that the square of each of these fractions which is different from $1/1 = 1$ is also a fraction with numerator 1, does not allow us to conclude that $1 = 1/1$ is the smallest of the fractions in question, since there does not exist a smallest such fraction.

In order to bring out still more clearly that the existence of a convex figure with unit perimeter and maximum area is not trivial, let us consider another example. Suppose that one tries to solve the following problem which, in its form, reminds one of the isoperimetric problem: Among all convex figures with perimeter less than 1, find the figure of greatest area. At first glance this problem appears to be as significant as the isoperimetric problem. Nevertheless we can easily convince ourselves that this problem has no solution. For each figure Φ of perimeter $p = 1 - \delta < 1$, a figure Φ can be found whose perimeter is also less then 1 but which has a greater area than Φ (for example the figure similar to Φ whose perimeter is $1 - \delta/2 > 1 - \delta$).

Thus the conclusion drawn from the result of Exercise 5-7—that the circle of radius $1/2\pi$ has the greatest area of all figures with perimeter 1— is not valid without a proof of the *existence* of a figure of maximum area.[†]

There are, however, elementary solutions of the isoperimetric problem which do not rest upon the theorem that there exists a figure with maximum area (see Exercise 5-8).[§]

5-8. Prove, by using the result of Exercise 5-5, that the circle has a greater area than any other figure with the same perimeter.

[†] For a proof of this existence which rests upon some concepts and methods of modern mathematics, see Appendix I (page 104).

[§] Some other proofs of the isoperimetric property of the circle are given in the books by D. A. Kryžanovskiĭ and W. Blaschke mentioned above (p. 51).

5-9. Prove that a polygon that can be inscribed in a circle has a greater area than any other polygon with corresponding sides of equal length.

Exercise 5-9 is a generalization of Exercise 5-4. We can state it in a form analogous to 5-5 b: *Of all convex polygons with given lengths of sides, that one has the greatest area which can be inscribed in a circle.* In order, however, for the exercise to be meaningful in this form, we must prove that there always exists a polygon with the prescribed side lengths which can be inscribed in a circle (naturally it must be assumed that each side is less than the sum of the other sides, for otherwise such a polygon could not be constructed). We will not go further into this matter here.[†]

We note further that Exercises 5-9 and 5-5 b, which are very similar in form, have different relations to the isoperimetric problem. The solution of Exercise 5-9 is extremely difficult, if we do not use the isoperimetric problem. On the contrary, however, Exercise 5-5 b can be solved directly and can itself be used for proving the isoperimetric property of the circle (see the solution of Exercise 5-8).

5-10. Prove that of all convex n-sided polygons with the same perimeter, the regular n-sided polygon has the greatest area.

Exercise 5-10 is obviously a generalization of Exercises 5-2 a and 5-2b.

5-11. (a) Prove that of all convex figures Φ that are bounded by a segment of length a and by an arc of length l, where $l > a$, a circular segment has the greatest area.

(b) Prove that of all convex figures Φ that are bounded by a segment of arbitrary length and by an arc of length l, the semicircle of radius l/π has the greatest area.

Exercise 5-11 (and more precisely, a somewhat more general problem) carries the name "the problem of Dido." Dido was the mythical Phoenician queen who founded the city of Carthage. According to legend, Dido made an agreement with a tribe which inhabited the coast of North Africa that a strip of land bounded by an ox hide would be given to her. However, Dido did not simply cover a small piece of ground with the hide as was the expectation of the owners of the coast, but instead devised a trick. She cut the hide into small strips and joined these together into a long rope. She then set herself the task of fencing off with this rope a strip of land having the greatest possible area. Thus the question Dido faced was not simply the isoperimetric problem, since

---

† The proof is also to be found in the book by D. A. Kryžanovskiĭ.

she could use the seacoast. By fencing off a strip of land along the coast, she obtained a greater territory than if she had chosen a strip inland. If we assume that the sea coast is a straight line, then we have at once Exercise 5-11 b.

5-12. Find a convex curve of length 1 which has a corner of angle α (see page 12) and which bounds a figure of maximum area.

In three-dimensional space the isoperimetric problem is formulated as follows: *Find the body of surface area 1 which has the maximum volume.* The solution is a sphere (with radius $1/2\sqrt{\pi}$). The proof of this theorem can be found, for example, in the previously mentioned books of D. A. Kryžanovskiĭ and W. Blaschke.

6

VARIOUS EXERCISES ON
MAXIMA AND MINIMA

In this section we collect some exercises about greatest and least values of numerical functions which are related to convex figures. In Sections 2 and 3 we have already had a series of similar exercises (*cf.* Exercises 2-4 through 2-6, 2-7 a, 3-5, and 3-7 through 3-10); Section 5 was devoted exclusively to one important problem of this kind together with its applications. Some exercises on maxima and minima are also presented in Sections 7 and 8 (Exercises 7-9, 7-12, 7-14, 7-17, 7-18, 7-20, 8-6, 8-7, and 8-12).

The exercises of the present section are entirely independent of one another; the reader can begin with the solutions of the exercises that interest him most. For most of the exercises of this section, a knowledge of the contents of the preceding sections is not required (with the exception of Section 1, which gives an introduction to the entire book). Only Exercises 6-9 through 6-11 are exceptional in this regard. Exercise 6-9 can be solved only if one knows the contents of Section 4. This exercise represents a special case of a general theorem that has manifold applications (the so-called Minkowski Inequality; *cf.* for example the books by L. A. Lyusternik or W. A. Blaschke referred to on page xv). Exercise 6-10 and 6-11 can be solved with the aid of Exercise 6-9; for the solution of Exercise 6-11, the content of Section 5 is presupposed.

To understand a number of exercises in this section the reader needs the previously defined notions of diameter, width, perimeter, and area of a convex figure (*cf.* pages 9, 18, and 14).

The least circle which encloses a plane figure Φ is designated as the *circle circumscribed about the figure (the circumcircle).*[†]

[†] *Cf.* Appendix I, Exercise 3 (page 105).

6-1. Prove that a plane figure Φ cannot have two distinct circum-circles. Moreover prove that of necessity the circumcircle of a plane figure Φ contains two boundary points of Φ which are the ends of a diameter of the circle, or else it contains three boundary points of Φ which form an acute-angled triangle. Deduce from this that if Φ has diameter 1, then the radius R of the circumcircle of Φ satisfies the inequalities

$$0.5 \le R \le 1/\sqrt{3} = 0.577 \ldots .$$

Jung's Theorem follows directly from Exercise 6-2 (*cf.* Exercise 2-4, page 17).

A circle of maximum radius contained in a convex figure Φ is called a *circle inscribed in the figure (the incircle)*.[†] In contrast to the circumcircle, there need not be a unique circle inscribed in a convex figure (Diagram 77).

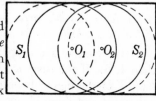

Diagram 77

6-2. Prove that a circle inscribed in a convex figure Φ must either contain two boundary points of Φ which are ends of a diameter of the circle, or else it contains three boundary points of Φ which form an acute-angled triangle; in the latter case there is a unique circle inscribed in Φ. Prove also that the radius r of a circle inscribed in a convex figure of width 1 satisfies the inequalities $1/3 \le r \le 1/2$. Blaschke's Theorem (Exercise 2-5) follows at once from Exercise 6-2.

We designate as a *center* of a convex figure Φ any inner point O of Φ having the property that the ratios in which the point O divides all chords through it lie within the narrowest bounds. The smallest of these ratios in which the center O divides a chord through it is called the *centralness coefficient of the figure* Φ. In the case of centrally symmetric figures (and only in such cases), the centralness coefficient is equal to 1, and the center coincides with the center of symmetry, since all chords through the center of symmetry are divided by it exactly in the ratio $1 : 1$. If the centralness coefficient of a convex figure is nearly 1, then the figure is obviously almost centrally symmetric.[§]

6-3.** Prove that if Φ is a convex figure with center O and centralness coefficient λ, then at least three chords, A_1B_1, A_2B_2, A_3B_3, through O have the property that $A_1O/OB_1 = A_2O/OB_2 =$

[†] *Cf.* Appendix I, Exercise 4 (page 106).

[§] Other estimates for the degree of centralness of a convex figure are contained in Exercises 3-7, 3-8, and 3-10; see also the text preceding Exercises 2-6 and 2-7.

$A_3O/OB_3 = \lambda$ (Diagram 78). Deduce from this that the centralness coefficient of a convex figure cannot be less than $\frac{1}{2}$.

See also Exercise 2-7 a.

6-4.* Prove that of all convex curves of width 1, the equilateral triangle with altitude 1 has the smallest area.

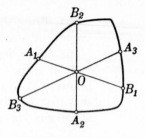

Diagram 78

Using Exercise 6-4 we can now solve the following problem: *What is the least possible area for a convex figure Φ that contains a segment of length 1 which can be rotated through 360° while remaining in Φ?*

It is easy to see that the width Δ of such a figure Φ cannot be less than 1, for if the distance between any pair of parallel supporting lines l and l' of the figure Φ were less than 1, a segment of length 1 perpendicular to l and l' could not be contained in Φ (Diagram 79); hence such a segment could not be rotated through 360° and remain always within Φ.

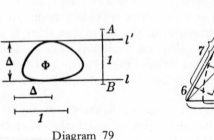

Diagram 79

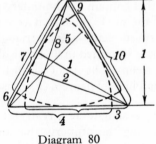

Diagram 80

Therefore, according to Exercise 6-4, it follows that the area of a convex figure Φ, within which a segment of length 1 can be rotated through 360°, cannot be smaller than the area of an equilateral triangle of altitude 1 (and therefore not less than $\sqrt{3}/3$). On the other hand, it is completely clear that in an equilateral triangle of altitude 1, we can rotate a segment of length 1 through 360° (Diagram 80).

Once we are convinced that an area less than $\sqrt{3}/3$ is not possible for a convex figure within which a segment of length 1 can be rotated through 360° (visually we can speak of a space in which a stick of length 1 is to be rotated), then the question quite naturally arises of how small an area is possible for a figure which is not convex but in which a unit segment can be rotated through 360°.

The answer to this question is quite unexpected (see Exercise 6-6).

6-5.** (Lemma.) Given a triangle ABC, it is always possible, by means of segments that join the vertex B to points of the base AC, to subdivide that triangle into a certain (sufficiently large) number of congruent triangles ABA_1, A_1BA_2, ..., $A_{n-1}BC$, and to displace these triangles along the line AC so that their common part in their new position is smaller than an arbitrarily small positive number (after the displacement these triangles occupy a smaller space than previously since they overlap one another; Diagram 81).

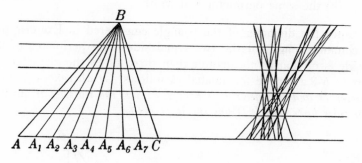

Diagram 81

6-6.* Theorem of A. S. Besikovitch. Prove that a (nonconvex) plane figure of arbitrarily small area exists within which a segment of length 1 can be rotated through $360°$.

Thus there exists a figure whose area is less, say, than 0.000001 sq. inch and within which a segment of length 1 mile can be rotated through $360°$.

6-7.* Prove that a triangle has a smaller area than any other convex figure with the same diameter and the same width.

It is easy to see that the diameter D of a triangle is equal to its longest side and that the width Δ equals the altitude on this side. We conclude immediately from this that for a triangle, $\Delta \leq \sqrt{3}\, D/2$. In fact, if D is the length of the largest side of any triangle, then the opposite angle is the largest in the triangle; hence at least one of the angles adjacent to this side does not exceed $60°$; thus it follows that the altitude perpendicular to the side of length D equals the product of one of the other two sides (which by hypothesis is not greater than D) and the sine of the included angle (which is not greater than $60°$), so this altitude does not exceed $D \cdot \sin 60° = \sqrt{3}\, D/2$. The equality $\Delta = \sqrt{3}\, D/2$ holds only for the case of an equilateral triangle.

Hence Exercise 6-7 can be formulated as follows: *Of all convex figures of diameter D and width Δ, where $\Delta \leq \sqrt{3}\, D/2$, the triangle has the least area.* (For the case $\Delta = D$, this problem is studied in the next section; see Exercises 7-12 and 7-20.)

6-8. Prove that an isosceles triangle, each of whose equal sides is not less than its base, has an area which does not exceed that of any other convex figure of

(a) the same perimeter and diameter
(b) the same perimeter and width.

Since the diameter of the triangle considered in Exercise 6-8 a is the common length of the two equal sides, the perimeter of such a triangle is obviously not greater than three times the diameter. Hence Exercise 6-8 a can be formulated as follows: *Of all convex figures with diameter D and perimeter L, where $L \leq 3D$, the isosceles triangle whose equal sides have length D has the least area.*

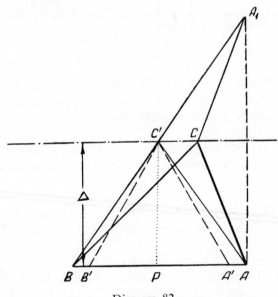

Diagram 82

By the *width* of the triangle ABC described in Exercise 6-8 b we understand the altitude on either of the equal sides AB or CB. The perimeter of this triangle is not less than the perimeter of the isosceles triangle ABC' with the same altitude $C'P = \Delta$ as that from C to side AB; hence $AC' = BC'$, while in the case of the first triangle $AB = BC$ (see Diagram 82, where the point A_1 is symmetric to A relative to CC'; $AC' + C'B = A_1B$ and $AC + CB = A_1C + CB$). The perimeter of the triangle ABC' is not less than the perimeter of the equilateral triangle $A'B'C'$ with the same altitude Δ (for in the triangle ABC' the side AB is the largest: $BC' < BC = AB$). Hence the perimeter of ABC is not less than that of the equilateral triangle $A'B'C'$ of altitude Δ, that is, not less than $3 \cdot 2\Delta/\sqrt{3} = 2\sqrt{3}\,\Delta$. Hence we can formulate the theorem of Exercise 6-8 b as follows: *Among all convex figures of width Δ and perimeter L, where $L > 2\sqrt{3}\,\Delta$, that of least area is the isosceles triangle in which the altitudes on the equal sides have length Δ.*

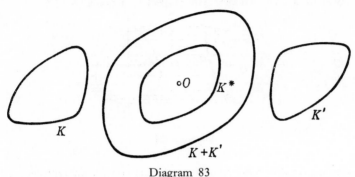

Diagram 83

6-9. Let K be any convex curve and K' be the curve obtained from K by reflection in some point O; let K^* be a curve similar to the sum of K and K' in the ratio of $\frac{1}{2}$ (Diagram 83).[†] Prove that:

(a) the curve K^* has a center of symmetry;
(b) the diameter and width of the curve K^* equal the diameter and the width of the curve K respectively;
(c) the length of the curve K^* equals the length of the curve K,
(d) the area bounded by the curve K^* is not less than that bounded by the curve K.

Since the result of Exercise 6-9 plays an important role in further developments, we shall try to explain here in yet another way the meaning of the construction used.

The relatively greater difficulty of problems that deal with convex figures compared with the geometry problems considered in high school courses can be explained by the fact that in the theory of convex figures rather general figures are studied, so that we can use no special properties of the form of these figures. Hence, any possibility of replacing a figure being studied by a new figure with

---

[†] The curve K^* can be defined as follows:
$$K^* = \tfrac{1}{2}(K + K')$$
(see the footnote on page 42). Thus, K^* may be called the "arithmetic mean" of the curves K and K'.

more symmetry than the original one is very valuable (we shall not for the moment define precisely the meaning of the term "figure with more symmetry"; it is intuitively understandable). In this connection the *method of symmetrization* occupies a significant place in the theory of convex figures; its basis is that of replacing figures by related figures. There is a whole series of different methods for symmetrizing convex figures. In the theory of plane convex figures, two kinds of symmetrization are of particular importance, that with respect to an axis and that with respect to a point.

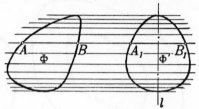

Diagram 84

Symmetrization with respect to an axis consists in replacing a convex figure by a new figure with a fixed axis of symmetry l by means of the following construction: Each chord AB of a convex figure Φ perpendicular to the line l is displaced along the line of AB into a new position A_1B_1 so that it is symmetric with respect to l. The figure Φ' formed by all the chords A_1B_1 in their new positions is called the *image of the figure under symmetrization with respect to the axis l* (Diagram 84). The basic properties of symmetrization with respect to an axis and some applications of this transformation will be found by the reader in the book by D. A. Kryžanovskiĭ, *Izoperimetri* or in the book by W. Blaschke, *Circle and Sphere* listed in the bibliography.[†]

The definition of symmetrization with respect to a point is more complicated. This transformation takes any convex figure Φ into a centrally symmetric figure $\overline{\Phi}$. By analogy with symmetrization with respect to a line, symmetrization with respect to a point could be defined as follows: Each chord AB of a curve through an interior point O is displaced along the line of AB into a new position $A'B'$

[†] We recommend that the reader try to prove for himself the following properties of symmetrization with respect to an axis:

If Φ' is the image of a convex figure Φ under symmetrization with respect to an axis, then

  a) the figure Φ' is convex;
  b) the area of Φ' equals that of Φ;
  c) the perimeter of Φ' does not exceed that of Φ.

symmetric with respect to O (Diagram 85). However, this method of symmetrization is seldom used.[†]

The following method of symmetrization with respect to a point has proved to be significantly more important. We regard the convex figure Φ as the intersection of infinitely many strips formed by the parallel supporting lines of Φ. Then each of these strips is displaced perpendicular to its original direction into a new position symmetric with respect to some point O. The figure $\overline{\Phi}$ which is the

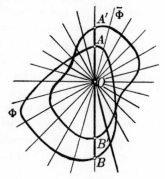

Diagram 85

intersection of the displaced strips is called the image of the figure Φ under symmetrization with respect to the point O (Diagram 86 a). In Diagram 86 b, the symmetrization of a convex polygon M is shown. It is easy to see that the convex curve K^* in the hypothesis

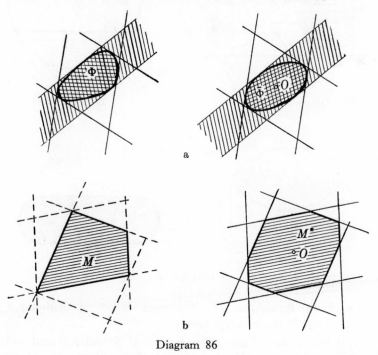

a

b

Diagram 86

§ One reason is that this method of symmetrization can change a convex figure into a nonconvex one (see, for example, Diagram 85).

of Exercise 6-9 coincides exactly with the curve obtained from K by means of this type of symmetrization with respect to a point.

In the theory of convex bodies in space, three methods of symmetrization are very important: symmetrization with respect to a plane, defined analogously to symmetrization with respect to a line in the plane; symmetrization with respect to a point, defined exactly as in a plane (where the strips between any two parallel supporting lines of the figure are, of course, replaced by strips between any two parallel supporting planes of the body); and finally symmetrization with respect to a line, in which each section of the convex body perpendicular to some axis l is replaced by a circle of the same area as the section and having its center on the axis l (Diagram 87).

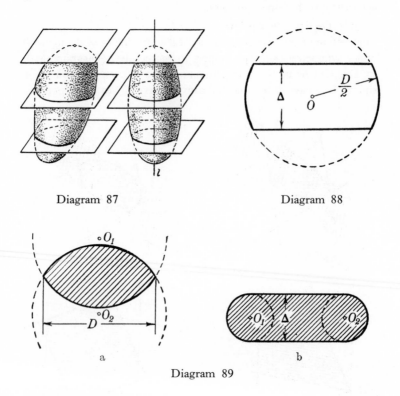

Diagram 87   Diagram 88

Diagram 89

6-10. (a) Prove that of all convex curves of diameter 1, the circle bounds the greatest area.

(b) Prove that of all convex figures of diameter D and width Δ, the figure shown in Diagram 88 has the greatest area. This figure is cut from a circle of radius $D/2$ by two parallel lines equidistant from the center of the circle and separated by the distance Δ.

6-11. (a) Prove that of all convex figures of diameter D and perimeter L ($L \leq \pi D$; *cf.* Exercise 7-17 a), the figure of greatest area is shown in Diagram 89 a. It consists of two equal circular segments with chord length D and arc length $L/2$.

(b) Prove that of all convex figures of width Δ and perimeter L ($L \leq \pi \Delta$; see Exercise 17-18 a), the figure shown in Diagram 89 b has the greatest area. This figure is bounded by parallel and equal segments whose distance apart is Δ, and by two semicircles of diameter Δ.

All maximum and minimum problems connected with convex figures can be divided into two groups. To the first belong problems in which it is required to find among all convex figures the one for which a certain number, characterizing the figure, assumes a maximum or a minimum value (problems about unconditional maxima or minima); Exercise 6-3 is an example of this group.

The second group contains a significantly larger number of problems; in these it is required to find the greatest or smallest value of a certain number related to a convex figure; however, the convex figure under consideration must satisfy further conditions given in the statement of the problem (problems about conditional maxima or minima).[†]

In the main, these subsidiary conditions require that some other numerical characteristic of the convex figure shall assume a prescribed value. The best known problem of this sort is the isoperimetric problem: *To find the maximum area of a convex figure, under the hypothesis that the length of the boundary curve of the figure has a prescribed value, say l* (see Section 5).

Many examples of similar problems can be found in the present section. In particular, in the exercises of this section and in some exercises of Sections 5 and 7, the largest and smallest values of the following are determined: a) the diameter D of a convex figure, b) the width Δ, c) the area S, and d) the perimeter L, under the assumption that some of the others of these quantities assume preassigned values. We find, in fact, the following:

1. *If the diameter of a convex figure is* D, *then*

(a) $D \geq \Delta > 0$. Both parts of this inequality are obvious.

(b) $\pi D^2/4 \geq S > 0$. The first part of this inequality forms the content of Exercise 6-10 a; the second is obvious.

[†] This division of maximum and minimum problems is naturally not restricted just to problems about convex figures.

(c) $3.14D \approx \pi D \geq L > 2D$ ($\approx$ means "is approximately equal to"). The first part of this inequality expresses the content of Exercise 7-17 a; the second is trivial.[†]

2. *If the width of a convex figure is $\varDelta$, then*

(a) $\infty > D \geq \varDelta$. Both parts of this inequality are obvious.

(b) $\infty > S \geq \sqrt{3}\,\varDelta^2/3$. The first part of this inequality is trivial; the second is the content of Exercise 6-4.

(c) $\infty > L \geq \pi\varDelta$. The first part of this inequality is obvious; the second forms the content of Exercise 17-18 a.

3. *If the area of a convex figure is S, then*

(a) $\infty > D \geq \sqrt{4S/\pi}$. The first part of this inequality is obvious; the second follows from Exercise 6-10 a.

(b) $\sqrt{\sqrt{3}\,S} \geq \varDelta > 0$. The first part follows from Exercise 6-4; the second is obvious.

(c) $\infty > L \geq \sqrt{4\pi S}$. The first part of this inequality is obvious; the second follows from Exercise 5-8.

4. *If the perimeter of a convex figure is L, then*

(a) $L/2 > D \geq L/\pi \approx 0.318L$. The first part of this inequality is obvious;[†] the second follows from Exercise 7-17 a.

(b) $L/\pi \geq \varDelta > 0$. The first part of this inequality follows from Exercise 7-18 a; the second is obvious.

(c) $L^2/4\pi \geq S > 0$. The first part of this inequality forms the content of Exercise 5-8; the second is obvious.

Problems in which it is required to find the greatest or least value of some number related to a convex figure are more difficult if several (two or more) other numerical characteristics of the figure have prescribed values (maximum or minimum problems with several subsidiary conditions). Some problems of this sort are treated in this and the next

---

[†] It is obvious that the perimeter of a convex figure $\varPhi$ of diameter D cannot be less than $2D$; for if A and B are two (boundary) points of $\varPhi$ whose distance apart is D, then neither of the two arcs into which A and B divide the boundary of $\varPhi$ can have length smaller than D. On the other hand, we can find a convex figure of diameter D whose perimeter is arbitrarily close to $2D$. As an example of such a figure, consider a rhombus, one of whose diagonals is D, while the other is very small.

section. All of these problems are connected with the same four numbers: D, Δ, S, and L. However, they do not exhaust all possible problems of a similar sort related to these four numbers, since a large number of such problems are still unsolved.

Thus, the maximum of S is determined for given D and Δ in Exercise 6-10 b; in Exercises 6-7, 7-12, and 7-20, the maximum for given D and Δ is determined under the restrictions $\Delta \leq \sqrt{3}/3$ and $\Delta = D$, respectively. The minimum of S for given D and Δ, where $D > \Delta > \sqrt{3}\,D/3 \approx 0.866\,D$, was found in 1952 (after the publication of the original edition of this book). The minimum is attained by the figure shown in Diagram 90, which consists of three circular arcs of radius Δ whose centers lie at the vertices of the equilateral triangle of side length D, and by the six tangents that are drawn from the vertices of this triangle to these arcs.[†] In Exercises 7-17 b and 7-18 b, the maximum and minimum values of L' for given D and Δ, are determined. In Exercise 6-11 a, the maximum of S for given D and L is found, and in Exercises 6-8 a, 7-12, and 7-20, the minimum of S for given D and L is determined under the condition that $L \leq 3D$ and

Diagram 90

that $L = \pi D$. The minimum of S for given D and L, where $3.14D \approx \pi D > L > 3D$, was first found in 1954 (it is satisfied by the curvilinear triangle which generalizes the curvilinear triangle of Reuleaux considered in the next section).[†] In Exercise 6-11 the maximum of S for given Δ and L is determined. In Exercises 6-8 b, 7-12, and 7-20, the minimum of S for given Δ and L is determined under the restrictions $L \geq 2\sqrt{3}\,\Delta$ and $L = \pi\Delta$; the minimum of S for given Δ and L, where $3.46\Delta \approx 2\sqrt{3}\,\Delta > L > \pi\Delta \approx 3.14\Delta$ was found in 1952 (it is constructed for a convex figure just as in Diagram 90).[§]

Even from this brief account one can see that there are many unsolved problems in the elementary theory of convex figures.

---

† The proof of this fact is closely related to the solution of Exercise 7-12. See the article by M. Scholander: "On Certain Minimum Problems in the Theory of Convex Curves." *Transactions of the American Mathematical Society*, vol. 73, no. 1, 1952, pages 139-173.

§ See the article by D. Hemmi: "The Minimum Area of Convex Curves for Given Diameter and Perimeter." *Proceedings of the Japan Academy*, vol. 30, no. 9, 1954, pages 91-96.

7

CURVES OF CONSTANT WIDTH

This section is concerned with an interesting class of convex curves, the so-called curves of *constant width*. These curves are also considered in Chapter 25 of an excellent elementary book by H. Rademacher and O. Toeplitz,[†] which can be used to supplement substantially the present section.

The exercises of the first half of this section (up to and including Exercise 7-14) are not related to the material of the preceding sections (except Section 1); a previous result is essential only for the solution of Exercise 7-12, namely Exercise 3-4 a. If Section 7 is read before Section 3, then in particular one needs only to acquaint himself with Exercise 3-4 a (by simply reading through the solution). Exercises 7-15 through 7-18 assume knowledge of the material explained in Exercises 4-1 through 4-11. Exercises 7-17 and 7-18 depend in an essential way upon Exercise 6-9. If Section 7 is read before Section 6, then these exercises must be omitted. Finally, Section 4 must be understood in order to follow the concluding part (in fine print) of this section.

The *width of a convex curve in a given direction* is the distance between a pair of supporting lines of the curve perpendicular to this direction (see Diagram 68, page 46). If the width of a curve is the same in all directions, then it is called a curve of *constant width* (Diagram 91 a). For such a curve we simply speak of its *width* instead of its width in a given direction.

The simplest example of a curve of constant width is a circle. Its width equals its diameter. However there are, besides the circle, infinitely

[†] *Von Zahlen und Figuren*, tr. by H. S. Zuckerman under the title *The Enjoyment of Mathematics*, Princeton University Press, 1957.

many other curves of constant width. For example, consider an equilateral triangle *ABC* of side *h*, and let each two of its vertices be joined by a circular arc of radius *h*, whose center is at the third vertex (Diagram 91 b). This curve is called a *Reuleaux triangle*. Given any two parallel supporting lines of a Reuleaux triangle, one of them passes through some

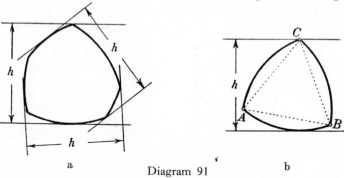

a

Diagram 91

b

vertex of the triangle *ABC* (these are also corner points of the curve), while the other is tangent to the opposite circular arc. Hence the distance between two parallel supporting lines of a Reuleaux triangle is *h*.

Beginning with Reuleaux triangles, it is easy to find other examples of curves of constant width. Consider again an equilateral triangle with side of length *h*. About each vertex of the triangle let us draw inside the corresponding angle an arc of radius $\rho > h$; join the end points of the resulting three arcs by smaller arcs of radius $\rho' = \rho - h$ about the vertices of the triangle (Diagram 92), and let $\rho + \rho' = H$. Given any two parallel supporting lines of the resulting curve, one is tangent to an arc of the larger circle and the other to an arc of the smaller circle, and both arcs have the same center. Thus it is evident that this curve has constant width *H*.

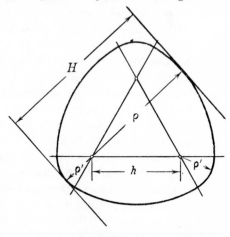

Diagram 92

If we draw two pairs of parallel supporting lines to a curve of constant width *h* so that the lines of the one pair are perpendicular to the lines of the other, then we obtain a square of side *h*. In this way a square can be circumscribed about a curve of constant width so that a side of the circumscribed square has any desired direction

(Diagram 93 b). In other words, the square can be rotated as much as desired and remains always circumscribed about the given curve of constant width. Or, a curve of constant width can be freely rotated within square so that it always maintains contact with the sides of the square the (remains inscribed in the square; see Diagram 93 b). It is clear that this property completely characterizes curves of constant width.

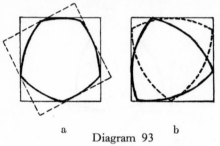

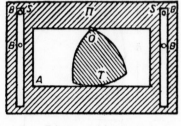

a   b
Diagram 93   Diagram 94

Curves of constant width, especially the Reuleaux triangle, are the simplest curves of this type except for the circle, and are used in practice in various mechanisms. For example, the fact that a Reuleaux triangle can be freely turned within a square while it touches all the sides is used in boring square holes, and borers in the shape of a Reuleaux triangle are used for this purpose.

Consider still another example. Let Π be a plane plate with two vertical slits S and a rectangular opening A (Diagram 94). In each of the slits S there are two bolts B, which are fastened to an immovable base so that the plate Π can move freely up and down but not sideways. In the opening A there is a disc T in the form of a Reuleaux triangle which is fastened to an axis O perpendicular to the plane of the sketch. We cause the disc T to move about the axis O and observe the motion of the plate Π. It is easy to see that when T moves through 120º the plate Π is raised (Diagram 95 a); movement of the disc through 60º more causes no movement of the plate (Diagram 95 b); on moving the disc through the next 120º, the plate drops to its initial position (Diagram 95 c); movement through the last 60º, which constitutes the conclusion of a rotation, leaves the plate again motionless (Diagram 95 c). In this fashion the rotation of the disc T is changed into a linear motion of the plate Π. The fact that each interval of movement of the plate is followed by an equal interval of rest permits the application of this mechanism as a gripper for moving the film in a movie projector.[†]

† To avoid blurring of the image, the film in a movie projector must move intermittently; that is, the movement of the film (objective closed) must alternate with temporary motionlessness of the film (objective open). The mechanism which makes this movement of the film possible is called a *gripper*.

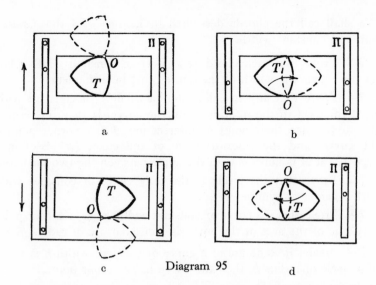

Diagram 95

7-1. Calculate the perimeter of a Reuleaux triangle and its area. Which is greater, the area of a circle or the area of a Reuleaux triangle of equal width? Also determine the size of the interior angles at the corner points of a Reuleaux triangle.

7-2. Draw a curve of constant width h which consists of five, seven, or in general, of any arbitrary odd number of circular arcs of radius h. What is the length of each of these curves?

Curves of constant width h which consist of circular arcs of diameter h play an important role in the succeeding developments (*cf.* the text in small type, pages 76-80).

7-3. Prove that the distance between two points of a curve of constant width h cannot exceed h.

7-4. Prove that each supporting line has only one point in common with a curve of constant width h. In a curve of constant width, each chord joining the contact points of two parallel supporting lines is perpendicular to those lines and hence has length h.

Plane curves with the property that the distance between any two points of the curve does not exceed a certain quantity h, and such that for each point of the curve there exists another point of the curve at a distance h from it, are occasionally called *curves of constant diameter*. From Exercise 7-4 it follows that *every curve of constant width is also a curve of constant diameter*. It is easy to prove that conversely *each curve of constant diameter is also a curve of constant width*. (Prove this!) Hence we need not study curves of constant diameter any further; they are identical with curves of constant width.

We shall call the chords described in Exercise 7-4 the *diameters* of a curve of constant width.

7-5. Prove that each chord of a curve of constant width whose length equals the width of the curve must be a diameter.

7-6. Prove that any two diameter of a curve of constant width must intersect in the interior or on the curve. If they intersect on the curve, then their point of intersection A is a corner point of the curve, and the exterior angle of the curve (see Section 1, page 12) at A is not less than the angle between the two diameters.

7-7. Prove that the circle is the only curve of constant width with a center of symmetry.

7-8. Prove that if a curve of constant width h has a corner point, then one of the arcs of the curve is a circular arc of radius h.

Conversely, if some arc of a curve of constant width h is an arc of a circle of radius h, then the curve has a corner point.

7-9. Prove that the interior angle at a corner point A of a curve of constant width cannot be less than 120°. The only curve of constant width in which a corner has an interior angle of 120° is a Reuleaux triangle.

7-10. (Lemma) Let $ABCD$ be a rhombus, and let MN and PQ be two line segments which are perpendicular to the diagonal BD and whose distance apart is h (Diagram 96).

(a) Prove that the perimeter of the hexagon $AMNCQP$ does not depend on the position of MN and PQ.

(b) Prove that the area of the hexagon $AMNCQP$ assumes its maximum value when MN and PQ are at an equal distance $h/2$ from the diagonal AC of the rhombus; the area is a minimum when MN passes through the vertex B (or PQ passes through the vertex D) of the rhombus.

7-11. By examining equiangular polygons of 2^n sides which are circumscribed about an arbitrary curve K of constant width h and also about a circle of diameter h, derive Barbier's Theorem: *All curves of constant width h have length πh.*

7-12.* Examine equiangular polygons with $3 \cdot 2^n$ sides which are circumscribed about an arbitrary curve K of constant width h, about a circle of diameter h, and about a Reuleaux triangle T of width h. Prove that the circle has the greatest area, and the Reuleaux triangle the least, of all curves of constant width.

From Barbier's Theorem (Exercise 7-11), it follows that the theorem in the first part of Exercise 7-12 is also a consequence of the isoperimetric problem (see Exercise 5-8).

7-13. Given any convex curve of constant width, prove that the circle inscribed in K and that circumscribed about K must be concentric, and that the sum of their radii equals the width of the curve (Diagram 97).

7-14.* Prove that the Reuleaux triangle is the curve of constant width h with the greatest circumradius (and hence with the least in-radius; see Exercise 7-13). The circle, on the other hand, has the smallest circumradius (and the greatest in-radius).

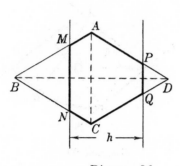
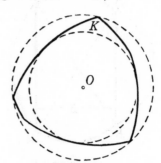

Diagram 96   Diagram 97

In problems about curves of constant width the notion of the addition of convex curves (see Section 4) turns out to be quite useful. It follows at once from Exercise 4-11 that the sum of two curves of constant width is also a curve of constant width; this theorem allows us to construct from any curves of constant width new examples of such curves. We have used this fact already: as an example of a curve of constant width, we considered the sum of a Reuleaux triangle and a circle (Diagram 92).

7-15. Prove that the sum of an arbitrary curve of constant width h with the same curve turned through 180° is a circle of radius h. Obtain from this theorem a new proof of Barbier's Theorem (see Exercise 7-11).

7-16. (Converse of Exercise 7-15.) If the sum of a curve K with the curve K' obtained by rotating K through 180° is a circle, then K is a curve of constant width.

From Exercises 7-15 and 7-16 it follows that we can also define a curve of constant width as *a curve which yields a circle when it is added to the curve obtained by rotating it through 180°.* All the properties of curves of constant width are easily derived from this definition.

7-17. (a) Prove that of all convex curves of diameter 1 (see page 9), curves of constant width 1 have the greatest length.

(b) In a curve $\bar{K}$ of constant width D, let AB and PQ be two parallel chords such that the diagonals AQ and BP of the trapezoid $ABQP$ are diameters of the curve (Diagram 98). We denote the distance between the lines AB and PQ by $\varDelta$. Prove that the curve K, formed from the arcs AP and BQ of $\bar{K}$ and the chords AB and PQ has the greatest length of all convex curves of diameter D and width $\varDelta$ (see pages 9 and 18).

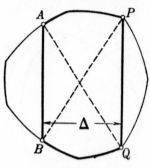

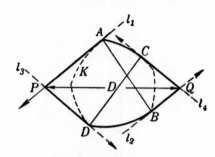

Diagram 98   Diagram 99

7-18. (a) Prove that curves of constant width 1 have the least length of all convex curves of width 1.

(b) Let AB and CD be two diameters of a curve $\bar{K}$ of constant width $\varDelta$; let l_1 and l_2 be two supporting lines of K perpendicular to AB, and let l_3 and l_4 be supporting lines perpendicular to CD. Denote by P the intersection of l_1 and l_3, and by Q the intersection of l_2 and l_4 (Diagram 99). Let D be the distance between the points P and Q. Prove that the curve K shown in Diagram 99, formed from the segments AP, PD, BQ, QC and the arcs AC and BD of $\bar{K}$ has the smallest length of all curves of width $\varDelta$ and diameter D.

From Exercises 7-17 and 7-18 we obtain the following estimates for the length L of a convex curve K of diameter D and width $\varDelta$:

$$\pi D \geq L, L \geq \pi\varDelta; \quad 2[D(\pi/2 - \text{arc cos } \varDelta/D) + \sqrt{H^2 - h^2}]$$
$$\geq L \geq 2[\varDelta(\pi/2 - \text{arc cos } \varDelta/D) + \sqrt{D^2 - \varDelta^2}].$$

(Here H and h are respectively the maximum and minimum altitudes among all the altitudes of equilateral triangles circumscribed about K.)

We now prove: *If K is any curve of constant width h, a curve of constant width h can be constructed which consists of circular arcs of radius h and which is arbitrarily close to K (in the sense of the distance between curves defined in Section 4).*

To prove this, consider a polygon $A_1A_2 \ldots A_{2n}$ circumscribed about K, having an even number of sides, whose opposite sides A_kA_{k+1} and $A_{n+k}A_{n+k+1}$ $(k = 1, 2, \ldots, n-1)$, A_nA_{n+1} and $A_{2n}A_1$ are parallel, and a polygon $B_1B_2 \ldots B_{2n}$ inscribed in K with vertices that are just the points of contact of the circumscribed polygon with the curve (Diagram 100; the possibility that any adjacent vertices of the

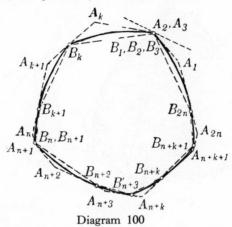

Diagram 100

circumscribed or of the inscribed polygon may coincide, say A_2 and A_3 or B_1, B_2, and B_3 in our drawing, is not to be excluded). We shall show the existence of a curve of constant width h consisting of circular arcs of radius h, which is inscribed in $A_1A_2 \ldots A_{2n}$ and circumscribed about $B_1B_2 \ldots B_{2n}$.

If B_k and B_{n+k} are two opposite vertices of the inscribed polygon, then the chord B_kB_{n+k} of the curve K is a diameter (since B_k and B_{n+k} are points of contact of K with a pair of parallel supporting lines). From this it follows that the length of the chord B_kB_{n+k} is h (Exercise 7-4); likewise the length of the chord $B_{k+1}B_{n+k+1}$ is h.

We now replace the opposite arcs B_kB_{k+1} and $B_{n+k}B_{n+k+1}$ of K by new circular arcs of radius h in such a way that the curve retains its constant width h and remains inscribed in $A_1A_2 \ldots A_{2n}$. For this purpose we draw circles of radius h about the points B_k and B_{k+1}; let C_k denote the point of intersection of these circles which lies on the same side of the chord B_kB_{k+1} as the points B_{n+k}, B_{n+k+1} (Diagram 101 a). The point C_k is at distance h from the points B_k and B_{k+1}. Now we draw a circular arc of radius h about C_k which joins B_k and B_{k+1}. We replace the arc $B_{n+k}B_{n+k+1}$ of K by the circular arcs $B_{n+k}C_k$, and C_kB_{n+k+1} of radius h with centers at B_k, B_{k+1}, and the arc B_kB_{k+1} by a circular arc with center at C_k.

It is evident that the new curve K' obtained this way is again a curve of constant width h. In fact, if one of two parallel supporting lines l and l' of K' touches the arc $B_{n+k}C_k$, then the other passes through the vertex B_k; if l goes through C_k, then l' is tangent to the arc B_kB_{k+1}; if l touches the arc C_kB_{n+k+1}, then l' passes through the vertex B_{k+1}. Thus the curve K' remains inscribed in the polygon $A_1A_2 \ldots A_{2n}$ and circumscribed about the polygon $B_1B_2 \ldots B_{2n}$.[†]

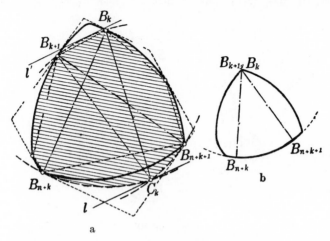

a   b

Diagram 101

In case B_k and B_{k+1} coincide, the diameters B_kB_{n+k} and $B_{k+1}B_{n+k+1}$ intersect on the curve, so that the arc $B_{n+k}B_{n+k+1}$ is a circular arc of radius h about the point $B_k = B_{k+1}$ (Diagram 101 b; see Exercises 7-6 and 7-8). If we carry out the same construction for every pair of opposite arcs of K, we obtain a curve K_0 of constant width, consisting only of circular arcs of radius h, which is inscribed

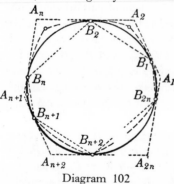

Diagram 102

in the polygon $A_1A_2 \ldots A_{2n}$ and circumscribed about the polygon $B_1B_2 \ldots B_{2n}$ (Diagram 102).

It remains only to show that by proper choice of the polygon $A_1A_2 \ldots A_{2n}$ we can make the distance between K_0 and K as small as we please. It follows at once from the fact that K and K_0 are both inscribed in $A_1A_2 \ldots A_{2n}$ and circumscribed about $B_1B_2 \ldots$ B_{2n} that the distance between these curves is no greater than the

---

[†] In this construction, of course, we can interchange the roles of the points A_k, A_{k+1} and A_{n+k}, A_{n+k+1}; in this case we obtain another curve K'' which also has the desired property.

distance between the polygons; for if an r-neighborhood of $A_1A_2...A_{2n}$ encloses the polygon $B_1B_2 ... B_{2n}$ and the r-neighborhood of $B_1B_2 ... B_{2n}$ encloses the polygon $A_1A_2 ... A_{2n}$, then K cannot extend beyond the r-neighborhood of K_0, nor K_0 beyond the r-neighborhood of K. Thus if we prove that *the distance between* $A_1A_2 ... A_{2n}$ *and* $B_1B_2 ... B_{2n}$ *can be made as small as we wish*, it will follow that the distance between K_0 and K can also be made as small as we wish.

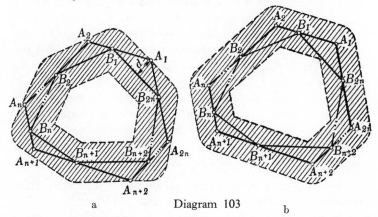

a   Diagram 103   b

Moreover it is obvious that the distance between the polygons $A_1A_2 ... A_{2n}$ and $B_1B_2 ... B_{2n}$ is equal to the largest of the distance between the vertices A_1, A_2, ..., A_{2n} and the corresponding sides $B_{2n}B_1, B_1B_2, ..., B_{2n-1}B_{2n}$ of $B_1B_2 ... B_{2n}$. In fact, if d is this distance, then $A_1A_2 ... A_{2n}$ lies entirely in the d-neighborhood of $B_1B_2 ... B_{2n}$ (Diagram 103 a) and conversely (Diagram 103 b). Now we assume that all angles of the polygon are equal, that is, all are equal to

$$\frac{(2n-2)\cdot 180^\circ}{2n} = \left(1 - \frac{1}{n}\right)\cdot 180^\circ$$

(the sum of the angles of a polygon of $2n$ sides equals $(2n-2)\cdot 180^\circ$). Consider the triangles $B_{2n}A_1B_1, B_1A_2B_2, ..., B_{2n-1}A_{2n}B_{2n}$. The base of each of these triangles is less than h (Exercise 7-3) and the angle at the vertices of the polygon is $(1 - 1/n)\,180^\circ$. Hence the altitude of each triangle is less than the altitude of a segment that includes an angle $(1 - 1/n)\,180^\circ$ above a chord of length h (Diagram 104).

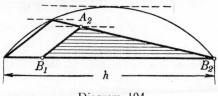

Diagram 104

However, as n increases, the height of this segment becomes as small as we please [it is easy to compute that it is equal to $(h/2) \tan (180^\circ/2n)$]. Hence, by choosing a sufficiently large number of sides for the polygon $A_1A_2 \ldots A_{2n}$ with $2n$ sides, we can make the distance between $A_1A_2 \ldots A_{2n}$ and $B_1B_2 \ldots B_{2n}$, and hence between K_0 and K, as small as we wish.

From the theorem just proved it follows at once that for each curve K of constant width h we can always find a sequence K_1, K_2, ..., K_n, ..., of curves of constant width h, where each of the curves consists of circular arcs of radius h, such that K is the limit of the sequence. For this purpose it is only necessary to require that the distance between K_1 and K be less than 1, the distance between K_2 and K be less than $\frac{1}{2}$, ..., the distance between K_m and K be less than $1/m$, etc. This theorem (called the *Approximation Theorem*[†]) is often useful in studying properties of arbitrary curves of constant width. In particular, the most difficult of the exercises stated earlier in this section (see Exercises 7-11 and 7-12) can be solved by using this theorem (see Exercises 7-19 and 7-20).

7-19. Obtain a new proof of Barbier's Theorem from the Approximation Theorem. (See Exercise 7-11.)

7-20.** From the Approximation Theorem, obtain a new proof that of all figures of constant width h the Reuleaux triangle bounds the smallest area.

A convex body in three-dimensional space is called a *body of constant width h* if the distance between any pair of parallel supporting planes is h. There are infinitely many bodies of constant width besides the sphere. However, examples of such bodies are more complicated than examples of plane curves of constant width, since there are no nonspherical bodies of constant width whose surfaces are entirely composed of portions of spheres. The simplest example of a nonspherical body of constant width is the body obtained by rotation of a Reuleaux triangle about its axis of symmetry (Diagram 105).

As examples of bodies of constant width which are not produced by rotation there are the "tetrahedra of constant width." These are

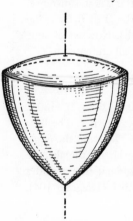

Diagram 105

---

† From the Latin *approximare*, meaning approach. Theorems of this kind, which permit the representation of complicated mathematical objects as limits of sequences of simpler objects, play a very important role in contemporary mathematics.

bodies which can be regarded as spatial analogues of the Reuleaux triangle. There are two different types of "tetrahedra of constant width." They are constructed as follows. Describe a sphere of radius h about each vertex of a regular tetrahedron of side h. The intersection of these four spheres forms the body shown in Diagram 106 a. Next we remove

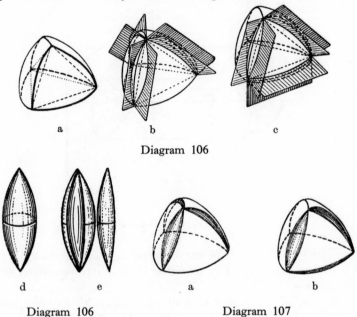

a   b   c

Diagram 106

d   e   a   b

Diagram 106   Diagram 107

the parts of the surface of this body which lie inside an angle between two surfaces, either the parts vertical to three tetrahedral edges which meet in a vertex (Diagram 106 b), or to three edges which bound a face (Diagram 106 c). These parts of the surface of the body are replaced by three pieces of surface generated by the rotation of the circular arcs bounding the given surface about the corresponding edges, that is, by portions of the surface of the spindle-shaped bodies shown in Diagram 106 d; a section of such a portion of surface is shown in Diagram 106 e. The two different types of bodies thus obtained are shown in Diagrams 107 a and 107 b. It is easy to verify that both types have constant width h. The two "tetrahedra of constant width" have the same surface and the same volume. We shall assume without proof that the "tetrahedra of constant width h" have the least volume among all bodies of constant width h.

Bodies of constant width h may have different surface areas; in other words, in space there is no analogue of Barbier's Theorem. However bodies of constant width in space have, instead, another remarkable property.

In three-dimensional space, the *projection* of a convex body P is the plane figure obtained by a parallel projection of P on some plane (Diagram 108). Since all projections of a body P of constant width h obviously produce plane figures of constant width h, it follows from Barbier's Theorem that all projections of P have exactly the same

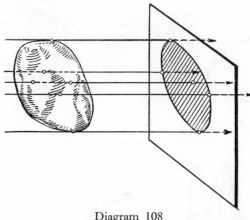

Diagram 108

perimeter πh (the length of the curve bounding the projection). A convex body is said to have a *constant perimeter* if all of its projections have the same perimeter.

Thus we see that *all bodies of constant width are also bodies of constant perimeter*. The converse also holds: *Every body of constant perimeter is a body of constant width*; however the proof of this theorem is complicated.[†]

† See T. Bonnesen and W. Fenchel: *Theorie der konvexen Körper* (Theory of convex bodies). Ergebnisse der Mathematik und ihrer Grenzgebiete 3, Berlin, 1934.

8

CURVES WHICH CAN
BE ROTATED IN AN
EQUILATERAL TRIANGLE
(Δ-CURVES) AND
RELATED CURVES

The contents of this section are closely related to those of the preceding one, which was devoted to curves of constant width. Hence this section should not be read before Section 7.

Knowledge of Section 1 is sufficient for the solution of the first eleven exercises and for Exercises 8-18 through 8-20. To solve Exercise 8-12, the theorem of Exercise 3-4 b is essential; if this section is read *before* Section 3, then it is necessary to examine Exercise 3-4 b carefully before attempting Exercise 8-12 (one need merely read through the solution). Exercises 8-13, 8-14, and 8-21 assume knowledge of Exercises 4-1 through 4-11. To understand the parts of this section which are in fine print (including Exercise 8-17), knowledge of all of Section 4 is necessary.

Curves of constant width (see Section 7) may be defined as convex curves that can be rotated in a square so that they always touch all sides of the square (see page 72, Diagram 93 b). It is natural to pose questions about the properties of convex curves that can be rotated freely inside other polygons. In this section we consider curves that can be rotated freely in the interior of an equilateral triangle so that they always remain in contact with all sides of the triangle (Diagram 109 a) or, what is the same thing, we consider curves all of whose circumscribed equilateral triangles are equal (Diagram 109 b). We shall call such curves *Δ-curves*. The simplest example of a *Δ* curve is the circle. Other examples are given in the first exercises of this section. The altitude *h* of every equilateral triangle circumscribed about a *Δ*-curve is called

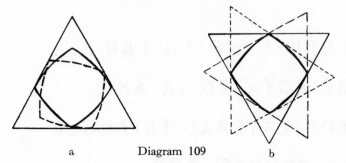

a   Diagram 109   b

the height of the *Δ*-curve. The properties of *Δ*-curves turn out to be very similar to those of curves of constant width, and many exercises of this section remind one of exercises in the previous section.

The conclusion of this section is devoted to certain generalizations of curves of constant width and *Δ*-curves. Several theorem referring to such generalizations are given without proof in this section. The reader is advised to attempt to prove then for himself.

8-1. (a) Let a circle whose radius equals the altitude of an equilateral triangle roll along one side of such a triangle. Prove that the arc cut out of the circle by the sides of the triangle always equals 60°. Prove also that the "lens" formed by reflection of these arcs in their corresponding chords (Diagram 110) always remains within the triangle. In what follows we shall call the boundary curve of this lens a *Δ-biangle*. The *Δ*-biangle is a *Δ*-curve.

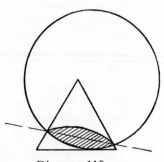

Diagram 110

Compute the length of a *Δ*-biangle of height *h* and also the area that it bounds. Which is greater, the area of a circle of radius $\frac{1}{3}h$ or the area of a *Δ*-biangle of height *h*?

(b) At each contact point of an equilateral triangle with an inscribed *Δ*-biangle, a line is constructed perpendicular to the side of the triangle. Prove that these three perpendiculars intersect in a point. In addition, find the locus described by the point of intersection of these perpendiculars when the Δ-biangle rotates inside the equilateral triangle and also the locus of this point when the equilateral triangle rotates so that it remains circumscribed about the Δ-biangle when the latter is stationary.

8-2. (a) About the vertices of a square of side h we draw four circles of radius h. Prove that the boundary curve of the figure resulting from the intersection of these circles is a Δ-curve of height h (Diagram 111). Compute the length of this curve and the area bounded by it.

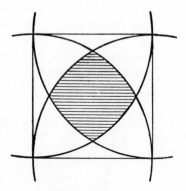

Diagram 111

(b) Circumscribe an equilateral triangle about the Δ-curve given in Exercise 8-2 a; erect perpendiculars to the sides of this triangle at the points where the curve touches the sides. Prove that these three perpendiculars intersect in a point. Find also the locus described by this point of intersection of the perpendiculars when the given Δ-curve rotates inside the equilateral triangle, and the locus it describes when the equilateral triangle rotates so that it remains circumscribed about the stationary Δ-curve.

8-3. Let K be a Δ-curve and let T be an equilateral triangle circumscribed about K whose sides touch K at the points A, B, C. Prove that the side of each equilateral triangle circumscribed about triangle ABC is not greater than the side of T.

8-4. * Prove that the perpendiculars to the sides of an equilateral triangle circumscribed about a Δ-curve K intersect in a point if the perpendiculars pass through the points of contact of the triangle with K.

This theorem generalizes the theorem of Exercise 8-1 b and 8-2 b.

The theorem of Exercise 8-4 has a simple kinematic meaning. It is proved in mechanics that the perpendiculars to the paths of all points of a moving body are at each instant either parallel to each other or else they meet in a point, which is called the *instantaneous center of rotation* of the body (Diagram 112). If a Δ-curve is rotated in the interior of an equilateral triangle so that it always remains in contact with the sides of the triangle, then it is easy to see that the paths traced by the points of contact of the curve with the sides of the triangle are each, at the moment of contact, tangent to a side of the triangle. Hence the perpendiculars to these paths at their contact points with the triangle coincide with the perpendiculars to sides of the triangle, and the point mentioned in Exercise 8-4 is the instantaneous center of rotation of the Δ-curve.

These kinematic concepts also make it possible to give simple proofs of a series of other theorems (in particular Barbier's) about Δ-curves and related curves and to simplify the construction of examples of such curves. The simplification which can be achieved by the use of these theorems stands out clearly if we compare what has been said here with the purely geometric proof given in the solution of Exercise 8-4.

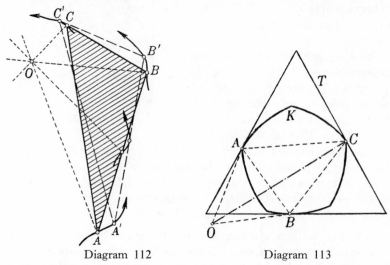

Diagram 112   Diagram 113

8-5. Prove that each supporting line of a Δ-curve can have only one point in common with the curve.

8-6. Prove that the diameter (see page 9) of a Δ-curve K of height h cannot exceed h. If the diameter is equal to h, then K is a Δ-biangle.

8-7. Prove that a Δ-curve has no corner with an interior angle of less than 60°. The only Δ-curve with an interior angle equal to 60° is a Δ-biangle.

8-8. Prove that the circle is the only Δ-curve that is carried into itself by a rotation of 120° about some point.

8-9. Let A, B, C be the points of intersection of a Δ-curve K with the sides of an equilateral triangle T circumscribed about K; moreover let O be the vertex outside the triangle ABC of the equilateral triangle ABO constructed on the side AB (Diagram 113). Prove that $OC = h$, the height of the Δ-curve K.

8-10.* Construct a Δ-curve of height h consisting of five or seven or, in general, of any number not divisible by three, circular arcs of radius h. Find the length of the curve constructed.

The Δ-curves of height h which are composed of circular arcs of radius h will play a significant role in further developments (see the fine print on pages 89-92).

8-11.* By considering polygons with $3 \cdot 2^n$ sides and equal angles circumscribed about a general Δ-curve of height h and also about a circle O of radius $\frac{1}{3}h$, prove *Barbier's Theorem for Δ-curves*: all Δ-curves of height h have the same length, namely, $2\pi h/3$.

8-12.** By considering equiangular polygons with $3 \cdot 2^n$ sides circumscribed about any Δ-curve K of height h, about a circle O of radius $\frac{1}{3}h$, and about a Δ-biangle D of height h, prove that among all Δ-curves of height h, the circle encloses the greatest area and the Δ-biangle the least area.

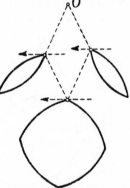

That the circle has the greatest area of all Δ-curves of given height h follows also from the isoperimetric problem (see Exercise 5-8) using Barbier's Theorem for Δ-curves (see Exercise 8-11).

Just as in the theory of curves of constant width, the concepts considered in Section 4 prove to be very useful in questions about Δ-curves. It follows directly from the theorems of Exercises 4-7 and 4-8 that *the sum of two Δ-curves is also a Δ-curve*. This theorem makes it possible to construct new examples of Δ-curves beginning with any known examples.

Diagram 114

Thus in Diagram 114, for example, the sum of two equal Δ-biangles is shown, where one biangle is obtained from the other by a 90° rotation; in Diagram 115 a the sum of a Δ-biangle and a circle is shown; Diagram 115 b represents the sum of the curve in Exercise 8-2 with a circle. All these curves are also Δ-curves.

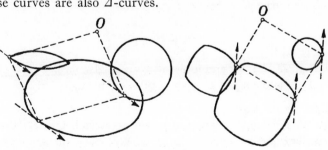

a   Diagram 115   b

8-13. If K is any Δ-curve, and K' and K'' are curves obtained by rotating K through 120° and 240° respectively, prove that the sum $K + K' + K''$ is a circle. Obtain from this fact a new proof of Barbier's Theorem for Δ-curves (see Exercise 8-11).

8-14. (Converse of Exercise 8-13) Prove that if the rotation of a curve K through 120° and 240° produces curves K' and K'' respectively such that $K + K' + K''$ is a circle, then K is a Δ-curve.

It follows from Exercises 8-13 and 8-14 that a *Δ-curve can be defined as a curve which yields a circle when added to the curves obtained by rotating it through 120ꞌ and through 240°*. All the properties of Δ-curves can easily be obtained from this definition.

We can also give a definition of Δ-curves which is similar to the basic definition for curves of constant width given at the beginning of Section 7. By analogy with the width of a curve in a given direction, we speak of *the height of a convex curve in a given direction* when referring to the height of an equilateral triangle which is circumscribed about the

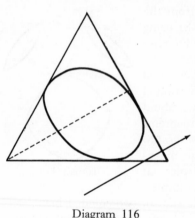

Diagram 116

curve and which has a side perpendicular to the given direction (see Diagram 116). Hence Δ-curves may also be described as curves whose height in every direction is the same, or as *curves of constant height*. The largest of the heights of a curve for all possible directions we call the *greatest height* of the curve (*cf.* the definition of the diameter of a convex curve, page 9) and the smallest of all heights of a curve is its *least height* or simply its *height* (see the definition of the width of a convex curve, page 18).

8-15. Prove that the greatest height H and the least height h of a convex curve K satisfy the inequality

$$h \leq H \leq 2h$$

and that $H = h$ if and only if K is a Δ-curve. Prove also that $H = 2h$ if and only if K is an equilateral triangle.

8-16. Prove that:

(a) Of all convex curves of given greatest height H, the curves of constant height H (that is, Δ-curves) have the greatest length, and the equilateral triangle of altitude $H/2$ has the least length;

(b) Of all convex curves of given height h, the Δ-curves of height h have the least length, and the equilateral triangle of altitude h has the greatest length;

(c) Of all convex curves of given greatest height H and given least height h, the greatest length is possessed by the curves that consist of three segments of the sides of an equilateral triangle of altitude h and three arcs of a Δ-curve of height H (Diagram 117 a);

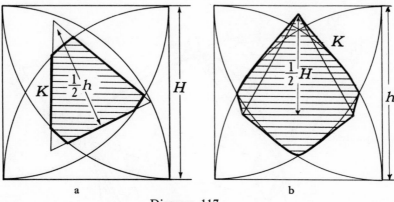

Diagram 117

the least length is possessed by the curves that consist of three arcs of a Δ-curve of height h and of six segments, which lie respectively on the lines of support at the ends of these arcs, and which intersect by pairs in the vertices of a triangle of greatest height H (Diagram 117 b).

From Exercise 8-16 the following estimates may be stated for the length L of a convex curve of given greatest height H, or given least height h, or given greatest height H and least height h:

(a) $H \sqrt{3} \leq L \leq \dfrac{2\pi H}{3};$

(b) $\dfrac{2\pi h}{3} \leq L \leq 4h \sqrt{3};$

(c) $2\left[h\left(\dfrac{\pi}{3} - \arccos \dfrac{h}{H}\right) + \sqrt{H^2 - h^2}\right] \leq L \leq 2\left[H\left(\dfrac{\pi}{3} - \arccos \dfrac{h}{H}\right)\right.$

$$\left. + \sqrt{H^2 - h^2}\right].$$

For Δ-curves, an approximation theorem can also be proved which is similar to that for curves of constant width (see page 80). In fact, we can show that for any Δ-curve K of height h, a Δ-curve K_0 of the same height can be constructed which consists of circular arcs of radius h and which approximates the curve K as closely as we wish. The proof of this theorem resembles that of the analogous theorem for curves of constant width.

Consider a polygon $A_1A_2 \ldots A_{3n}$ of $3n$ sides circumscribed about K so that equilateral triangles are formed by the lines of the first side, the $(n + 1)$'st side, and the $(2n + 1)$'st side, similarly by the lines of the second side, the $(n + 2)$'nd side, and the $(2n + 2)$'nd

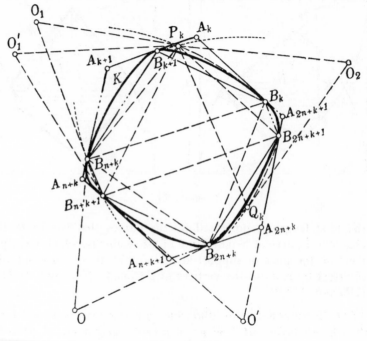

Diagram 118

side, and, in general, by the lines of the sides A_kA_{k+1}, $A_{n+k}A_{n+k+1}$, $A_{2n+k}A_{2n+k+1}$ (for example, a circumscribed equiangular polygon with $3n$ sides). The points of contact of the sides of this polygon with K are denoted by B_1, B_2, ..., B_{3n}. We shall prove that a Δ-curve of height h exists, consisting of circular arcs of radius h, which is inscribed in $A_1A_2 \ldots A_{3n}$ and circumscribed about $B_1B_2 \ldots B_{3n}$.

By means of the following construction we simultaneously replace the arcs B_kB_{k+1}, $B_{n+k}B_{n+k+1}$, $B_{2n+k}B_{2n+k+1}$ of K by new curves consisting of circular arcs of radius h. On the sides $B_{n+k}B_{2n+k}$ and $B_{n+k+1}B_{2n+k+1}$ of triangles $B_kB_{n+k}B_{2n+k}$ and $B_{k+1}B_{n+k+1}B_{2n+k+1}$, we construct outside these triangles the equilateral triangles $B_{n+k}B_{2n+k}O$ and $B_{n+k+1}B_{2n+k+1}O'$ (Diagram 118). About the points O and O' we draw circular arcs of radius h. Let P_k denote the point of intersection of these circles which lies on the same side of the line OO' as do B_k and B_{k+1}. Next, on the sides P_kB_{n+k} and P_kB_{n+k+1} of the triangles $P_kB_{n+k}B_{2n+k}$ and $P_kB_{n+k+1}B_{2n+k+1}$, we construct outside these triangles the equilateral triangles $P_kB_{n+k}O_1$ and $P_kB_{n+k+1}O_1'$. Since triangle $O_1B_{n+k}B_{2n+k}$ is congruent to triangle OP_kB_{n+k}, and triangle $O_1'B_{n+k+1}B_{2n+k+1}$ is congruent to triangle $O'P_kB_{n+k+1}$, it follows that $O_1B_{2n+k} = OP_k = h$ and $O_1'B_{2n+k+1} = O'P_k = h$.

Now we draw circles of radius h about the points O_1 and O_1'. We denote by Q_k the point of intersection of these circles lying on the same side of the line of centers O_1O_1' as the points B_{2n+k} and B_{2n+k+1}. Finally, on the common side P_kQ_k of triangles $P_kQ_kB_{n+k}$ and $P_kQ_k B_{n+k+1}$, and outside these triangles, we construct an equilateral triangle $P_kQ_kO_2$; then $O_2B_{n+k} = O_1Q_k = h$, $O_2B_{n+k+1} = O_1'Q_k = h$, ($\Delta O_2B_{n+k}P_k = \Delta O_1Q_kP_k$ and $\Delta O_2B_{n+k+1}P_k = \Delta O_1'Q_kP_k$); hence we can join the points B_{n+k} and B_{n+k+1} by a circular arc of radius h about the point O_2.

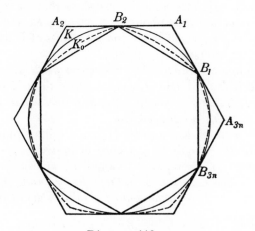

Diagram 119

Next we replace the arc B_kB_{k+1} of K by the circular arcs B_kP_k and P_kB_{k+1}, the arc $B_{2n+k}B_{2n+k+1}$ of K by the circular arcs $B_{2n+k}Q_k$ and Q_kB_{2n+k+1}, and the arc $B_{n+k}B_{n+k+1}$ by a circular arc $B_{n+k}B_{n+k+1}$ about O_2. It is evident that the new curve K^* thus obtained is also a Δ-curve. If a regular triangle circumscribed about K^* touches any of the constructed circular arcs, then it is easy to establish that the other two sides of this triangle pass through vertices of the curve and the altitude of the triangle equals h (cf. the solution of Exercise 8-10).

If we carry out such a replacement for each triple of arcs B_kB_{k+1}, $B_{n+k}B_{n+k+1}$, $B_{2n+k}B_{2n+k+1}$, and B_nB_{n+1}, $B_{2n}B_{2n+1}$, $B_{2n}B_1$ of K, where

$k = 1, 2, ..., n - 1$, we obtain a $\varDelta$-curve K_0 of height h, which consists entirely of circular arcs of radius h and which is circumscribed about the polygon $B_1 B_2 ... B_{3n}$ and inscribed in the polygon $A_1 A_2 ... A_{3n}$ (Diagram 119).

The rest of the proof is the same as that for the approximation theorem for curves of constant width. The theorem we have just established can be expressed as follows : *Every $\varDelta$-curve K of height h is the limit of a sequence of $\varDelta$-curves, $K_1, K_2, ..., K_n, ...,$ each of height h and composed of circular arcs of height h.*

8-17. Obtain from the Approximation Theorem a new proof of Barbier's Theorem for $\varDelta$-curves (see Exercise 8-11).

By analogy with $\varDelta$-curves, we can also study convex curves that rotate freely within a regular polygon of n sides and always maintain contact with the sides (here n may be any fixed integer; for $n = 3$ we obtain $\varDelta$-curves and for $n = 4$ curves of constant width). We can prove a series of theorems about such curves similar to those considered in the present section. For example, we can show that if a regular polygon P of n sides is circumscribed about such a curve K, and perpendiculars to the sides of P are erected at the contact points of P and K, then these n perpendiculars intersect in a point.[†]

By examining an equiangular polygon of $n \cdot 2^k$ sides circumscribed about a curve K and a circle O, we can prove that *the length of a curve K which rotates inside a regular polygon of n sides equals the length of the circle inscribed in this n-sided polygon.*

This last theorem can also be obtained quite simply by using the theorem about the length of the sum of convex curves. By analogy with the solutions of Exercises 7-15 and 8-13 we can, in fact, prove the following: *If a curve K can be rotated freely inside a regular n-sided polygon so that it is in constant contact with all sides of the polygon, then*

$$K + K^{(1)} + K^{(2)} + ... + K^{(n-1)}$$

is a circle, where $K^{(1)}$ is obtained by rotating K through $360°/n$, $K^{(2)}$ by rotating K through $2 \cdot 360°/n$, ..., and $K^{(n-1)}$ by rotating K through $(n - 1) 360°/n$.[§] Since the length of the sum of curves equals the sum of their lengths (see Section 4, page 46), it follows at once that curves that can be rotated freely inside a regular polygon of n sides must all have the same length (*cf.* the solutions of Exercises 7-15 and 8-13).

[†] See the text in fine print on page 85; the kinematic proof sketched there for the theorem in Exercise 8-4 can be transferred unchanged to the more general case.

[§] To prove this we must establish the following simple theorem: *The only curve that can be rotated freely inside a regular polygon of n-sides and that is invariant under a rotation of $360°/n$ about some point is a circle.*

In contrast to the theorems of Exercises 7-16 and 8-14, it should be noted that even if the sum of a curve K and $(n - 1)$ curves obtained from K by rotation through $360^o/n$, $2 \cdot 360^o/n$, ..., $(n - 1) \, 360^o/n$, is a circle, it still does not follow that K can be rotated freely inside a regular polygon of n sides (*cf.* page 96).

There are infinitely many curves which are not circles, but which can be rotated freely inside a regular polygon of n sides while always remaining in contact with the sides of the polygon.[†] For $n > 4$, however, the simplest examples of such curves become more complicated than the Reuleaux triangle or the $\varDelta$-biangle. It is also not known, for $n > 4$, which of the curves that can be rotated freely inside a regular polygon of n-sides bounds the least area.

We now consider another generalization of curves of constant width and $\varDelta$-curves.

It is obvious that about any convex curve a rectangle can be circumscribed so that its sides have arbitrarily chosen directions (*cf.* page 8). The curves of constant width may be defined as curves for which all the circumscribed rectangles are equal squares (*cf.* page 72, especially Diagram 93 a). We now consider convex curves with the property that *all their circumscribed rectangles have the same perimeter*.[§]

Naturally all curves of constant width have this property. However there are also many curves with this property which are not curves of constant width. The simplest examples of such curves are given in Exercises 8-18 and 8-19, immediately following. It turns out that for these curves certain properties of constant width curves remain valid (see first of all, Exercise 8-20).[¶]

8-18. Let the altitudes of an equilateral triangle be continued beyond the corresponding vertices; on these extensions let segments be laid off equal to the sides of the triangle. Join the vertices of the triangle by circular arcs circumscribed about the end points of

[†] We can prove that every arc of a convex curve satisfying certain fairly general conditions can be extended to form a convex curve of this sort if the angle between the tangents at the end points of the arc is not greater than $360^o/n$.

[§] The most obvious generalization of curves of constant width would be those curves for which all the circumscribed rectangles are the same, but are not squares, that is, those curves that rotate freely inside a rectangle and always remain in contact with its sides. It is easy, however, to prove that no such curves exist.

In fact, if a curve rotates freely between two parallel lines (which are sides of any rectangle) and always touches them, then the distance between each pair of parallel supporting lines of this curve equals the distance between the given parallel lines. Hence the curve in question is a curve of constant width, and all its circumscribed rectangles are squares.

[¶] The connection between these curves and curves of constant width is shown in Exercise 8-21.

the extended altitudes (Diagram 120). Prove that all rectangles circumscribed about the convex curve formed from the three circular arcs have the same perimeter. Compute the length of this curve and the area it bounds if the perimeter of a rectangle circumscribed about the curve is $4l$.

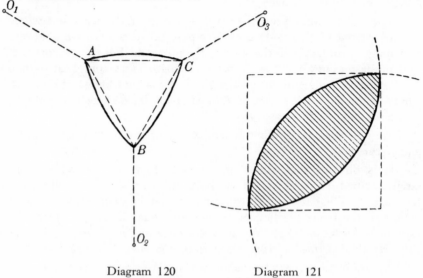

Diagram 120   Diagram 121

8-19. Two circles are drawn about the opposite vertices of a square with radii equal to the side of the square. Prove that the perimeters of all rectangles circumscribed about the intersection of these two circles are equal (Diagram 121). Compute the length of the curve bounding this figure and the area of the figure if the perimeter of a circumscribed rectangle is $4l$.

8-20.* (Generalization of Barbier's Theorem) If all the rectangles circumscribed about a convex curve K have perimeter $4l$, then the length of K is πl.

From Exercises 4-7 and 4-8 we infer: *If each of the curves K_1 and K_2 has the property that all its circumscribed rectangles are of equal perimeter, then $K = K_1 + K_2$ also has this property.* This fact makes it possible to construct new examples of curves whose circumscribed rectangles all have equal perimeters, starting from known curves with this property. In Diagram 122, for example, the sum of the curve of Exercise 8-18 and a circle is shown; in Diagram 123 the sum of the curve in Exercise 8-19 and a circle is shown.

8-21. If the perimeters of all rectangles circumscribed about a convex curve K are equal, then $K + K'$ is a curve of constant width if K' is obtained from K by a 90° rotation; conversely, if $K + K'$ is a curve of constant width, and K' is obtained from K by a 90° rotation, then the perimeters of all rectangles that are circumscribed about the convex curve K are equal. Obtain from this statement a new proof of the generalization of Barbier's Theorem (see Exercise 8-20). What is $K + K'$ if K is the curve of Exercise 8-18 or the curve of Exercise 8-19?

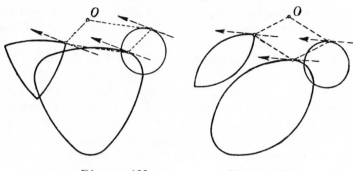

Diagram 122   Diagram 123

A curve whose circumscribed rectangles all have the same perimeter may also be defined as a *curve that yields a curve of constant width when added to any curve obtained from it by a rotation through 90°*. Still another definition for such a curve is that it is a convex curve that yields a circle when added to the three curves obtained by rotating it through angles of 90°, 180°, and 270°; this follows easily from the definition of curves of constant width given on page 75. Thus, for example, in Diagram 124 the curves K, K', K'', K''', each of which is obtained from its predecessor by a 90° rotation, have a circle as sum. This definition is completely analogous to the definition of curves of constant width (see page 75) and to the definition of Δ-curves (see page 87).

We can also prove the follow-ing: Every curve K of constant width h can be represented as the sum of a curve K_1, all of whose circumscribed rectangles have peri-meter $2h$, and the curve K_1' obtained by rotating K_1 through 90°. This theorem is quite simple to prove for curves of constant width h which consist of circular arcs of radius h. The general theorem follows from this special case by means of the

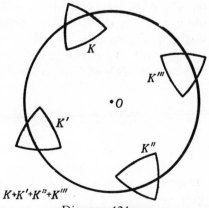

$K + K' + K'' + K'''$

Diagram 124

Approximation Theorem (*cf.* Section 7, page 80) and Theorem 1 in Appendix I.

We can also study curves K with the property that all equiangular polygons of n sides (for any fixed integer n) circumscribed about K have the same perimeter. For $n = 4$, we obtain the curves studied in Exercises 8-18 through 8-21; for $n = 3$, we obtain the Δ-curves considered in Exercises 8-1 through 8-5. Special cases of such curves are the curves that can be rotated freely inside a regular n-sided polygon while always maintaining contact with the sides of the polygon (see page 92).

There are, however, infinitely many curves with the desired property which are different from the curves that can be rotated freely in a regular n-sided polygon, and simple examples of these can be constructed. For example, it is easy to verify that the perimeters are the same for all equiangular n-sided polygons circumscribed about a curve consisting of $n - 1$ equal circular arcs, the angular measure of each of which is equal to the angles of a regular n-sided polygon (Diagram 125;

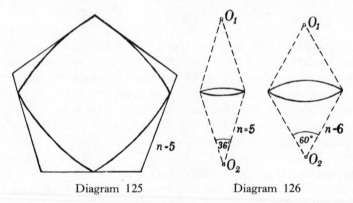

Diagram 125   Diagram 126

for $n = 4$ the curve constructed becomes the curve of Exercise 8-18; for $n = 3$, it is the Δ-biangle defined in Exercise 8-1). We also readily establish the equality of the perimeters of all equiangular n-sided polygons that are circumscribed about a curve consisting of two equal circular arcs with angular measure

$$\frac{[3 + (-1)^n]\,180^\circ}{2n} = \begin{cases} \dfrac{180^\circ}{n} \text{ for } n \text{ odd,} \\[2mm] \dfrac{360^\circ}{n} \text{ for } n \text{ even} \end{cases}$$

(Diagram 126; for $n = 4$ this curve coincides with the curve of Exercise 8-19; for $n = 3$, with the Δ-biangle). It seems plausible that this curve bounds a smaller area than any other curve with the property that all equiangular n-sided polygons circumscribed about it have the same perimeter; it would be interesting to prove or refute this conjecture.

By examining equiangular polygons of $n \cdot 2^k$ sides circumscribed about a curve K with the property that all its circumscribed equiangular n-sided polygons have perimeter nl, it is easy to establish that *the length of K equals the perimeter of the circle which is inscribed in the regular n-sided polygon of side l* (*cf.* solution of Exercise 8-20).

The last theorem can be derived in a simpler way from the theorem about the length of the sum of convex curves (see Section 4, page 46) if one uses the following easily established theorem:

The perimeters of all equiangular polygons circumscribed about a curve K are equal if and only if the sum of the curve K and the $n - 1$ curves obtained by rotating K through $360°/n$, $2 \cdot 360°/n$, ..., $(n - 1) \, 360°/n$ is a circle (*cf.* Exercises 8-13, 8-14, and 8-21).

Another generalization of curves of constant width is the class of *convex curves all of whose circumscribed rectangles are squares* (not necessarily equal!). The square itself serves as the simplest example of such a curve not having constant width. It is possible to show that *all rectangles circumscribed about a curve K are squares if and only if K is the sum of two curves K_1 and K_1', where K_1' results from a $90°$ rotation of K_1.*[†] Thus, for example, the square is the sum of two equal and mutually perpendicular segments (see Exercise 4-1, page 43). If a curve K_1 has the property that all rectangles circumscribed about it have the same perimeter, then $K_1 + K_1'$ is a curve of constant width (*cf.* Exercise 8-21 and the remark on page 95).

We can also study curves that rotate freely inside an *irregular* n-sided polygon while maintaining contact with all its sides. However it is far from true that such curves exist for every n-sided polygon (see for example, the footnote on page 93). It is possible to show that for a given triangle there exists a curve which is not a circle and which rotates freely in the triangle while maintaining continuous contact with the sides, if and only if all angles of the triangle are commensurable.[§]

This result is also correct for all n-sided polygons, when $n \neq 4$; if the angles of an n-sided polygon, $n \neq 4$, in which a circle is inscribed are *commensurable*, then there exists a curve which is not a circle and

---

[†] If $K = K_1 + K_1'$ and K_1' is obtained by a $90°$ rotation of K_1, it is easy to show that every rectangle circumscribed about K must be a square. The converse is obtained easily in case K is a polygon with the given property. The general theorem can be derived with the aid of the following approximation theorem: every curve K all of whose circumscribed rectangles are squares is the limit of a sequence of polygons $K_1, K_2, ..., K_n, ...$ having the same property (in the sense of the definition given in Section 4, page 50).

[§] See I. M. Kamenetskiĭ: "Rešenie geometriceskoi zadači L. Lyusternika" (The solution of a geometrical problem of L. Lyusternik). Uspehi mat. nauk, vol. II, 2, 1947, pages 199-202. (The proof is not elementary.)

which rotates freely inside the *n*-sided polygon while always touching all sides; if the angles of an *n*-sided polygon are *incommensurable*, such a curve does not exist.[†] For quadrilaterals this theorem does not hold; regardless of whether the angles of a rhombus are commensurable or not, there exist noncircular curves that can rotate freely inside a rhombus and always remain in contact with its sides (curves with constant width equal to the height of the rhombus have this property).

The curves inside which a regular triangle can be freely rotated so that the vertices glide along the curve are, in a certain sense, "dual" to the *Δ*-curves. It is easy to show, for example, that the curve shown in Diagram 127, consisting of two circular arcs with central angle 120°,

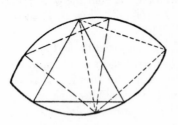

Diagram 127

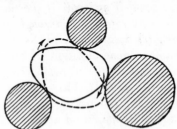

Diagram 128

has this property. It has been conjectured that this curve and the circle are the only *convex* curves in which a regular triangle can be rotated (there are infinitely many *nonconvex* curves of this sort); it would be interesting to prove or refute this conjecture.

Nothing seems to be known about curves inside of which a general triangle or general *n*-sided polygon, can be rotated.

A generalization of the problems about curves that can be rotated inside a triangle while touching all its sides, and of the problems about curves within which a triangle can be rotated, is offered by a problem

[†] The given result appears remarkable at first sight; however the same situation appears quite often in similar problems. As a further example we cite a problem related to a special case of a general problem of L. A. Lyusternik (which is described at the end of this section) namely: *to find all convex curves which can be seen from all points of a fixed circle subtending a constant angle* α. It turns out that in case the angle α is incommensurable with π, then the only such curve is a circle concentric with the circle C. The same is true of $\alpha = (m/n)\,\pi$, where m and n are relatively prime odd integers. If at least one of the two integers m or n is even (and n is not zero), then there are infinitely many noncircular curves with the given property. The circle has the greatest length of all curves with the desired property; the least length, however, is that of a certain *n*-sided, curvilinear polygon which consists of elliptical arcs (in case $m/n = 1/2$ this *n*-sided polygon degenerates into a double segment, the diameter of the circle C). In this connection see J. W. Green: "Sets Subtending a constant angle on a circle," *Duke Mathematical Journal*, 17, No. 3, 1950, pages 263-267.

posed several years ago by L. A. Lyusternik.[†] He sought to establish
the conditions for the existence of convex figures other than circles
which can be rotated freely while maintaining continuous contact with
three given circles in the plane (Diagram 128), where any of these
circles may become a line ("a circle of infinite radius") or a point
(" a circle of zero radius"). If in place of three circles we consider three
lines, then we obtain the problem about curves that can be rotated
inside a triangle. If three points are considered, we obtain the problem
about curves in whose interior a triangle can be rotated. The complete
solution of the problem of L. A. Lyusternik (which is of practical significance in the technique of measurement) is probably extremely difficult

[†] Uspehi Mat. nauk, vol. 1, parts 3-4, 1946.

Appendix I

LIMIT THEOREM FOR CURVES

We shall prove the following important theorem, which may be called "the principle of the limit curve."

THEOREM 1. *If infinitely many convex curves are given lying entirely inside a circle, then one can always select from them a sequence of curves $K_1, K_2, ..., K_n, ...$ which has a limit.* The limit of this sequence can be either a convex curve, a segment, or a point.

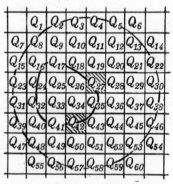

Diagram 129

PROOF. Denote the set of all convex curves in question by L and the circle in which they lie by O; then subdivide the plane into squares of side $\frac{1}{8}$ and denote those squares in which points of the circular region O lie by $Q_1, Q_2, ..., Q_r$. Let $L(Q_\alpha, Q_\beta, ..., Q_\rho)$ be the set of all curves that have points in common with each of the squares $Q_\alpha, Q_\beta, ..., Q_\rho$, but no points in common with the other squares. Clearly each of the given curves belongs to a certain set $L(Q_\alpha, Q_\beta, ..., Q_\rho)$. In Diagram 129, for example, the curve

100

indicated has points in common with the squares $Q_{16}, Q_{17}, Q_{18}, Q_{24},$ $Q_{26}, Q_{27}, Q_{32}, Q_{35}, Q_{40}, Q_{41}, Q_{42}, Q_{43}$ only. It is obvious that many sets $L(Q_\alpha, Q_\beta, ..., Q_\rho)$ need not contain any curves. For example the set $L(Q_{27}, Q_{42})$ certainly contains no curve, since a convex curve cannot consist of two separated pieces.

The number of the sets $L(Q_\alpha, Q_\beta, ..., Q_\rho)$ is finite. There exist, in fact, exactly $\binom{r}{1}$ sets formed from curves that lie exactly in one square, exactly $\binom{r}{2}$ sets whose curves lie in two squares, etc. Thus there are

$$\binom{r}{1} + \binom{r}{2} + ... + \binom{r}{r} = 2^r - 1$$

sets $L(Q_\alpha, Q_\beta, ..., Q_\rho)$, many of which, however, contain no curves at all. Thus it follows that at least one of the sets $L(Q_\alpha, Q_\beta, ..., Q_\rho)$ must contain infinitely many curves. For if each set $L(Q_\alpha, Q_\beta, ..., Q_\rho)$ contained only a finite number of curves, then all these sets together would include a finite number of curves, whereas the set of all the curves was assumed to be infinite.

Hence some set $L(Q_{\alpha_0}, Q_{\beta_0}, ..., Q_{\rho_0})$ must contain infinitely many curves. Denote this set by L_1. *If K' and K'' are two curves belonging to L_1, then the distance between them is less than* $\frac{1}{4}$. Let A be any point of K' and let Q_δ be the square in which A lies. Then there is a point B on K'', likewise in Q_δ, since K' and K'' both belong to L_1. Thus there is a point B on K'' whose distance from A is equal to or less than $\sqrt{2}/8$ (the diagonal of a square of side $\frac{1}{8}$). All points of K' lie therefore in a $\frac{1}{8}\sqrt{2}$-neighborhood of K''. On the other hand, K'' lies in a $\frac{1}{8}\sqrt{2}$-neighborhood of K'; the distance between these curves is thus equal to or less than $\frac{1}{8}\sqrt{2}$ and hence is less than $\frac{1}{4}$.

Let K_1 be any curve of L_1 and let $K_1^* = K_1 + O_{1/2}$, where $O_{1/2}$ is a circle of radius $\frac{1}{2}$, that is, K_1^* is the outermost boundary curve of a $\frac{1}{2}$-neighborhood of K_1. Then each curve K' of L_1, together with its $\frac{1}{4}$-neighborhood, lies inside K_1^* (since each curve K' of L_1 lies entirely in the interior of $K_1 + O_{1/2}$).

We now subdivide the plane into squares of side $\frac{1}{16}$ and denote by $Q_1', Q_2', ...$, those squares having points in common with the circular region O. Just as before, we define $L(Q_\alpha', ..., Q_\rho')$ to be all curves of L_1 which intersect the squares $Q_\alpha', ..., Q_\rho'$ and have no points in common with the remaining squares. From these sets we choose a certain set containing infinitely many curves and denote this set by L_2. Just as above, we show that the distance between any two curves of L_2 is less than or equal to $\frac{1}{8}$ (since the sides of the squares are chosen only half as large). If we choose any curve K_2 of L_2 and write $K_2^* = K_2 + O_{1/4}$, where $O_{1/4}$ is a circle of radius $\frac{1}{4}$, then all curves of L_2 and their $\frac{1}{8}$-neighborhoods lie inside K_2^*. Since K_2 is a curve of L_1 (the entire set L_2 is contained in L_1), it follows that K_2 and its $\frac{1}{4}$-neighborhood lie inside K_1^*. That is, K_2^* lies entirely within K_1^*.

Next we subdivide the plane into squares of side $\frac{1}{32}$ and once more carry out the same construction. We obtain a set L_3, from which we select any curve K_3, and let $K_3^* = K_3 + O_{1/8}$. Then K_3^* lies entirely inside K_2^*.

Continuing this process, we construct a sequence K_1, K_2, ..., K_n, ... of curves of L and a sequence of auxiliary curves K_1^*, K_2^*, ..., K_n^*, ..., where K_1^* encloses K_2^*, K_2^* encloses K_3^*, etc.; the distance between K_n and K_n^* is $1/2^n$ since $K_n^* = K_n + O_{1/2^n}$, where $O_{1/2^n}$ is a circle of radius $1/2^n$.

We denote by Φ_n^* the convex figure bounded by K_n^*. We now prove that *there is at least one point belonging to all of the figures* Φ_1^*, Φ_2^*, ..., Φ_n^*, ... We draw supporting lines l_n to each of the figures Φ_n^* so that all these supporting lines are parallel and have the same orientation. We denote the half-plane to the left of l_n by Π_n, that is, the half-plane in which Φ_n^* lies. The intersection of all the half-planes Π_1, Π_2, ..., Π_n, ... is a certain half-plane Π which is bounded by a line l parallel to l_1, l_2, ..., l_n, ... It is clear that the line l intersects each of the figures Φ_n^*, so Φ_1^* cuts out a certain segment M_1 on l, Φ_2^* a certain segment M_2, etc. Thus M_1 contains M_2; M_2 contains M_3; etc. A common point of all these segments is also a common point of all the figures Φ_1^*, Φ_2^*, ...

To prove the existence of a common point for all the segments M_1, M_2, ..., we consider the ray N_1 lying to the left of the right end point of M_1, the ray N_2 lying to the left of the right end point of M_2, etc. Each of these rays is a convex figure; and N_1 contains N_2, N_2 contains N_3, and so on. The intersection of all these rays is a convex figure bounded on one side and is thus a ray. It is clear that the end point C of this ray belongs to all of the segments M_1, M_2, ... Hence the figures Φ_1^*, Φ_2^*, ..., Φ_n^* ... have a common point, and we may speak of the (nonempty) intersection of all these figures, denoted by Φ^*. The boundary K^* of this figure is either a convex curve (if Φ^* is a two-dimensional convex figure), a segment, or a point.

It is evident immediately that l is a supporting line of Φ^*. In fact, we have noted that points of Φ^* lie on this line (for example the point C). Moreover, since each Φ_n^* is to the left of l_n and is therefore in the plane Π_n, the intersection of all these figures must be in Π, the intersection of all the half-planes Π_n. Hence Π lies to the left of l, and l is a supporting line of Φ^*. If l' is parallel to l and similarly oriented, and if l' lies to the right of l, then after a certain

n all figures Φ_n^* lie to the left of l'. The points of l' do not lie in Π and thus l' does not belong to all half planes Π_n; that is, after a certain n, the half-planes Π_n and also the figures Φ_n^* all lie to the left of l'.

Now we choose any positive distance, ϵ. Let P be a polygon which is circumscribed about the curve K^* and whose exterior angles are so small that the distance between P and K^* is less than $\epsilon/2$.[†] Further, let P' be a polygon enclosing P whose sides are parallel to the sides of P; we assume that the sides of P' are sufficiently close to those of P so that the distance between P and P' is also less than $\epsilon/2$;[§] hence the distance between K^* and P' is less than ϵ (see Exercise 4-15, page 49).

Denote the sides of P' by l_1', l_2', ..., l_k'. Then there is an integer n_1 such that all the figures Φ_n^* for which $n > n_1$ lie to the left of l_1'. There is an integer n_2 such that for $n > n_2$ the figures Φ_n^* lie to the left of l_2', etc. Thus, if n is larger than n_1, n_2, ..., n_k, the figures Φ_n^* lie to the left of all the sides l_1', l_2', ..., l_k'. They are therefore enclosed in P' and hence are in the ϵ-neighborhood of K^*. Thus, after a certain n, all the curves K_n^* are at a distance less than ϵ from K^*; that is K^* *is the limit of the sequence* K_1^*, K_2^*, ..., K_n^*, ...

We now prove that K^* is also the limit of the sequence K_1, K_2, ..., K_n ... . Let n_ε be such that if $n > n_\varepsilon$, then the distance between K^* and K_n is less then $\epsilon/2$. We may also take n_ε so large that for $n > n_\varepsilon$ the inequality $1/2^n < \epsilon/2$ holds. Hence the distance between K_n^* and K_n is less than $\epsilon/2$ when $n > n_\varepsilon$.

In this way we establish that the distance between K^* and K_n is less than ϵ for $n > n_\varepsilon$; that is, K^* *is the limit of the sequence* K_1,

---

[†] The distance between a convex curve and a polygon circumscribed about it is less than $d \tan \alpha$, where d is the diameter of the curve and α is the greatest exterior angle of the polygon. In fact, in Diagram 130 the segment $A_1B_1 = C_1A_1$ $\tan \alpha_1$, where $C_1A_1 \leq d$, since C_1 and A_1 are points of the convex figure; moreover $\alpha_1 \leq \alpha' \leq \alpha$.

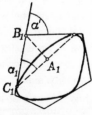

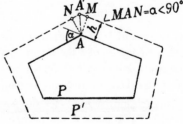

Diagram 130   Diagram 131

[§] If all exterior angles of P are less than $90°$ and if the sides of P' are at distance h from the corresponding sides of P, then the distance between P and P' is less than $h \sqrt{2}$ (Diagram 131). If K^* is a segment or a point, P' can be taken to be a rectangle sufficiently close to K^*.

$K_2, ..., K_n, ...$. This limit may be a convex curve, a segment, or a point. This proves the theorem.

THEOREM 2. (Bolzano-Weierstrass Theorem) *From every infinite set of points inside a circle it is always possible to choose a sequence of points having a limit.*

These theorems enable us to prove in certain cases that a convex figure having a stated property exists (although nothing can be established about the *shape* of the figure by use of these theorems). We consider some examples.

Exercise 1 (see page 55). *Prove that among all convex curves of perimeter 1, there exists a curve of greatest area.*

Solution. Let F be any convex figure of perimeter 1 and let its area be S. Choose a fixed line l and a point O on it. To the right of O lay off a segment OM of length S (in fixed units of length). In this way we can assign a certain point M of the line l to each convex figure of perimeter 1. The larger the area of F, the further to the right M lies on l. The points M corresponding to all convex figures of perimeter 1 form a certain set Φ on the line l.

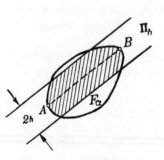

Diagram 132

We show that this set is a one-dimensional convex figure. If M is a point of Φ and α is the length of OM (that is, if there exists a figure F_a of perimeter 1 and area α), and if N is a point of OM such that $ON = \beta$, $\beta < \alpha$, then N also belongs to Φ (that is, there exists a convex figure of perimeter 1 and area β).

Consider two points A and B of F_α. Let Π_h be the strip enclosed by two parallels to AB each at a distance h from AB (Diagram 132). For large values of h the intersection of F_a and Π_h is F_a; the ratio of the area to the square of the perimeter is therefore α. For small values of h, the area of the intersection becomes arbitrarily small; the perimeter approaches twice the length of $\overline{AB}$. Thus the ratio of the area to the square of the perimeter becomes arbitrarily small. By continuity (Section 3) it follows that there is some value of h such that in the figure of intersection of F_α and Π_h the ratio of the area to the square of the perimeter equals β. By a similitude enlargement of this figure (without change of shape; see trans. note, page 111), so that its perimeter becomes 1, we obtain a figure F_β of area β. Hence the point N belongs to the set Φ.

Thus Φ is a convex figure. Moreover since Φ is bounded (there is no figure of perimeter 1 and arbitrarily large area; see page 54), Φ is a segment on l whose left end point is O and whose right end point is some point M^* (see Section 1, page 6). Let α^* be the length of OM^*; then for each positive α less than α^*, there is a convex figure of perimeter 1 and area α. We select convex figures F_n of perimeter 1 such that the area of F_n is $\alpha - 1/n$ and place all these figures in a circle of radius 1. By Theorem 1 there is then a sequence F_{n_1}, F_{n_2} ..., of selected figures with limit F^*. On the basis of what was proved in Section 4 (see page 50) we may conclude that the perimeter of F^* is 1 and its area is α^*. Thus F^* is a convex figure of perimeter 1 with the greatest area.

The theorem just proved tells us nothing about the shape of this greatest figure. However it supplements Steiner's reasoning so that together they provide a rigorous solution of the isoperimetric problem (see Exercises 5-1 a, 5-6, and 5-7). No noncircular figure can, in fact, be maximal. By what has been proved, a biggest figure exists. Therefore it must be a circle.

Exercise 2 (see page 17). *Prove that Helly's Theorem is valid for infinitely many bounded convex figures.*

Solution. Let F_1, F_2, ..., F_n, ... be bounded convex figures, any three of which have a common point. From Exercise 2-2 it follows that any n of these figures have a common point. Let A_3 be a point of F_1, F_2, and F_3; A_4 a point of F_1, F_2, F_3, F_4; ...; A_n a point of F_1, F_2, ..., F_n, etc. By the Bolzano-Weierstrass Theorem (we now use the boundedness of the figures F_1, F_2, ..., F_n, ...; otherwise the set of points A_n might not lie within a fixed circle), we can select from the sequence of points A_1, A_2, ..., A_n, ... a subsequence A_{n_1}, A_{n_2}, ..., A_{n_k} ... having the limit A. Then *the point A belongs to all the figures F_1, F_2, ..., F_n, ...* .

To see this, assume that A does not belong to one of the figures, say F_m; that is, A is neither a boundary point nor an interior point of F_m. Then a circle K_r of radius r can be drawn about A which lies entirely outside F_m. From the sequence of numbers n_1, n_2, ..., n_k, ... we choose a number n_t so large that $n_t > m$ and A_{n_t} is at a smaller distance from A than r. Then A_{n_t} belongs to all the figures F_1, F_2, ..., F_m, ... F_{n_t} and also lies inside K_r, contrary to our assumption that F_m contains no interior point of K_r. This contradiction proves that A belongs to all the figures F_1, F_2, ..., F_n, ...

Exercise 3 (see page 58). *Prove that a circle can be circumscribed about a given bounded figure F and thus that among all circles enclosing F, there is a smallest.*

Solution. Let C be a circle enclosing F and let r be its radius. We choose a fixed line l and a point O on it. To the right of O we lay off on l a segment OM of length r. In this way we assign a certain point M of l to each circle that encloses F. The points M form a set Φ. If a circle of radius r encloses F, then each circle concentric with it and having a larger radius also encloses F; thus if a point belongs to Φ, then each point to its right on l belongs to Φ. Therefore Φ is a one-dimensional convex figure, a ray on l issuing from some point M^*; M^* is the leftmost point of the ray Φ. Let $OM^* = r^*$. For each $r > r^*$ there is a circle of radius r which encloses F. We will show that *there is a circle of radius r^* which encloses F.*

Let C_n be a circle of radius $r + 1/n$, $n = 1, 2, \ldots$ which encloses F. By Theorem 1, we can select from the sequence of circles C_1, C_2, ..., C_n, ... a subsequence that has a limit C^*. Then C^* is a circle (see Exercise 4-17). Obviously F does not extend beyond C^*, since F is enclosed by all the circles C_1, C_2, ..., C_n, ... The radius of C^* is clearly equal to r^*. This follows easily from the fact that the length of C^* is the limit of the lengths of the circles C_n (see page 50).

In a completely analogous way we can solve

Exercise 4 (see page 59). *Prove that a circle can be inscribed in a given bounded convex figure, and thus that among all circles contained in F there is a largest.*

Exercise 5 (see page 9). *Let F be a bounded figure. Prove that there are two points A and B of F such that the length of AB is greater than or equal to the distance between any two points of F.*

Solution. We choose a fixed line l and a point O on it. For every pair of points of F, lay off on l to the right of O the segment OM whose length is equal to the distance between the pair of points. All such points M form a set Φ on l, which (as in Exercises 1 and 3) is a segment OD of length d.

We select point A_n, B_n of F whose distance from each other is $d - 1/n$. From the sequence of points A_1, A_2, ..., A_n, ... we select a convergent sequence A_{n_1}, A_{n_2}, ..., A_{n_k}, ... The corresponding subsequence B_{n_1}, B_{n_2}, ..., B_{n_k}, ... of the sequence B_1, B_2, ..., B_n, ... may fail to converge. However, if we select from it a convergent sequence B_{m_1}, B_{m_2}, ..., B_{m_k}, ..., then the corresponding sequence A_{m_1}, A_{m_2}, ..., A_{m_k}, ... also converges. Let A and B be the limits of these last two sequences. It is clear that the distance between A and B is d.

It only remains to show that the two points A and B belong to F. We prove this, say, for A. Let p be any natural number and A_{m_t} a point of the sequence A_{m_1}, A_{m_2}, ..., A_{m_k}, ... such that the distance between A and A_{m_t} is less than $1/p$. The point A_{m_t} belongs to F; hence there are points of F which are arbitrarily close to A. Thus A also belongs to F (see Appendix II, Property I).

We state two further exercises which can be solved analogously.

Exercise 6 (see page 18). *Let Φ be a bounded figure. We can draw two parallel supporting lines to the figure such that the distance between them is less than or equal to the distance between any other two parallel supporting lines of Φ.*

Exercise 7 (see the solution of Exercise 2-12, page 136). *If Φ_1 and Φ_2 are two convex figures at least one of which is bounded, then there exists a point A_1 of Φ_1 and a point A_2 of Φ_2 such that the length of $A_1 A_2$ is less than or equal to the length of every other segment that joins a point of Φ_1 to a point of Φ_2.*

We observe finally that Theorem 1 often implies the existence of a largest (or smallest) figure but does not imply the *uniqueness* of this figure. Thus, for example, the circumcircle of a figure is always unique (see Exercise 6-1, page 59); however there can be several incircles (see page 59, Diagram 77).

ON THE CONCEPTS OF
CONVEX AND NONCONVEX
FIGURES

In Section 1 we stated conditions under which a plane figure is called *convex*. However, what is meant by a plane *figure?* The present supplement is presented to clarify the meaning that the authors attribute to the word "figure."

From the most general point of view we could take a "figure" to be any point set in the plane. To determine a point set, we give a rule which makes it possible to decide rigorously whether an arbitrarily selected point belongs to the set or not. For example, if we consider all the points that lie in the interior of a certain circle, we obtain a circular region (without boundary); if in addition we adjoin all points of the perimeter to the set, then we obtain another set (a circular region with boundary).

A set in the plane is convex if for each two distinct points in the set, the entire line segment joining them is also in the set. A circular region with its boundary is a convex set and so is a circular region without its boundary. If we adjoin to a circular region only a part of its boundary, we again obtain a convex set. Geometrically all these sets are represented by a single figure; for geometry it suffices to examine one of them, for example, the circular region with its boundary. If we wish to study arbitrary convex sets (which do not necessarily contain all their boundary points), then the formulation of a whole series of theorems would become much more difficult (for example a "supporting line" would then not need to have a point of contact in common with the figure). Hence in this book we shall designate as "figures" only those sets that have the following properties:

Property I. *If a set M is a "figure," then all points of its boundary belong to M.*

Thus the interior points of a set M and the exterior points with respect to this set are defined exactly as in Section 1 (page 5); all other points (regardless of their membership in M) are points of the boundary of M.

In the study of convex figures, we will always assume in this book that they possess property I (see Section 1, page 5). In studying nonconvex figures this property will also be assumed, along with the following:

Property II. *If A is a point of the boundary of a figure F and K is a circle* (which can be taken arbitrarily small) *about A, then there are interior points as well as exterior points of F within K.*

A circle and a point A outside it furnish an example of a set having Property I, but not Property II: the point A is a point of the boundary of this set; however it has a neighborhood containing no interior points of the given set.

Even when we restrict ourselves to sets with Properties I and II (and indeed to those which are connected, that is, consist of one piece), our definition of "figure" is still too broad (although many theorems are true even for such nonconvex figures, for example Exercises 1-5 and 1-9, since in their proofs only Properties I and II are used). Among sets with Properties I and II there are, for example, three different sets having the same boundary, so that the three sets abut, so to speak, "on three sides."[†] Furthermore there are sets with Properties I and II, for example, an annulus (the part of the plane between two concentric circles), whose boundary consists of two different curves. These peculiarities do not appear in convex figures. Since nonconvex figures are of interest to us only in comparison with convex figures, it is reasonable to exclude sets like the ones described above. In this book we shall therefore limit ourselves to the study of figures with

Property III. *The boundary of F consists of a simple curve* (which is closed when F is bounded, and whose ends may extend to infinity if F is not bounded).

Within the scope of this book we cannot enter into a discussion of the exact meaning of a *simple curve*.[§] Visually, a simple curve can be represented as a curve which results from the continuous motion of a pencil, and which never crosses itself.

[†] See P. S. Aleksandrov: *Kombinatornaya Topologiya* (Combinatorial topology). Gostehizdat, Moscow-Leningrad, 1947, pages 68-69.

[§] *Ibid.*, page 65.

We have supposed in this book (unless the contrary was explicitly stated) that *a figure is a point set with Properties I-III*. We must not suppose, however, that therefore a figure must be extremely simple in the ordinary sense of the word. Among *simple closed* curves there are, for example, some to which no finite length can be assigned (*nonrectifiable* curves). As already mentioned (page 14), this cannot happen for convex curves. Moreover, even the visually clear concept of a convex curve is not at all simple. For example there are convex curves which have on every arc (however small and wherever located on the curve) infinitely many corner points.

For closed simple curves in the plane the following famous theorem holds.

JORDAN CURVE THEOREM. *Every simple closed curve K divides the plane into two regions* (an interior and an exterior).

This means that the points of the plane not on K form two sets or regions R_i and R_e having the following properties: (1) Any two points that belong to the *same* one of these two regions can be joined by a path that lies entirely in the given region and thus does not intersect K. (2) If A and B are two points belonging to *different* regions, then every path joining these points intersects the curve K. This theorem justifies the expressions "a point lies in the *interior*" or "in the *exterior*" of a simple closed curve.

The Jordan Curve Theorem makes it possible to assert that every bounded figure in the sense of our definition (that is, every bounded set satisfying Properties I-III) is a point set situated in the *interior* of, and *on*, a certain simple closed curve. In those cases where we speak of the length of a curve or of the area of the figure bounded by it (Sections 5 and 6) we must, of course, restrict ourselves to simple closed curves for which these concepts hold. The proof of the Jordan Curve Theorem in its full generality is quite difficult, although it can be carried out in a reasonably elementary fashion.[†] For polygons, the proof of this theorem is relatively simple.[§]

[†] See, for example, the supplement to Chapter V of Courant and Robbins: *What Is Mathematics?* (mentioned on page 27); also Chapter 2 of the book by P. S. Aleksandrov (mentioned on page 109), and E. I. Volpert: "Èlementarnoe dokazatelstvo teoremy Žordana" (An elementary proof of the Jordan Curve Theorem). Uspehi mat. nauk, vol. V, 5, 1950, pages 168-172 and A. F. Filippov, *ibid.*, pages 173-176.

[§] See, for example, A. D. Aleksandrov, *Vypuklye Mnogogrannika* (Convex Polyhedra). Gostehizdat, Moscow-Leningrad, 1950, pages 69-72, mentioned in the Introduction, or the addenda by P. K. Raševskii to the translation of the book by D. Hilbert, *Foundations of Geometry*, Moscow-Leningrad, 1948, pages 409-419.

Translators' Note

SIMILITUDES

Let O be any point of the plane and λ be any positive number. To each point A different from O, we associate a point A' which is on the ray from O through A and is such that $OA' = \lambda \cdot OA$. If points A and B are not collinear with O, it is easily verified that the triangle AOB is similar to the triangle $A'OB'$, and thus that a general segment AB is mapped into a segment $A'B'$ such that $A'B' = \lambda \cdot AB$. The correspondence is called a *similitude*, since it carries any figure into a figure similar to the original one in the ratio $\lambda : 1$. The two figures are similarly oriented with respect to O, the *center of similitude*.

We can let λ have negative values by making the convention that in such a case A' is selected not on the ray OA but on the oppositely directed collinear ray, and so that $OA' = |\lambda| \cdot OA$. In particular, for $\lambda = -1$, the similitude is the same as a reflection in O, or a rotation of 180° about O.

Let K be the boundary of a convex figure Φ and let P_n be a polygon of n sides inscribed in K. Under a similitude, P_n is mapped into a polygon P'_n inscribed in K', and it is easily seen that the perimeter of P'_n is $|\lambda|$ times the perimeter of P_n, while the area of P'_n is λ^2 times the area of P_n. By increasing the number of sides of P_n, so that all sides approach zero, we conclude from the limit that the perimeter of Φ' is $|\lambda|$ times that of Φ, while the area of Φ' is λ^2 times that of Φ.

By the use of a similitude we can therefore increase (or decrease) the size of a figure without changing its shape to make its perimeter (or its area) assume any desired positive value.

SOLUTIONS

1-1. Prove that the intersection of two or more convex figures is also a convex figure.

Let Φ_1 and Φ_2 be two convex figures and let Φ be their intersection. Let A and B be any two points of the intersection (Diagram 133). By the definition of the intersection of two figures, points A and B belong both to the figure Φ_1 and to the figure Φ_2. Since the figure Φ_1 is convex, all points of the segment AB belong to Φ_1, and because of the convexity of Φ_2 all of them belong also to Φ_2. Hence the entire segment belongs to the intersection Φ of figures Φ_1 and Φ_2; this means that the intersection Φ is convex.

In just the same way, we prove that the intersection Φ of any finite number of convex figures Φ_1, Φ_2, ..., Φ_n is convex: If A and B are any two points of Φ, then A and B belong simultaneously to all the

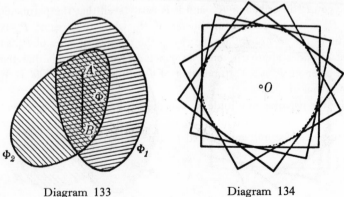

Diagram 133　　　　　　　　Diagram 134

figures Φ_1, Φ_2, ..., Φ_n; since all these figures are convex, all points of the segment AB belong simultaneously to all figures Φ_1, Φ_2, ..., Φ_n; that is, they are contained in their intersection.

> *Note.* This theorem remains true if infinitely many figures Φ_1, Φ_2, ... are given. The proof proceeds as before. In Diagram 134, for example, equal squares with a common center are represented. It is easy to see that the intersection of all such squares (there are infinitely many of them) is a circle, that is, a convex figure.

1-2. Show that every convex polygon is the intersection of a finite number of half-planes.

A convex polygon Φ lies entirely on one side of every straight line that is a prolongation of one of its sides. Indeed, if there were a point C which belonged to Φ and which did not lie on that side of the line AB (A and B are two adjacent vertices of Φ) in which the polygon Φ abuts upon the side AB (Diagram 135), then the segment MC, for example, which joins an interior point M of the segment AB to the point C would not lie completely in Φ. The polygon Φ would therefore not be convex.

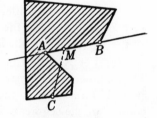

Diagram 135

Thus a convex polygon Φ is contained in one of the half-planes whose boundary line contains a given side of Φ.

The intersection of all such half-planes is the polygon Φ.[†]

1-3. Prove: (a) If A and B are interior points of a convex figure Φ, then all points of the segment AB are interior points of Φ. (b) If A is an interior point and B a boundary point of a convex figure Φ, then all points of segment AB except B are interior points of Φ. (c) If A and B are boundary points of a convex figure Φ, either all points of the segment AB are boundary points of Φ or all the points of segment AB except points A and B themselves are interior points.

(a) Let A and B be two interior points of the figure Φ. From the definition of interior points, there are two circles C and C' whose centers are respectively the points A and B, and all of whose points belong to the

---

[†] If we start from the definition of a convex figure given on page 12, then we can show that every convex figure is the intersection of finitely or infinitely many half-planes.

figure Φ (Diagram 136 a). Let MN and PQ be the common exterior tangents to the circles C and C'. Since Φ is convex, the entire curvilinear figure $MPQN$ in Diagram 136 a belongs to Φ. Consequently every point D of the segment AB is the center of a certain circle all of whose points belong to the figure Φ (this circle is inscribed in the figure $MPQN$).

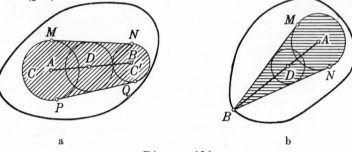

a   b

Diagram 136

(b) The proof differs very little from the proof of assertion (a); we need only replace the circle C' by a point B and the figure $MPQN$ by the figure MBN shaded in Diagram 136 b.

(c) Let A and B be two boundary points of the convex figure Φ. The segment AB may consist entirely of boundary points (Diagram 137 a). This is the first case described in the exercise. If any point C of the segment AB is an interior point of Φ, then, according to assertion (b), all points of the segments CA and CB, except for A and B, must be interior points of Φ. This is the second case described in the exercise (Diagram 137 b).

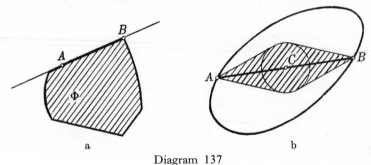

a   b

Diagram 137

1-4. Prove that every line passing through an interior point of a convex figure cuts the boundary of the figure in at most two points. If the convex figure is bounded, then every line passing through an inner point of the figure cuts the boundary of the figure in exactly two points.

Let Φ be a convex figure, O an interior point of Φ, and l a straight line passing through the point O. Since the line l is itself convex, its intersection with the figure Φ (according to Exercise 1-1) is a convex figure lying on the line (a one-dimensional convex figure) and is therefore a segment, a ray, or the entire line. If this intersection is a segment, then its end points A and B are boundary points of the figure Φ (Diagram 138); hence the line l contains two boundary points of Φ. If this intersection is a ray, (line l_1 in Diagram 138) then its initial point A' is the only boundary point of the figure Φ lying on the line.

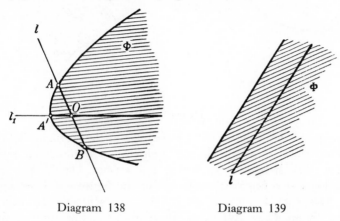

Diagram 138   Diagram 139

Finally, if the entire line l is contained in the figure (Diagram 139), then there is no boundary point of the figure Φ on this line.[†]

If the figure Φ is bounded, then its intersection with the line is bounded, and hence it is a segment. Thus, every line l which passes through an interior point of a bounded convex figure Φ contains exactly two boundary points of this figure.

1-5. If every line passing through an arbitrary interior point of a bounded figure cuts the boundary in two points, then the figure is convex.

Our assertion is equivalent to the assertion that for every bounded nonconvex figure Φ, a line can be found which cuts the boundary of the figure in more than two points. We now prove this assertion.

Let Φ be a bounded nonconvex figure. In this case two points A and B of the figure Φ can be found such that the segment AB does not entirely belong to the figure Φ. Let C denote a point of the segment AB

---

† If a convex figure contains an entire line, then we can prove that it is either a strip (see Diagram 4 b, page 4), a half-plane (see Diagram 4 a), or the entire plane.

not belonging to Φ (Diagram 140 a). We can always assume that the point A is an interior point of Φ. Indeed, if A were a boundary point of Φ and if A' were an interior point sufficiently close to A (see the definition of a boundary point of a figure, page 5), then the segment $A'B$ would also contain points exterior to the figure Φ (Diagram 140 b).

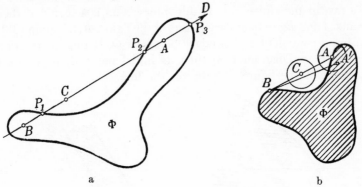

Diagram 140

Therefore, let A be an interior point. On the segment BC there is a boundary point P_1 of the figure Φ (which may even coincide with B), since the point B belongs to Φ, but C does not. On the segment AC there is likewise a boundary point P_2 of the figure Φ (A belongs to Φ and C does not). Finally, if we prolong the segment AB beyond A, then we obtain a ray AD which emanates from the interior point A of the figure Φ. On this ray there is also a boundary point P_3 of figure Φ (since Φ is bounded). Thus, on the line through the interior point A of the figure Φ there are at least three boundary points, P_1, P_2, P_3 of Φ, as we wished to show.

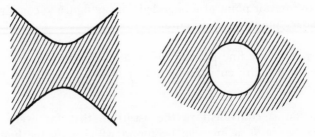

Diagram 141

Note. If the figure Φ were unbounded, then the point P_3 might not exist, since the prolongation of the line AC beyond A could belong entirely to the figure Φ. For example, if Φ were one of the figures shown in Diagram 141, then every line would cut the boundary in no more than two points, although the figure is not convex.

1-6. Prove that two parallel supporting lines that are a maximum distance apart each contain a single boundary point of the figure, and that the line segment joining these two boundary points is perpendicular to the two supporting lines.

Let l_1 and l_2 be two parallel supporting lines of the figure Φ whose distance apart has a maximum value, and let A_1 and A_2 be two boundary points of Φ lying on l_1 and l_2 respectively. We assert that the segment A_1A_2 is perpendicular to each of the lines l_1 and l_2. Otherwise the distance between l_1 and l_2 would be less than the length of the segment A_1A_2 (Diagram 142) and therefore less than the distance between the two supporting lines l_1' and l_2' of Φ which are perpendicular to A_1A_2, which is contrary to hypothesis.

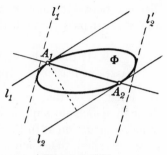

Diagram 142

Since A_1 and A_2 are arbitrary boundary points of the figure Φ belonging to l_1 and l_2 respectively, it follows from the perpendicularity of A_1A_2 to l_1 and l_2 that neither l_1 nor l_2 can have an entire segment in common with Φ (that is, the case depicted in Diagram 143 is impossible). In other words, each of these lines contains exactly one boundary point of Φ.

1-7. Prove that the greatest distance between two points of a convex figure is identical with the greatest distance between parallel supporting lines.

Let Φ be a convex figure and let l_1 and l_2 be two parallel supporting lines whose distance apart has the largest possible value d; let A_1 and A_2 be points common to Φ and to l_1 and l_2 respectively. Since the segment

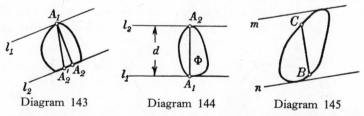

Diagram 143   Diagram 144   Diagram 145

A_1A_2 is perpendicular to the lines l_1 and l_2 (cf. Exercise 1-6), the length of A_1A_2 equals d (Diagram 144). Therefore, we have only to prove that the distance between any two points of Φ cannot exceed the value d. If B and C are two points of Φ and if m and n are supporting lines perpendicular to BC (Diagram 145), then the length of the segment BC does not exceed the distance between the lines m and n, which is in turn no larger than d. Consequently, the length of BC cannot be greater than d.

1-8. If A and B are two points of a convex figure Φ whose distance d has a maximum value, then the lines through the points A and B and perpendicular to AB are supporting lines of Φ.

We construct two supporting lines l and m of the convex figure Φ perpendicular to the segment AB. The entire figure Φ is enclosed in the strip between l and m. Hence, the segment AB of length d and perpendicular to l and m lies within the strip. Since, however, the distance between l and m cannot exceed d (cf. Exercise 1-7), the lines l and m must pass through the end points A and B of the segment.

1-9. If through every boundary point of a bounded figure there passes at least one supporting lines, then the figure is convex.

We must show that every nonconvex figure Φ has a boundary point through which no supporting line can be passed. By carrying out the same construction as in the solution of Exercise 1-5 (see Diagram 140 a), we easily show that such a point exists, say P_2. The line AB through P_2 is indeed not a supporting line, since it passes through the interior point A. No other line through P_2 is a supporting line since the points A and B of Φ lie on different sides of the line.

Note. The assertion of this exercise is also true for unbounded figures; however, we will not give a proof.

1-10. Prove that every polygon inscribed in a bounded convex curve is convex.

We consider any side AB of a polygon $ABC...P$ inscribed in the curve K bounding the convex figure Φ. The points A and B divide the curve K into two arcs K_1 and K_2 (Diagram 146); according to the definition of an inscribed polygon, all of the remaining vertices C, ..., P lie on one of these two arcs, say on the arc K_2. The line AB forms with the arc K_2 a convex curve K^*. This curve is the boundary of one of the two convex figures into which Φ is divided by the line AB (these figures are convex

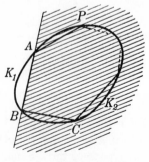

Diagram 146

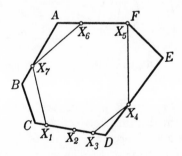

Diagram 147

since they are the intersections of Φ with the half-planes into which the line AB divides the plane). The line AB is a supporting line of the convex curve K^*; hence the arc K_2 and with it all points $C, ..., P$ are on one side of AB. It follows from the fact that all vertices of the polygon $ABC ... P$ lie on one side of the prolongation of each side that this polygon is convex (*cf.* the solution of Exercise 1-2).

> *Note.* Certain sides of the polygon $ABC ... P$ can be prolongations of one another. For example, consider the seven-sided polygon $X_1X_2X_3X_4X_5X_6X_7$ which is inscribed in the convex hexagon $ABCDEF$ in Diagram 147. The sides X_1X_2 and X_2X_3 are prolongations of each other, so that the point X_2 is actually not a vertex of the inscribed polygon and the figure $X_1X_2X_3X_4X_5X_6X_7$ is in reality not a seven-sided polygon, but a hexagon. Nevertheless, in such cases we shall say that such points as X_2 are also vertices of the inscribed polygon. In this way, the formulation and solution of many exercises are simplified.

1-11. Prove that if every set of n points of a bounded curve K comprises the vertices of a convex polygon, then the curve is convex.

We suppose that the figure Φ, bounded by the curve K and satisfying the hypothesis of the exercise, is not convex, and we carry out once more the construction used in the solution of Exercise 1-5. We draw the line CD through the point C and any interior point D of Φ not lying on the line AB (Diagram 148) and consider all points Q of the line CD which have the property that the segment DQ belongs entirely to Φ. These points form a convex figure, namely the segment Q_1Q_2, which does not intersect the line AB. Then one of the two points Q_1, Q_2, say Q_1, has the smaller distance from line AB and lies within the

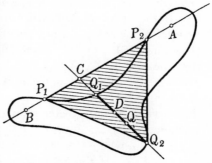

Diagram 148

triangle formed by the points P_1, P_2, Q_2. Consequently the points P_1, P_2, Q_1, Q_2 are not vertices of a convex quadrilateral, contrary to hypothesis.

> *Note.* It follows from this solution that in the hypothesis of this exercise we need only require that *any four points of the curve K be vertices of a convex quadrilateral*. The convexity of the curve K follows from this requirement alone.

1-12. Prove that if a bounded convex curve has only a finite number of corner points, then the sum of the exterior angles of all corner points is at most 360°. If the sum of all exterior angles is exactly 360°, then the curve is a convex polygon.

Let X_1, X_2, ..., X_n be all the corner points of a curve K, written in cyclic order. Then the polygon $X_1X_2 ... X_n$ is inscribed in the curve K. The interior angle at the point X_k of the curve K is at least equal to the interior angle at the vertex X_k of the polygon $X_1X_2 ... X_n$ (Diagram 149). This means that the exterior angle at the point X_k of the

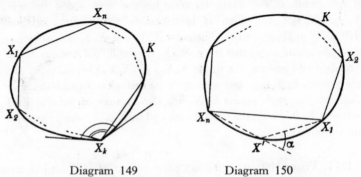

Diagram 149   Diagram 150

curve K is at most equal to the exterior angle at the vertex X_k of the polygon $X_1X_2 ... X_n$. Hence the sum of all exterior angles at the corner points of the curve K does not exceed the sum of the exterior angles of the polygon $X_1X_2 ... X_n$. As is well known, this latter sum equals 360°.[†]

If the curve K is distinct from the convex polygon $X_1X_2 ... X_n$, then let X' be any point of the curve which does not lie on this polygon (Diagram 150). Let the corner points of the curve K be so numbered that the points X_1, X_2, ..., X_n, X' appear in cyclic order. We shall examine the inscribed polygon $X_1X_2 ... X_nX'$. Just as above, we can again infer that the sum of the exterior angles at the corner points of the curve K is not greater than the sum of the exterior angles at the vertices X_1, X_2, ..., X_n of the polygon $X_1X_2 ... X_nX'$. The sum is equal to $360° - \alpha$, where α is the exterior angle at the point X' of the polygon $X_1X_2 ... X_nX'$. If the curve K is not a convex polygon, then the sum of the exterior angles at its corner points is less than 360°.

2-1. Let four convex figures be given in the plane, each three of which have a common point. Prove that all four figures have at least one common point.

[†] The first assertion of this exercise is valid even when the convex figure has an infinite number of cornerpoints. However, the proof of this assertion requires knowledge of some simple concepts of analysis.

We denote our convex figures by Φ_0, Φ_1, Φ_2, Φ_3. Let A_0 be a common point of Φ_1, Φ_2, Φ_3 and let A_1 be a common point of Φ_0, Φ_2, Φ_3. Also let A_2 be a common point of Φ_0, Φ_1, Φ_3 and let A_3 be a common point of Φ_0, Φ_1, Φ_2. Since the points A_0, A_1, A_2 belong to Φ_3, the entire triangle $A_0A_1A_2$ is contained in Φ_3 (see Diagram 6 on page 6). Analogously, the triangle $A_0A_1A_3$ belongs to Φ_2; the triangle $A_0A_2A_3$ belongs to Φ_1, and the triangle $A_1A_2A_3$ to Φ_0. Two cases can arise:

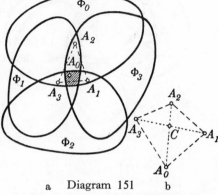

1) One of the points A_0, A_1, A_2, A_3 lies inside (or on oneside) of the triangle formed by the other three. Suppose, for example, that A_0 lies inside the triangle $A_1A_2A_3$ (Diagram 151 a). Then A_0 belongs to all four figures. This argument remains valid even if the triangle $A_1A_2A_3$ becomes a segment (for example, if A_2 lies on the side A_1A_3).

2) None of the points lies in the triangle formed by the other three; that is, the points A_0, A_1, A_2, A_3 are vertices of a convex quadrilateral (Diagram 151 b). Then the intersection C of the diagonals of this quadrilateral belongs to all four triangles under consideration and hence to all four figures Φ_0, Φ_1, Φ_2, Φ_3.

a   Diagram 151   b

2-2. Helly's Theorem. Let n convex figures be given in the plane, and suppose each three of them have a common point. Prove that all n figures have a common point.

The proof is by induction. If the number of figures is 4, then the theorem holds, as is proved in Exercise 2-1. We now show that it is true for $n + 1$ figures if it is true for n figures, let Φ_1, Φ_2, ..., Φ_n, Φ_{n+1} be the given convex figures, any three of which have a common point. We denote the intersection of the figures Φ_n and Φ_{n+1} by $\overline{\Phi}_n$. Then Φ_1, Φ_2, ..., Φ_{n-1}, $\overline{\Phi}_n$ are again n convex figures (Exercise 1-1) any three of which have a common point. Indeed, there exists by hypothesis a common point for any three of these figures which are distinct from $\overline{\Phi}_n$. A common point of the figures Φ_k, Φ_l, $\overline{\Phi}_n$ (that is, a common point of the figures Φ_k, Φ_l, Φ_n, Φ_{n+1}) exists by Exercise 2-1, since any three of the figures Φ_k, Φ_l, Φ_n, Φ_{n+1} have a common point. Thus, any three of the figures Φ_1, Φ_2, ..., Φ_{n-1}, $\overline{\Phi}_n$ have a common point and since the number of these figures is n, the inductive hypothesis implies that there is a point belonging to all these figures and hence to each of the figures Φ_1, Φ_2, ..., Φ_n, Φ_{n+1}.

2-3. Let n points be given in the plane such that each three of them can be enclosed in a circle of radius 1. Prove that all n points can be enclosed in a circle of radius 1.

We must show that there is a point O of the plane (the center of the desired circle) whose distance from all the given points is not greater

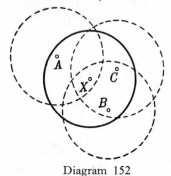

than 1, that is, that there exists a point O of the plane which belongs to all circles of radius 1 about the given points.

According to Helly's Theorem, it suffices to show that any three of the circles in question intersect. By virtue of the hypothesis of the exercise, any three points can be enclosed in a circle of radius 1 (Diagram 152). The center X of this circle is a point belonging to the three unit circles about the points A, B, D (since it is at most at distance 1 from each of the points A, B, C).

Diagram 152

Note. The theorem just proved is also true if infinitely many points are given, for if any three of an infinite number of circles intersect, then all the circles intersect.

2-4. Jung's Theorem. Let n points be given in the plane such that each pair of them are at a distance of at most 1 from each other. Prove that all these points can be enclosed in a circle of radius $1/\sqrt{3}$.

It is sufficient to show that any three of the given points can be enclosed in a circle of radius $1/\sqrt{3}$. It will then follow at once from Exercise 2-3 that *all* the points can be enclosed in a circle of radius $1/\sqrt{3}$ (in Exercise 2-3 the radius 1 was chosen; that the radius here is to be $1/\sqrt{3}$ is, of course, a trivial matter).

No side of a triangle ABC formed from any three of the given points is greater than 1. If this triangle is obtuse or right-angled, then it is completely enclosed by the circle that is constructed on the largest side as diameter. The radius of this circle is not greater than $\frac{1}{2}$ and is therefore smaller than $1/\sqrt{3}$. If the triangle ABC is acute-angled, then the radius of the circumscribing circle can likewise not be greater than $1/\sqrt{3}$, for at least one of the angles of this triangle, say angle A, is not less than 60° (the sum of all three angles is equal to 180°). Hence, the side BC, as chord of an arc not less than 120° but less than 180°, is not smaller than $r\sqrt{3}$, where r is the radius of the circumcircle of the triangle ABC (the chord of an arc of 120° has length $r\sqrt{3}$). Hence, we have $BC \geq r\sqrt{3}$, and since $BC \leq 1$, it follows that $r\sqrt{3} \leq 1$ and thus $r \leq 1/\sqrt{3}$.

Note. The approximation given in Jung's Theorem cannot be improved: three points lying at the vertices of an isosceles triangle of side length 1 serve as an example of a system of points in which the distance between any two points is not greater than 1 and which cannot be enclosed in a circle whose radius is less than $1/\sqrt{3}$ (an isosceles triangle of side length 1 is an example of a figure of diameter 1 which cannot be enclosed in a circle of radius less than $1/\sqrt{3}$).

2-5. Blaschke's Theorem. Prove that every bounded convex figure of width 1 contains a circle of radius $\frac{1}{3}$.

We must prove that there is a circle of radius $\frac{1}{3}$ which is entirely contained in the given convex figure Φ. In other words, it is to be shown that within the figure Φ there exists a point O (center of the desired circle) whose distance from all supporting lines of Φ is at least $\frac{1}{3}$.

If such a point exists, then the circle of radius $\frac{1}{3}$ about this point is entirely enclosed by the figure Φ, for the point O has distance not less than $\frac{1}{3}$ from every boundary point A of Φ (the point O has distance at least $\frac{1}{3}$ from the supporting line through A; see Diagram 153 a).

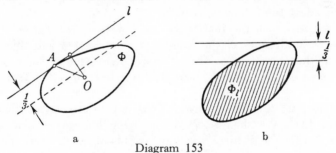

Diagram 153

All points of Φ at a distance not less than $\frac{1}{3}$ from a given supporting line l of Φ form a bounded figure Φ_l which we obtain upon removing from Φ a strip of width $\frac{1}{3}$ which lies between the supporting line l and a parallel to l situated at a distance of $\frac{1}{3}$ from l. (Diagram 153 b). According to Helly's Theorem it suffices to show that any three of the figures Φ_l intersect; from this it will follow directly that there is a point O belonging to all the figures Φ_l. This point can be chosen as the center of the desired circle.

We construct three supporting lines l, m, n to the figure Φ. Either these lines form a triangle that completely encloses the figure Φ

(Diagram 154 a) or they do not form such a triangle (Diagram 154 b). We now consider the first case and denote by T the triangle formed by the lines l, m, n.

Since the width of Φ is 1, the width of the triangle T circumscribed about Φ cannot be less than 1. Thus the altitudes of T are not less than 1; hence the intersection of the medians of this triangle has a distance of

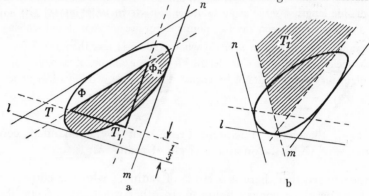

Diagram 154

at least $\frac{1}{3}$ from each of the lines l, m, n. (This point is at a distance of $\frac{1}{3}$ the corresponding altitude from each side.) If we remove three strips from our triangle consisting of all the points at distance less than $\frac{1}{3}$ from one of the sides, there still remains within the triangle T a certain triangle T_1 (in the limiting case T_1 can consist of but one point; this does not affect the following proof).

It remains to show that there are points of the figure Φ whose distance from all sides of the triangle T is at least $\frac{1}{3}$ and thus that Φ intersects the triangle T_1. This intersection obviously belongs to all three figures Φ_l, Φ_m, and Φ_n (see Diagram 154; only the figure Φ_n is shown).

We assume that the figure Φ does not intersect the triangle T_1 (Diagram 155). We then select a line lying between Φ and T_1 (see Exercise 2-12) and displace the line parallel to itself until it touches the triangle T_1. The line r thus obtained is either parallel to one of the sides of T or it forms with two of the three lines l, m, and n (say with and m) a triangle t completely enclosing the figure Φ. If r were parallel to one of the sides of T, then Φ would have to lie inside a strip of width $\frac{1}{3}$, which is impossible. If we prove that the width of t is less than 1, it follows that the figure Φ of width 1 cannot be enclosed in this triangle, that is, the second case cannot occur either, and therefore the assumption that Φ does not intersect the triangle T is false.

We denote the vertices of the triangle t by L, M, and R and the vertex of T_1 lying on the side LM by P. Since the point P is at distance

$\frac{1}{3}$ from both the lines l and m, the line RP is the bisector of the angle LRM. Now let $LR \geq MR$ (if $LR \leq MR$ we reason analogously). Since $LP : MP = LR : MR$, it follows in this case that $LP \geq MP$. From the points M and P, drop perpendiculars MM_1 and PP_1 to the line l. Since $PP_1 = \frac{1}{3}$, it follows that

$$MM_1 = PP_1 \cdot \frac{LM}{LP} = \frac{1}{3}\left(\frac{LP + PM}{LP}\right) \leq \frac{1}{3} \cdot 2 < 1.$$

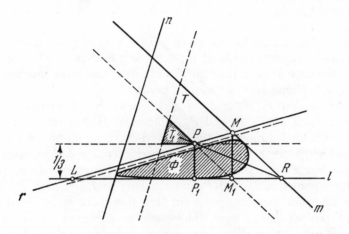

Diagram 155

Thus we see that the altitude MM_1 of the triangle t is less than 1, which concludes the proof.

If the lines l, m, n do not form a triangle enclosing the figure Φ, the proof changes hardly at all. The existence of points whose distance from each of the lines l, m, and n is at least $1/3$ is easier to prove in this case than in the previous one. In the case to be investigated, these points form an unbounded convex figure T_1 (see Diagram 154 b; if the lines l and m are parallel, the existence of such points follows from the fact that the distance between l and m is not less than 1 and thus is certainly greater than $\frac{1}{3} + \frac{1}{3}$). The remainder of the proof is the same as that given above.

Note. The approximation given by Blaschke's Theorem cannot be improved. An equilateral triangle of altitude 1 is a convex figure of width 1 in which no circle can be drawn with radius greater than $1/3$.

Other examples of Blaschke's theorem are given in the solutions to Exercises 2-7 b and 3-9 a.

2-6. (a) Let n points A_1, A_2, ... A_n be given in the plane. Prove that a point O exists in the plane such that on each side of any line l through the point O there are at least $n/3$ of the given points (including points lying on the line l itself). (b) Let a bounded curve K of length L be given in the plane. (K may consist of separated pieces.) Prove that there is a point O of the plane such that each line through the point O divides the curve K in two parts, each having a length of not less than $L/3$. (c) Let Φ be a plane bounded figure (which may possibly consist of separated pieces) with area S. Prove that there is a point O in the plane such that every line through O divides the figure into two parts, each having an area of not less than $S/3$.

(a) Let A_1, A_2, ..., A_n be the given points. Consider all half-planes in which more than two-thirds of the n given points lie (including points on the boundary lines of the half-planes). We shall show that any three of these half-planes have a common point.

Suppose that P_1, P_2 and P_3 are three such half-planes. Since in each of the half-planes P_1 and P_2, more than $2n/3$ of the given points lie and since the number of the points is n, the number of the given points which lie in both P_1 and P_2 must exceed $n/3$. Moreover since the half-plane P_3 contains more than $2n/3$ of the given points, at least one of the points in P_1 and P_2 must belong to P_3, that is, P_1, P_2, P_3 have at least one common point (in fact, this point is one of the pre-assigned points). Since every half-plane is a convex figure, Helly's Theorem implies that there is a point O belonging to all of the half-planes under consideration.

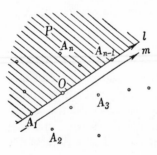

Diagram 156

We show that O is the desired point. Let l be any line through O (we assume that the line l has been given a definite direction). Let P be either of the half-planes into which l divides the plane, say the half-plane to the left of l (Diagram 156). We must prove that there are at least $n/3$ of the given points in the half-plane P (including the line l).

Assume the contrary. Then there are more than $2n/3$ of the given points to the right of l, not counting the points that belong to l itself. Draw a line m parallel and to the right of l sufficiently close to l so that none of the given points lie between l and m. Then there are just as many of the given points to the right of m as to the right of l, that is, more than $2n/3$. Hence the half-plane to the right of m must contain the point O, which is impossible, since O lies on the line l and is therefore to the left of m.

This contradiction proves that the half-plane P contains at least $n/3$ of the given points.

The attentive reader may have detected a gap in the solution of this exercise. The half-planes to which we have applied Helly's Theorem are in point of fact *unbounded* convex figures, whereas we especially emphasized in the text that Helly's Theorem may be false for infinitely many unbounded figures. This defect can easily be remedied, however. Let C be a large enough circle so that all the points A_1, A_2, ..., A_n lie in it. We then consider, in the proof above, not just the half-planes in each of which more than $2n/3$ given points lie, but rather only those *parts* of the half-planes which are contained in the circle C. Then we obtain bounded convex figures any three of which have a common point. Thus the proof given is in fact correct.

(b) and (c) These exercises are solved analogously to Exercise 2-6 (a) except that in place of half-planes containing more than $2n/3$ given points, we consider half-planes containing parts of the curve K each of whose arc lengths is greater than $2L/3$, or (in the case of c) half-planes containing portions of the figure Φ, the area of each of which is greater than $25/3$. We leave it to the reader to complete the proof of these theorems for himself.

Note. The estimates in Exercises 2-6 a to 2-6 c cannot be improved. Three arbitrary non collinear points furnish an example of a set of points admitting no point O such that on each side of any line through O there are more than $n/3$ points. Three non-intersecting small circles (circular areas) about the vertices of any triangle (Diagram 157) constitute an example of a curve K (figure Φ) for which the estimate in Exercises 2-6 b and 2-6 c cannot be improved.

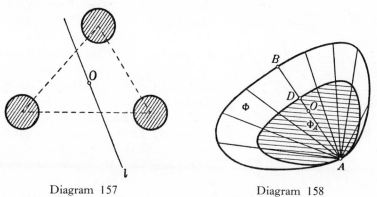

Diagram 157   Diagram 158

2-7. (a) Prove that inside every bounded convex figure Φ there exists a point O such that every chord AB of Φ which passes through O is divided into two segments AO and BO, each of whose lengths is not less then $\frac{1}{3}$ the length of the segment AB. (b) Derive from the assertion of Exercise 2-7 a new proof of Blaschke's Theorem.

(a) Let Φ be a given convex figure and let A be any boundary point of Φ (Diagram 158). We draw through A all possible chords of the figure Φ and lay off on any such chord AB the segment AD whose length is $\frac{2}{3}$ the length of AB. All of the points D thus obtained form the boundary of a certain figure Φ_A which is similar to the figure Φ and which lies in a position similar to that of Φ. The center of similitude (see Translators' Note, page 111) is the point A and the proportionality factor is $\frac{2}{3}$. Now let O be the point whose existence is to be proved, and let AB be a chord of the figure through this point. Since by definition of the point O the inequality $AO \leq \frac{2}{3} AB$ must hold, the point O belongs to the figure Φ_A.

The assertion that there exists a point O of the figure Φ such that on each chord AB through O the segment AO is not greater than $\frac{2}{3} AB$, *regardless of how the boundary point A of the figure Φ is chosen*, is equivalent to the assertion that there exists a point O belonging to every figure Φ_A which is similar to the figure Φ and whose center of similitude A lies on the boundary of Φ and whose ratio of similarity is $\frac{2}{3}$. Since all the figures Φ_A are convex (obviously all figures that are similar to a convex figure are convex), it is sufficient, by Helly's Theorem, to show that any three of the figures under consideration have a common point.

Let Φ_A, Φ_B, and Φ_C be three such figures similar to the figure Φ

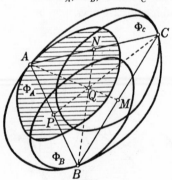

Diagram 159

whose centers of similitude are the boundary points $A, B,$ and C respectively (Diagram 159). We draw the three chords AB, BC, and AC of the figure Φ. Let M, N, and P be the midpoints of the sides of the triangle ABC and let Q be the intersection of the medians AM, BN, and CP of this triangle. The point M belongs to the figure Φ (since M lies on the segment BC and the figure Φ is convex). From a well-known property of the medians of a triangle, the segment AQ equals $\frac{2}{3} AM$; hence the point Q belongs to the figure Φ_A. We show by analogy that Q also belongs to the figures Φ_B and Φ_C. Thus Φ_A, Φ_B, and Φ_C possess a common point. The assertion of the exercise follows from this.

Note. The estimate in Exercise 2-7 a cannot be improved. It is easy to prove that within a triangle there is no point O such that both segments of each chord through O are greater than $\frac{1}{3}$ of the entire chord. In fact, let O be an interior point of the triangle ABC and let A_1, B_1, and C_1 be the respective intersections of OA, BO, and CO with the sides BC, AC, and AB of the triangle (Diagram 160 a). If $A_1O > \frac{1}{3} A_1A$, then O lies within (not on the

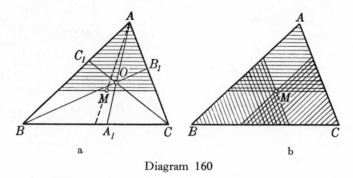

Diagram 160

boundary!) of the triangle cut off from ABC by a line parallel to BC and passing through the intersection M of the medians. If $B_1O > \frac{1}{3} B_1B$, then O is similarly situated within the triangle cut off from ABC by a parallel to AC through M. If $C_1O > \frac{1}{3} C_1C$, then O lies within the triangle cut off from ABC by a parallel to AB through M. These three triangles have no common interior point, however (Diagram 160 b); hence no such point O of triangle ABC can exist.

(b) We suppose that the width of the convex figure Φ equals 1, and prove that the point O, whose existence is asserted in Exercise 2-7 a, is the center of a circle of radius $\frac{1}{3}$ which is entirely enclosed by Φ. For this purpose, it suffices to show that the point O has a distance at least $\frac{1}{3}$ from each boundary point A. Through a point A we draw a supporting line l of the figure Φ. Let B designate the point of intersection of the figure Φ with the supporting line l_1 of Φ parallel to l (see Section 1, page 8). The distance between l and l_1 cannot be less than the width 1 of Φ. Let C and C_1 be the intersection points of the line BO with the boundary of the figure Φ and the line l, respectively (Diagram 161). Since $CO \geq \frac{1}{3} CB$ (by definition of the point O), it follows that

$$C_1O = CO + CC_1 \geq \tfrac{1}{3}(CB + 3CC_1) \geq \tfrac{1}{3} C_1B.$$

Hence the distance of the point O from the line l is at least $\frac{1}{3}$ the distance between the lines l and l_1, that is, at least $\frac{1}{3}$. It thus follows that the distance between the points O and A is at least $\frac{1}{3}$.

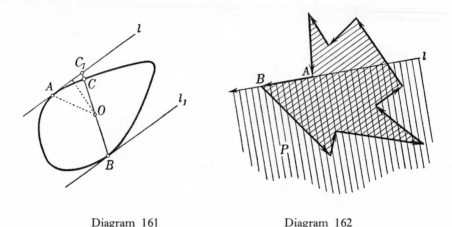

Diagram 161   Diagram 162

2-8. M. A. Krasnoseľskiĭ's Theorem. Prove that if for every three points A, B, C of an arbitrary polygon K there exists a point M such that all three segments MA, MB, MC lie entirely inside the polygon, then there exists in the interior of K a point O all of whose connecting segments with points of the polygon K likewise lie entirely inside the polygon.

Let K be the given polygon. Let any sense of orientation be designated on its boundary, for example the "counterclockwise" sense, that is, the orientation such that when traversing the boundary in this sense, then in the neighborhood of each side exterior points of the polygon K lie to the right and interior points to the left (Diagram 162). Let AB be a side of the polygon lying on a line l. We assume that l has the same direction as the side AB of the polygon K and denote by P the half-plane to the left of l. We call P the left *half-plane of the polygon K with respect to the side AB.*

We now prove that there is a point O belonging to the left half-planes with respect to all sides of the polygon K. (As is shown in what follows, this point satisfies the conditions of the theorem.) According to Helly's Theorem, it suffices to show that any three of the left half-planes have a common point. Let P_1, P_2, P_3 be three left half-planes with respect to any three sides of the polygon K, and let A_1, A_2, A_3 be any points on the corresponding lines (Diagram 163). By the hypothesis of the theorem, there is a point M such that the segments A_1M, A_2M, and A_3M lie inside the polygon K. From this it follows that when the three sides mentioned are traversed, the point M lies on the same side as the interior points of the polygon K, that is, to the left. Thus the point M lies in all three left half-planes P_1, P_2, P_3.

Now let O be a common point of all left half-planes of the polygon K. We prove that O is the desired point. First we show that O lies inside K.

If we assume that O lies outside of the polygon K and that X is the boundary point of the polygon K which is nearest to the point O (or that it is one of several nearest boundary points—see Diagram 164),

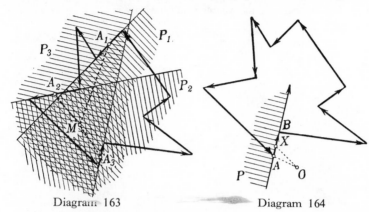

Diagram 163   Diagram 164

then except for X, the segment OX lies entirely outside K. If the point X were a vertex of the polygon K (it would then coincide with A), then a point (sufficiently close to X) could be chosen on one of the two sides through this vertex so that it was not a vertex of the polygon and was such that except for this point, the entire segment connecting it with O would lie outside the polygon. Therefore, if O lies outside K, then a point X of K can certainly be found which is *not a vertex* and is such that except for X the segment OX lies outside K. If now AB is the side on which the point X lies, then O is on the same side of AB as the exterior points of the polygon, that is, to the right, contrary to the fact that O belongs to all left half-planes of the polygon K and, in particular, to the left half-plane P with respect to the side AB.

The point O therefore lies within K. It remains to show that the entire segment OC lies within K if C is any point of the polygon K.

We assume the contrary and select on the segment OC a point M lying outside the polygon K. Let P be that point of the intersection of the segment CM with the boundary of the polygon K (Diagram 165 a) nearest to M.

If P is not a vertex of the polygon K and AB is the side on which the point P lies, then the point O lies on the same side of AB as M, that is, on the same side as the exterior points of the polygon, thus on the right side. This contradicts the fact that the point O belongs to all left half-planes of the polygon K.

If P is a vertex of K, then on each of the sides through P a point P' can be found (sufficiently close to P) which is not a vertex of the polygon

K and is such that on the segment OP' there is a point M' outside the polygon K (Diagram 165 b). The above argument is now repeated to complete the proof.

The segment joining any point C of the polygon K with the point O therefore lies within K, as we wished to show.[†]

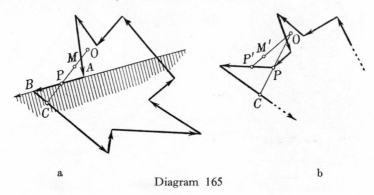

a

Diagram 165

b

Note. Krasnosel'skiĭ's Theorem holds not only for polygons, but also for any plane figure. The proof for the general case does dot differ basically from the one just given.[§]

2-9. In the plane, n parallel line segments are given. Prove that if for each three of them there exists a line that intersects the three line segments, then there also exists a line that intersects all the line segments.

We introduce in the plane a system of coordinates, taking for the Y-axis any line parallel to the segments to be considered and as the X-axis a line perpendicular to the Y-axis. Let (x_i, y_i') and (x_i, y_i''), $i = 1, 2, ..., n$, be the coordinates of the end points of the ith segment, where $y_i' < y_i''$. In order that the line l with equation $y = kx + b$ shall intersect this segment (Diagram 166) it is obviously necessary that the inequalities

$$y_i' \leq kx_i + b, \qquad y_i'' \geq kx_i + b \qquad \text{✳}$$

be satisfied.

[†] In this proof we used Helly's Theorem in a situation in which the convex figures to be investigated (half-planes) are unbounded; this fact does not invalidate the proof, however, since in the case of finitely many figures, their boundedness is not needed for the validity of Helly's Theorem.

[§] Since there are infinitely many "left half-planes," Helly's Theorem cannot be applied immediately (because of the unboundedness of the half-planes). Therefore in the proof we make use of the procedure that we used in solving Exercise 2-6.

Next consider the point L with coordinates (k, b). It is clear that if we know the line l (not parallel to the Y-axis) we can find the point L, and conversely, if the point L is given, the line is completely defined. The correlation

$$y_i' = kx_i + b$$

or

$$b = -x_i k + y_i'$$

signifies that the point L lies on the line with slope $-x_i$ and Y-intercept y_i'. Moreover, the correlation

$$y_i'' = kx_i + b \quad \text{or} \quad b = -x_i k + y_i''$$

signifies that the point L lies on another line parallel to the first. Finally the inequality $*$ given above signifies that the point L lies in the *strip* between these lines (Diagram 167). *Thus the line l intersects the ith segment*

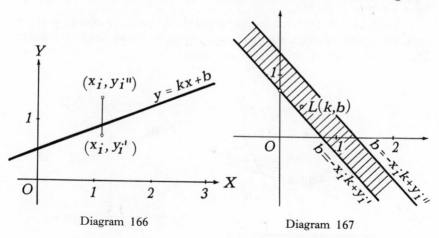

Diagram 166   Diagram 167

if and only if the point L lies in the strip Φ_i bounded by two parallel lines (the position of these lines is determined by the ends of the ith segment since they are the lines with slope $-x_i$ through (o, y_i') and (o, y_i'') respectively).

Since by hypothesis there is for each three segments a line (obviously not parallel to the Y-axis) which intersects them, it follows that each three of the n strips Φ_i, $i = 1, 2, ..., n$ corresponding to our n segments have a common point L. Applying Helly's Theorem, we conclude that all n strips Φ_i, $i = 1, 2, ..., n$ have a common point; that is, there is a line that intersects all the given segments.

Note. In exactly the same way, but using the Helly's Theorem for space (see below, Exercise 2-14), we can prove the following theorem: If for each *four* of n segments parallel to the Y-axis there exists a parabola $y = ax^2 + bx + c$ intersecting them, then there also exists a parabola intersecting all n of the segments.

2-10. (a) If among n half-planes each three have a common point, prove that all n half-planes have a common point (Helly's Theorem for half-planes). (b) Derive from the assertion of Exercise 2-10 a the conclusion that n convex polygons possess a common point when each three of the n (not necessarily bounded) polygons have a common point (Helly's Theorem for polygons).

(a) The proof is by induction. Suppose that we have already proved that k of the half-planes have a common point. We now show that the $(k + 1)$'st half-plane Π has a point in common with Φ, where Φ is the intersection of the first k half-planes, that is, the $k + 1$ half-planes have a common point.

The figure Φ is convex by Exercise 1-1; it is either a convex polygon (possibly unbounded), a segment (or a ray or an entire line), or a point. We consider each of these cases separately.

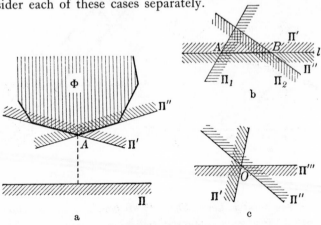

Diagram 168

1) Let Φ be a convex polygon (Diagram 168 a). We assume that Π does not intersect this polygon. Then let A be the vertex of the polygon Φ nearest to the half-plane Π (or one of these vertices if there are several). In this case the sides of the polygon Φ which pass through the vertex A are the boundaries of two of our half-planes Π' and Π''. From Diagram 168 a it is obvious that the half-planes Π, Π', Π'' have no common point, contrary to hypothesis. Hence Π must necessarily intersect Φ, as we wished to show.

2) Let Φ be a segment AB of a line l (Diagram 168 b). In this case there are among the first k half-planes two half-planes Π' and Π'' which border the line l from different sides. Moreover there is among them a half-plane Π_1 which intersects the line in the point A and contains the point B, and there is a half-plane Π_2 which contains point A and intesects the line l in the point B. Since the half-planes Π', Π'' and Π possess a common point, it follows that Π intersects the line l. Now if the half-plane Π had a ray in common with the line l lying completely outside the segment AB, and before the point A, then either the three half-planes Π, Π_1 and Π' or the three half-planes Π, Π_1 and Π'' would have no common point, as we can easily see. Similarly we can prove that Π cannot cut off from the line l a ray that lies outside the segment AB and beyond the point B. Hence Π intersects the segment AB, as we wished to show.

The proofs are analogous in the cases in which l is a ray or an entire line.

3) Let Φ be a point O. In this case there are among the first k half-planes three half-planes Π', Π'', and Π''' which intersect in the point O and whose position is shown in Diagram 168 c. If the half-plane Π did not contain the point O, then, as is easily shown, one of the sets of half-planes Π, Π', Π'' or Π, Π' and Π''' or Π, Π'' and Π''' could not possess a common point.

The assertion of the exercise follows by the usual induction argument from what has been proved in all these cases.

(b) Let n polygons Φ_1, Φ_2, ..., Φ_n, be given, any three of which have a common point. From the result of Exercise 1-2, each of these polygons is the intersection of a certain number of half-planes. We assert that all these half-planes have a common point.

In fact if three different polygons correspond to three half-planes Π, Π', Π'', then the intersection of the three half-planes Π, Π', Π'' contains the intersection of these three polygons. By hypothesis this intersection exists. If Π, Π', Π'' correspond to two polygons (two of them belong to half-planes whose intersection is a polygon) or if they belong to a single polygon, then these half-planes also have common points (in the first case the intersection of these half-planes contains the intersection of two of the polygons in question; in the second place it contains an entire polygon).

With the help of the result in Exercise 2-10 a, it follows from the above that all the half-planes possess at least one common point, which naturally belongs to all the polygons. This concludes the proof of the theorem.

2-11. If each pair of n segments of a line have a common point, prove that all n segments possess a common point.

We designate the left end points of the given segments by $A_1, A_2, ..., A_n$, and the right end points by $B_1, B_2, ... B_n$. Since the segments A_1B_1 and A_2B_2 intersect, it follows that the left end point A_1 of the first segment cannot lie to the right of the end point B_2 of the second segment, that is, either A_1 lies to the left of B_2 (Diagram 169 a), or A_1 coincides with B_2 (in the latter case this point is the only common point of segments A_1B_1 and A_2B_2 (see Diagram 169 b). Hence none of the left end

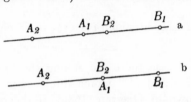

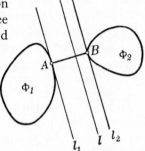

Diagram 169   Diagram 170

points $A_1, A_2, ..., A_n$ lies to the right of any of the right end points B_1, $B_2, ..., B_n$. We denote by A_0 the left end point of the segment lying furthest to the right, and by B_0 the right end point lying furthest to the left. If A_0 coincides with B_0, then $A_0 = B_0$ is the only point belonging to all the segments $A_1B_1, A_2B_2, ..., A_nB_n$. If the point A_0 lies to the left of B_0, then the entire segment A_0B_0 is contained in all the given segments.

2-12. If two bounded convex figures Φ_1 and Φ_2 of the plane do not intersect, then there exists a line l such that Φ_1 and Φ_2 lie on different sides of l.

Let Φ_1 and Φ_2 be two bounded convex figures with no common point; let A and B be two of their points whose distance has a least value (Diagram 170).[†] We pass lines l_1 and l_2 through the points A and B, respectively, perpendicular to the segment AB. We shall show that these lines are supporting lines of the figures Φ_1 and Φ_2 respectively.

Assume that l_1 is not a supporting line of the figure Φ_1. Then there is a point P of the figure Φ_1 on the same side of l_1 as the point B. Since Φ_1 is convex, the entire segment AP belongs to the figure Φ_1. There is a point on the segment AP whose distance from the point B is less than AB. In fact, either the foot Q of the perpendicular from B

† *Cf.* Appendix I, Exercise

on AP is such a point, if th's foot lies on AP (Diagram 171 a), or P itself is such a point, if the foot of the perpendicular lies on the extension of AP beyond the point P (Diagram 171 b). Since the angle PAB is acute, it follows that the foot of the perpendicular from B onto AP cannot lie on the extension of AP beyond the point A. This, however, is contrary to the hypothesis that AB is the shortest distance between

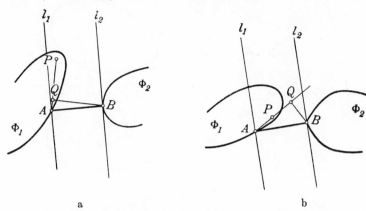

Diagram 171

points of the figures Φ_1 and Φ_2. Hence l_1 is a supporting line of Φ_1 and, by the same argument, l_2 is a supporting line of Φ_2.

Since l_1 and l_2 are supporting lines of the figures Φ_1 and Φ_2 respectively it follows immediately that every line parallel to the lines l_1 and l_2 and lying between them satisfies the conditions of the exercise.

> *Note.* The proof remains correct even when only one of the figures Φ_1 and Φ_2 is bounded. However, if Φ_1 and Φ_2 are both unbounded convex figures, then the proposition is no longer valid. Between figures that extend indefinitely there need be no least distance, for while the presence of arbitrarily near points means in the case of bounded figures that they intersect, nonintersecting, unbounded figures Φ_1 and Φ_2 may contain points which lie arbitrarily close to one another (Diagram 172). It is easy to see that the convex figures shown in Diagram 172 are not separated by a line.

> **2-13.** Using the results of Exercises 2-11 and 2-12, prove that four bounded convex figures of the plane possess a common point if each three of them have a common point.

Denote the given figures by Φ_1, Φ_2, Φ_3, Φ_4 and the convex figure which is the intersection of Φ_1, Φ_2, and Φ_3 by Φ (see Exercise 1-1). We must prove that the figures Φ and Φ_4 have a common point.

Assume that Φ and Φ_4 do not intersect. Then there is a line l such that the figures Φ and Φ_4 lie on different sides of it (Exercise 2-12). For convenience we assume that the line l is horizontal, and that Φ lies above l and Φ_4 below it (Diagram 173). Since any three of our given

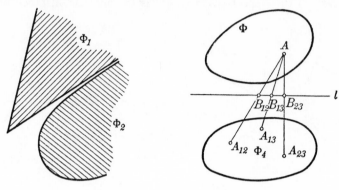

Diagram 172   Diagram 173

figures intersect, there exists a point A_{12} belonging to the figures Φ_1, Φ_2, and Φ_4, a point A_{13} belonging to the figures Φ_1, Φ_3, and Φ_4, and a point A_{23} belonging to the figures Φ_2, Φ_3, and Φ_4. All these points lie below the line l.

Let A be any point of the figure Φ. Since the figures Φ_1, Φ_2, and Φ_3 are convex, the segment $A_{12}A$ lies in the intersection of the figures Φ_1 and Φ_2, the segment $A_{13}A$ in the intersection of the figures Φ_1 and Φ_3, and the segment $A_{23}A$ in the intersection of the figures Φ_2 and Φ_3. The points B_{12}, B_{13}, and B_{23}, in particular (which are the intersections of these segments with the line l), belong to the figures mentioned. Thus each pair of the figures Φ_1, Φ_2 and Φ_3 have a common point on the line l. Since l intersects Φ_1, Φ_2, and Φ_3 in segments, and, from the above remark, any two of these segments have a common point, it follows (Exercise 2-11) that there is a point O of the line l which belongs to all three segments in question; that is, O belongs to all three of the figures Φ_1, Φ_2, Φ_3. However, this contradicts the assumption that the line l has no point in common with the intersection Φ of the figures Φ_1, Φ_2, Φ_3. The figures Φ and Φ_4 therefore intersect, and the proof is concluded.

2-14. Helly's Theorem in space. Let n convex bounded bodies be given, each four of which have a common point. Prove that all n bodies possess a common point.

We describe only the principal steps of the proof, which is analogous to the proof of Helly's Theorem for the plane as presented in the solutions of Exercises 2-11 through 2-13.

First we prove that any two nonintersecting, bounded, convex bodies can be separated by a plane and then show that five bounded convex bodies Φ_1, Φ_2, Φ_3, Φ_4, Φ_5 have a common point if each four of these bodies possess a common point. The proof is indirect. Assume that the body Φ_5 does not intersect the intersection Φ of the bodies Φ_1, Φ_2, Φ_3, Φ_4, and we construct a plane L which separates the bodies Φ and Φ_5. It then develops that the four bounded *plane convex* figures that arise from the intersections of the bodies Φ_1, Φ_2, Φ_3, Φ_4 with the plane L, satisfy the hypothesis of Helly's Theorem. Thus it follows that Φ must have a point in common with the plane L, which is a contradiction. The last step of the proof is similar to the solution of Exercise 2-2. By induction we pass from Exercise 2-1 to the general form of Helly's Theorem.

Note. If each four of five given convex bodies Φ_0, Φ_1, Φ_2, Φ_3, Φ_4 have a common point, then we can prove by arguments analogous to those in the solution of Exercise 2-1 that all five bodies have a common point. This method of proof for Helly's Theorem in space is more satisfactory than the one sketched above, in the sense that we need not assume the boundedness of the figures. It turns out, however, that this method of proof is much more complicated for the case of bodies in space than the proof of the corresponding theorem for plane figures, while the proof just sketched above is exactly modeled after the proof of Helly's Theorem for plane figures, and conceals no supplementary difficulties. If we define the points A_0, A_1, A_2, A_3, A_4 by analogy with the solution of Exercise 2-1, so that A_0 is the common point of the bodies Φ_1, Φ_2, Φ_3, Φ_4, etc., then the number of cases to be considered, corresponding to possible positions of the five points A_0, A_1, A_2, A_3, A_4, is considerably greater than the former two. However, even here, we can show that in every case there is a point belonging to all five bodies.

We leave it to the reader to carry out the proof in detail.

2-15. Formulate and prove theorems for three-dimensional space which are analogous to the theorems of plane geometry contained in Exercises 2-4 to 2-7 a.

We give here only the formulation of the theorems analogous to the theorems of Exercises 2-4 through 2-7 a. The proofs of these theorems are similar to the proofs of Exercises 2-4 through 2-7 a and it is left to the reader to construct them for himself (we emphasize the fact that a theorem for space similar to that of Blaschke cannot be derived from the theorem corresponding to Exercise 2-7 a).

Analogue of Jung's Theorem. In three-dimensional space, every body of diameter 1 can be enclosed in sphere of radius $\sqrt{6}/4$ ($\sqrt{6}/4$ is the radius of the sphere circumscribed about a regular tetrahedron of side 1).[†]

Analogue of Blaschke's Theorem. Inside each convex body of width 1 in three-dimensional space we can place a sphere of diameter $1/\sqrt{3}$.[§]

Analogue of Exercise 2-6 a. If n points A_1, A_2, ..., A_n are given in space, there always exists a point O such that at least $1/4$ of the given points lie on each side of any plane passing through the point O.

(b) and (c). If any surface C (any body P) is given, then there is always a point O such that, for any plane L through O, the area of those parts of C (the volume of those parts of P) which are on one side of L is not less than $1/4$ of the area of the surface C (of the volume of P).

Analogue of Exercise 2-7 a. Within every bounded convex body P there is a point O such that every chord AB of the body P through the point O is separated by O into two segments AO and OB, each of whose lengths is not less than $1/4$ of the length of AB.

The estimates in these theorems cannot be improved.

3-1. Given a figure Φ (not necessarily convex; it can, in fact, consist of several separate pieces) and any line l_0, prove the existence of a line parallel to l_0 which divides the figure Φ into two figures of equal area.

We select a direction on the line l_0 and draw a line l' parallel to the direction of l_0 such that the entire figure Φ lies to its left (Diagram 174). Now we displace l' to the left parallel to itself until it assumes the position l'' and the entire figure Φ lies to its right. Then the area of the part of the figure Φ which lies to the right of the displaced line l is a continuous

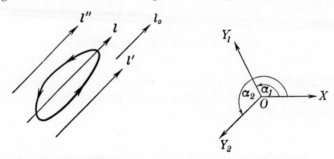

Diagram 174   Diagram 175

[†] The diameter of a body in space is the greatest distance between two of its points.

[§] In space, the *width of a convex body* is the least distance between pairs of parallel supporting planes.

function of the distance of this line from l'. If the distance is zero (that is, if l coincides with l'), then the function is equal to zero; if l coincides with l'', then the function is equal to the surface area of Φ. Hence there exists between l' and l'' a line l, parallel to l' and l'' (and therefore parallel to l_0), so that exactly half (of the area) of the figure Φ lies to the right of l. The line l therefore bisects the area of Φ. Obviously for every convex figure, and in general for every figure consisting of a single piece, the line obtained is unique.

3-2. (a) Let two convex figures Φ_1 and Φ_2 be given in the plane. Prove the existence of a line l which simultaneously divides the two figures Φ_1 and Φ_2 in half. (b) Given a convex figure Φ in the plane, prove that there exist two lines l and l^* perpendicular to each other which divide the figure Φ into four parts of equal size.

(a) We select a direction OX in the plane which is to serve as the initial ray for an angle. Each direction OY is determined by the angle α which it forms with the direction OX (more exactly by the angle α through which the direction must be rotated in the counterclockwise sense in order to bring it into coincidence with the direction OY; here α can assume every value from $0°$ to $360°$. (See Diagram 175).

For every angle α, there exists a unique line $l(\alpha)$ which halves the area of the figure Φ_1 and is parallel to the direction OY which forms the angle α with the initial ray OX (Diagram 176 a; see the solution

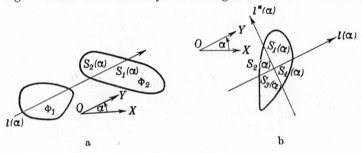

Diagram 176

of Exercise 3-1). Suppose that this line divides the figure Φ_2 into two unequal parts. Let $S_1(\alpha)$ be the surface area of that part of the figure Φ_2 lying to the right of $l(\alpha)$, and suppose that $S_1(\alpha) > S_2(\alpha)$, where $S_2(\alpha)$ is the area of the part of Φ_2 to the left of $l(\alpha)$. Replace the angle α by $\alpha + 180°$; clearly the line $l(\alpha + 180°)$ coincides with $l(\alpha)$ and is distinct from it in direction only. Hence

$$S_1(\alpha + 180°) = S_2(\alpha), \qquad S_2(\alpha + 180°) = S_1(\alpha);$$
$$S_1(\alpha + 180°) - S_2(\alpha + 180°) = S_2(\alpha) - S_1(\alpha) < 0.$$

As α increases to $\alpha + 180°$, the difference $S_1(\alpha) - S_2(\alpha)$ changes sign. Since $S_1(\alpha)$ and $S_2(\alpha)$ are clearly continuous functions of the angle α, $S_1(\alpha) - S_2(\alpha)$ is also a continuous function of α, and hence there must exist between α and $\alpha + 180°$ an angle α_0 for which

$$S_1(\alpha_0) - S_2(\alpha_0) = 0,$$

so that the line $l(\alpha_0)$ simultaneously bisects the figures Φ_1 and Φ_2.

(b) Just as in the solution of Exercise 3-2 a, we select a direction OX as the initial ray for measuring angles. To each direction OY determined by the angle α formed between OY and the initial ray OX there corresponds a unique line $l(\alpha)$ parallel to OY and bisecting the area of the figure Φ (see Exercise 3-1). Likewise there is a line $l^*(\alpha)$ perpendicular to OY which also bisects the figure Φ. We denote by $S_1(\alpha)$, $S_2(\alpha)$, $S_3(\alpha)$ and $S_4(\alpha)$ (Diagram 176 b) the four parts into which the lines $l(\alpha)$ and $l^*(\alpha)$ divide the figure Φ (the areas of these parts are functions of α). By construction we have

$$S_1(\alpha) + S_2(\alpha) = S_3(\alpha) + S_4(\alpha)$$

and

$$S_1(\alpha) + S_4(\alpha) = S_2(\alpha) + S_3(\alpha),$$

from which it follows at once that

$$S_2(\alpha) = S_4(\alpha) \quad \text{and} \quad S_1(\alpha) = S_3(\alpha).$$

The equality

$$S_1(\alpha) = S_2(\alpha)$$

must also hold if the four parts into which the lines $l(\alpha)$ and $l^*(\alpha)$ divide the figure Φ are to be equal. Assume that for some fixed angle α (Diagram 176 b), we have $S_1(\alpha) > S_2(\alpha)$ and hence $S_1(\alpha) - S_2(\alpha) > 0$. (An analogous proof holds in case $S_1(\alpha) - S_2(\alpha) < 0$.) If we replace the angle α by $\alpha + 90°$ (that is, if we rotate the line $l(\alpha)$ and $l^*(\alpha)$ by $90°$ counterclockwise), then $l(\alpha + 90°)$ coincides with $l^*(\alpha)$, and $l^*(\alpha + 90°)$ differs from $l(\alpha)$ only in orientation. Hence $S_1(\alpha + 90°)$ coincides with $S_2(\alpha)$ and $S_2(\alpha + 90°)$ with $S_3(\alpha) = S_1(\alpha)$; hence we have

$$S_1(\alpha + 90°) - S_2(\alpha + 90°) = S_2(\alpha) - S_1(\alpha) < 0.$$

Since $S_1(\alpha)$ and $S_2(\alpha)$ are obviously continuous functions of the angle α, their difference $S_1(\alpha) - S_2(\alpha)$ is also a continuous function of α. Thus there must exist a value α_0 between α and $\alpha + 90°$ such that

$$S_1(\alpha_0) - S_2(\alpha_0) = 0;$$

that is,

$$S_1(\alpha_0) = S_2(\alpha)_0.$$

Thus the mutually perpendicular lines $l(\alpha_0)$ and $l^*(\alpha_0)$ divide the figure Φ into four equal parts.

Note. It is evident at once that the figures considered in Exercises 3-2 a and 3-2 b need not be convex. We recommend to the reader that he determine for himself how to complete the proof in this general case.

3-3. Prove that a square can be circumscribed about every convex figure.

About each convex figure Φ a uniquely determined rectangle $L(\alpha)$ can be circumscribed, one of whose sides $a(\alpha)$ has a given direction OY, determined by the angle α formed by the direction OY and a fixed initial ray OX (Diagram 177). We denote by $b(\alpha)$ the length of the side of the rectangle perpendicular to $a(\alpha)$, and we suppose that $a(\alpha) \neq b(\alpha)$, say $a(\alpha) - b(\alpha) > 0$. If we replace the angle α by $\alpha + 90°$, the circumscribed rectangle is unchanged. Its side $a(\alpha + 90°)$ coincides with $b(\alpha)$ and $b(\alpha+90°)$ coincides with $a(\alpha)$, except for direction. Hence

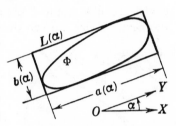

Diagram 177

$$a(\alpha + 90°) - b(\alpha + 90°) = b(\alpha) - a(\alpha) < 0.$$

Since the difference $a(\alpha) - b(\alpha)$ is a continuous function of α,[†] there must exist an angle α_0 between α and $\alpha + 90°$ such that

$$a(\alpha_0) - b(\alpha_0) = 0,$$

[†] We shall not go deeper here into the proof that the difference $a(\alpha) - b(\alpha)$ is a continuous function of α, since this is geometrically evident. The following idea lies at the basis of an exact proof. Consider a rectangle circumscribed about the figure Φ, one of whose sides forms the angle α with the initial ray OX. This rectangle will be denoted by $L(\alpha)$. If $\triangle\alpha$ (the increment of the angle α) is sufficiently small, then, as one easily shows, the points in which the convex figure Φ touches the sides of the rectangle $L(\alpha + \triangle\alpha)$ circumscribed about the figure Φ lie near the points in which the corresponding sides of the rectangle $L(\alpha)$ touch the figure Φ. (If the sides of the rectangle $L(\alpha)$ have an entire segment in common with the boundary of the figure Φ, then one of the contact points—one of the endpoints of the segment—lies in the neighborhood of the contact point of the corresponding side of $L(\alpha + \triangle\alpha)$ with the figure Φ.) Hence the position of the rectangle $L(\alpha + \triangle\alpha)$ differs but little from that of the rectangle $L(\alpha)$ for small $\triangle\alpha$; the rectangle $L(\alpha + \triangle\alpha)$ lies within a certain small "frame" circumscribed about $L(\alpha)$ (Diagram 178). From this it follows readily that each of the lengths $a(\alpha)$ and $b(\alpha)$, and hence the difference $a(\alpha) - b(\alpha)$, is a continuous function of the angle α.

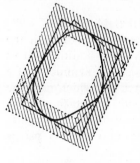

Diagram 178

and hence

$$a(\alpha_0) = b(\alpha_0).$$

Thus the rectangle $L(\alpha_0)$ circumscribed about the figure Φ, and with one side forming the angle α_0 with the initial ray OX, is a square.

3-4. (a) Prove that an equiangular hexagon with two equal opposite sides can be circumscribed about every convex curve.
(b) Prove that an equiangular hexagon having an axis of symmetry can be circumscribed about every convex curve.

(a) About every convex curve a unique equiangular hexagon (whose angles are all equal to 120°) can be circumscribed such that one side of the hexagon has a given direction OY formed by the angle α between the direction OY and the initial ray OX

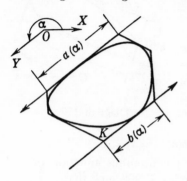

Diagram 179

(Diagram 179). We denote this side with direction OY by $a(\alpha)$ and the side opposite by $b(\alpha)$ and suppose that $a(\alpha) \neq b(\alpha)$, say $a(\alpha) > b(\alpha)$, that is, $a(\alpha) - b(\alpha) > 0$. When α is replaced by $\alpha + 180°$, the circumscribed hexagon is unchanged, and the sides $a(\alpha + 180°)$ and $b(\alpha)$ coincide, as do the sides $b(\alpha + 180°)$ and $a(\alpha)$. Thus $a(\alpha + 180°) - b(\alpha + 180°) = b(\alpha) - a(\alpha) < 0$. Since the difference $a(\alpha) - b(\alpha)$ is a continuous function of α, there must exist an angle α_0 between α and $\alpha + 180°$ for which

$$a(\alpha_0) - b(\alpha_0) = 0$$

and hence

$$a(\alpha_0) = b(\alpha_0).^{†}$$

Hence the hexagon $L(\alpha_0)$ has two equal opposite sides.

(b) If a hexagon whose angles are all equal (and equal to 120°) has axes of symmetry, then one of these axes must pass through the midpoints of opposite sides. (The hexagon may have additional axes of symmetry.) Indeed, we can easily see that an axis of symmetry of a polygon intersects the boundary either in a vertex (in which case the axis is an angle bisector) or in the midpoint of a side (in which case the axis is perpendicular to the side). Thus in the case of an equiangular hexagon whose opposite sides are parallel, an axis of symmetry passes

---

† The continuity of the function $a(\alpha) - b(\alpha)$ is geometrically evident. The exact proof is analogous to that sketched in the preceding footnote.

through the midpoints of opposite sides (Diagram 180 a) or through opposite vertices (Diagram 180 b). In the latter case the axis divides the hexagon into two congruent trapezoids (forming an angle of 60° with the base line), and the hexagon also has an axis of symmetry passing through the midpoints of opposite sides. We must therefore find a hexagon which is circumscribed about the convex figure and which has an axis of symmetry passing through the midpoints of opposite sides (perpendicular to those sides).

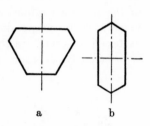

a   b

Diagram 180

About the convex figure Φ a unique equiangular hexagon can be circumscribed, one of whose sides has a given direction OY forming an angle α with the fixed intial ray OX. This hexagon we shall denote by $L(\alpha)$. The successive sides of this hexagon which are supporting lines of the figure Φ are denoted by l, m'', l', m, l'', m' (Diagram 181). The lines l, l', l'', m'', m, m' form two equilateral triangles. Let $A, A',$ A'' and B'', B, B' denote the vertices of these triangles (vertex A is opposite the side l; vertex B'' is opposite the side m'', etc.). If the

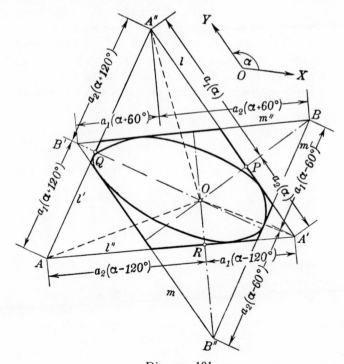

Diagram 181

hexagon $L(\alpha)$ has an axis of symmetry through the midpoint of the side l and perpendicular to it, then this axis passes through two vertices of the equilateral triangle in question, namely through the vertex A of the triangle $AA'A''$ and the vertex B of the triangle $BB'B''$ (by virtue of the previous remarks about axes of symmetry; Diagram 182). Conversely, if the perpendicular from vertex B to side l goes through the vertex A (if therefore the side $A'A''$ of the equilateral triangle $AA'A''$ is bisected by l), then the hexagon $L(\alpha)$ has an axis of symmetry.

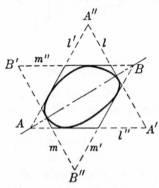

Diagram 182

Let us assume that the last assertion is false; that is, that the perpendicular from point B to line l divides the segment $A'A''$ into two unequal parts $a_1(\alpha)$ and $a_2(\alpha)$. Suppose that the segment $a_1(\alpha)$ with end point A' and lying along the side $A'A''$ is greater than the segment $a_2(\alpha)$ (see Diagram 181). From B' and B'', drop perpendiculars to the segments AA'' and AA', meeting these segments at points Q and R respectively. The lengths of the segments AQ, $A''Q$, AR, and $A'R$ are denoted by $a_1(\alpha + 120°)$, $a_2(\alpha + 120°)$, $a_1(\alpha - 120°)$, and $a_2(\alpha - 120°)$ respectively. Obviously the segmets $a_1(\alpha)$ and $a_2(\alpha)$ are converted into $a_1(\alpha + 120°)$ and $a_2(\alpha + 120°)$ or into $a_1(\alpha - 120°)$ and $a_2(\alpha - 120°)$, respectively, when the angle α is replaced by $\alpha + 120°$ or by $\alpha - 120°$. The perpendiculars from B, B', B'' are altitudes of the equilateral triangle $BB'B''$ and hence intersect in a point O. From this we obtain:[†]

$$a_1(\alpha)^2 + a_1(\alpha + 120°)^2 + a_1(\alpha - 120°)^2$$
$$= a_2(\alpha)^2 + a_2(\alpha + 120°)^2 + a_2(\alpha - 120°)^2.$$

Hence if $a_1(\alpha) > a_2(\alpha)$ it is impossible for both of the inequalities

$$a_1(\alpha + 120°) > a_2(\alpha + 120°)$$

and

$$a_1(\alpha - 120°) > a_2(\alpha - 120°)$$

to hold.

Let us suppose for example that

$$a_1(\alpha - 120°) < a_2(\alpha - 120°).$$

[†] It is obvious from Diagram 181 that $a_1(\alpha)^2 = A''O^2 - OP^2$, $a_1(\alpha + 120°)^2 = AO^2 - OQ^2$, $a_1(\alpha - 120°)^2 = A'O^2 - OR^2$ and $a_2(\alpha)^2 = A'O^2 - OP^2$, $a_2(\alpha + 120°)^2 = A''O^2 - OQ^2$, $a_2(\alpha - 120°)^2 = AO^2 - OR^2$, from which the relation we need is easily obtained.

The function $a_1(\alpha - 120°) - a_2(\alpha - 120°)$ is a continuous function[†] of the angle α. Therefore there exists an angle α_0 between $\alpha - 120°$ and α such that $a_1(\alpha_0) - a_2(\alpha_0) = 0$, that is, $a_1(\alpha_0) = a_2(\alpha_0)$. Hence the hexagon $L(\alpha_0)$ has an axis of symmetry passing through midpoints of opposite sides.

Note. We can assert somewhat more than the existence of a hexagon circumscribed about the convex figure Φ and having an axis of symmetry through the midpoints of opposite sides. In fact, if we change our proof slightly, we can show that there is a hexagon of the same type whose *axis of symmetry forms an angle $< 60°$ with a prescribed direction*.

We drop a perpendicular from A'' to the side BB' and one from A' to side BB'' of the triangle $BB'B''$. The segments determined by the perpendicular to the side BB' are denoted $a_1(\alpha + 60°)$, $a_2(\alpha + 60°)$ and those on BB'' by $a_1(\alpha - 60°)$, $a_2(\alpha - 60°)$ (see Diagram 181). It is easy to see that the segments $a_1(\alpha)$ and $a_2(\alpha)$ go over into $a_1(\alpha + 60°)$ and $a_2(\alpha + 60°)$ when α is replaced by $\alpha + 60°$ and into $a_1(\alpha - 60°)$ and $a_2(\alpha - 60°)$ when α is replaced by $\alpha - 60°$. We now prove easily that

$$a_1(\alpha + 60°) - a_2(\alpha + 60°) = a_1(\alpha - 120°) - a_2(\alpha - 120°)$$

and

$$a_1(\alpha - 60°) - a_2(\alpha - 60°) = a_1(\alpha + 120°) - a_2(\alpha + 120°),$$

since (in the case of the first equality) these two differences are equal to double the distance between the parallel lines through A'' and B'' respectively perpendicular to the line BB' (or AA'). Hence if $a_1(\alpha) > a_2(\alpha)$ we have

$$a_1(\alpha + 60°) < a_2(\alpha + 60°) \quad \text{and} \quad a_1(\alpha - 60°) < a_2(\alpha - 60°).$$

Since the difference $a_1(\alpha) - a_2(\alpha)$ is continuous as a function of α, it follows that there is an angle α_0 between α and $\alpha + 60°$ or between α and $\alpha - 60°$, where α corresponds to an arbitrary fixed direction, such that the hexagon $L(\alpha_0)$ has an axis of symmetry perpendicular to two sides of the hexagon, and this axis forms the angle α_0 with the initial ray. This proves our assertion. This remark will be useful in the sequel.

[†] The continuity of the function $a_1(\alpha) - a_2(\alpha)$ is geometrically trivial; the exact proof is similar to that sketched in the footnote on page 143.

3-5. Prove that every plane figure of diameter 1 (see page 9) can be inscribed in a regular hexagon of side length $1/\sqrt{3}$. Since each such regular hexagon can be inscribed in a circle of radius $1/\sqrt{3}$, this exercise strengthens *Jung's Theorem* considerably.

In the solution of Exercise 3-4 a it was proved that about each convex figure an equiangular hexagon can be circumscribed which has a pair of equal opposite sides. From this it follows immediately that about each (not necessarily convex) bounded figure Ψ such a hexagon can be circumscribed. Every hexagon circumscribed about the convex hull of the figure Ψ is indeed also circumscribed about the figure Ψ (see text, pages 31-32).

Suppose we have a plane figure Ψ of diameter 1. We circumscribe about this figure a hexagon $ABCDEF$ (Diagram 183 a) each of whose

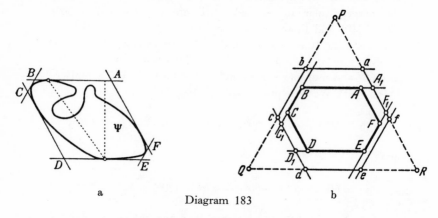

a

Diagram 183

b

angles is 120° and whose opposite sides AB and DE are equal. The distance between each pair of opposite sides is not greater than 1. If, for example, the distance between the supporting lines AB and DE were greater than 1, then the distance between the contact points of these supporting lines with the figure would also be greater than 1, contrary to the assumption that the diameter of Ψ equals 1.

We now enlarge the hexagon $ABCDEF$ by parallel displacement of its sides so that the distance between each pair of parallel sides is exactly equal to 1.

Let $abcdef$ be the new hexagon, constructed so that any two of its opposite sides are equidistant from the corresponding sides of the hexagon $ABCDEF$ (Diagram 183 b). We assert that the sides ab and de of the hexagon $abcdef$ are equal. Indeed, if we displace the opposite sides AF and DC of the hexagon $ABCDEF$ by equal amounts, we obtain a new hexagon $A_1BC_1D_1EF_1$ in which $AA_1 = DD_1$ and hence $A_1B = D_1E$. Likewise the sides A_1B and D_1E of the new hexagon are increased by equal segments if we displace the sides BC_1 and EF_1 by equal amounts, and they diminish in equal proportion if they themselves are displaced equally (Diagram 183 b).

It is now easy to show that $abcdef$ is the regular hexagon which we seek. To do this we lengthen the segments bc, de, and fa so that their lines form the equilateral triangle PQR (Diagram 183 b). Let the altitude of this triangle be H. Since the distance between opposite sides of $abcdef$ is 1, the altitudes of the equilateral triangles abP, cdQ, and efR are all equal to $H - 1$. Hence these triangles are congruent; it follows that $ab = cd = ef$. We prove similarly that $bc = de = fa$. Hence the hexagon $abcdef$ has equal sides and is therefore regular.

If the distance between any two opposite sides of a regular hexagon is 1, it is easy to verify that the sides of the hexagon are each equal to $1/\sqrt{3}$. (If the distance from the center of a regular hexagon to each side is $1/2$, then the distance from the vertices to the center, which is the radius of the circumcircle, equals $(1/2) \sec 30° = (1/2) \cdot (2/\sqrt{3}) = 1/\sqrt{3}$; hence the sides are also equal to $1/\sqrt{3}$.)

3-6. (a) Given a convex curve K and any line l in the plane, prove that three chords $A'B'$, $A''B''$, A_0B_0 of the curve K can be found which are parallel to the line l, and which have the property that the chord A_0B_0 is equidistant from the chords $A'B'$ and $A''B''$, and $A'B' = A''B'' = A_0B_0/2$. (b) Prove that a hexagon can be inscribed in every convex curve so that any two opposite sides of the hexagon are parallel to each other and to the diagonal joining the vertices not lying on these sides.

(**a**) We construct two supporting lines l_0' and l_0'' to the figure Φ which are parallel to the line l and draw a line m_0 also parallel to l, equidistant from l_0' and l_0''. Suppose that the lengths of the contact segments of lines l_0' and l_0'' with the curve K are respectively a_0' and a_0'' and that $a_0' \leq a_0''$ (if the lines l_0' and l_0'' have only one point in common with the boundary of Φ, then $a_0' = a_0'' = 0$). The length of the chord cut off from m_0 by K will be denoted by b_0. If $a_0' > b_0/2$, then three chords satisfying the hypotheses of this exercise lie on the lines l_0', l_0'', and m_0, and these chords are uniquely determined if $a_0' = a_0'' = b_0/2$; otherwise, they can be chosen in various ways (Diagram 184 a, b). However if $a_0' < b_0/2$, so that $b_0 > 2a_0'$ and $b_0 - 2a_0' > 0$, then we displace the line l_0' continuously parallel to itself in the direction toward the line l_0''. Let l' be a position assumed by l_0' after a displacement and let l'' be a line parallel to l' such that on its contact segment there is a chord of the same length a as the contact segment of l'. If $a_0' < a_0''$, then the line l'' may possibly coincide with l_0'', even though l' is different from l_0'

(Diagram 184 c). Let m denote the line parallel to the lines l' and l'' and equidistant from them. Let the length of the chord which the curve K cuts off from the line m be denoted by b. As l_0' is continuously displaced toward l_0'', the difference $b - 2a$ changes continuously. If a_1 is the

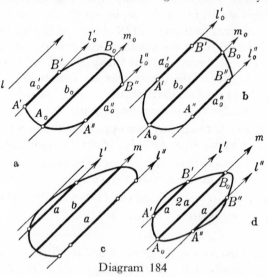

Diagram 184

length of the longest chord of the curve K in the direction of l, then a and b are both equal to a_1 and the difference $b - 2a = a_1 - 2a_1$ becomes less than zero. From the continuity of the difference $b - 2a$, regarded as a function of the distance between l_0' and l', it follows that for some position of the line l', the equation $b = 2a$ must hold (Diagram 184 d). This completes the proof.

Note. The triple of chords which has been described is, as we easily show, *unique* in the sense that the lines on which these chords lie are uniquely determined. Let $A'B'$, $A''B''$, A_0B_0 and $A_1'B_1'$, $A_1''B_1''$ and $A_{01}B_{01}$ be two different chord triples, with a common direction, both of which satisfy the requirements of this exercise. We will show that the chords A_0B_0 and $A_{01}B_{01}$ coincide. Assume that this is not the case (Diagram 185), and let h be the distance between the parallel lines A_0B_0 and $A_{01}B_{01}$. We also assume that $A_0B_0 \geq A_{01}B_{01}$ (if not we exchange the chord triples in what follows). Moreover let the chord A_0B_0 be on the same side of the chord $A_{01}B_{01}$ as the chord $A_1'B_1'$ (the reverse case is analogous). Then the chord $A'B'$ lies between the lines A_0B_0 and $A_1'B_1'$ (or on the line $A_1'B_1'$), since otherwise we would have $A'B' < A_1'B_1'$, contrary to the inequality $A_0B_0 \geq A_{01}B_{01}$. Thus the distance between the parallel chords A_0B_0 and $A'B'$ is smaller by h than the distance between $A_{01}B_{01}$

and $A_1'B_1'$. It then follows readily that the distance between the chords $A''B''$ and $A_1''B_1''$ is at least $2h$. We now consider the trapezoid $A_0B_0B_1''A_1''$. The points of intersection of the sides of this trapezoid with $A''B''$ and $A_{01}B_{01}$ will be denoted by M, N and P, Q. We now conclude that

$$MN - A_1''B_1'' \geq 2(A_0B_0 - PQ),$$

since the distance between the chords MN and $A_1''B_1''$ is at least twice as large as the distance between the chords A_0B_0 and PQ. On the other hand,

$$A_0B_0 - PQ > A_0B_0 - A_{01}B_{01} = 2A''B'' - 2A_1''B_1''$$
$$= 2(A''B'' - A_1''B_1'') > 2(MN - A_1''B_1'').$$

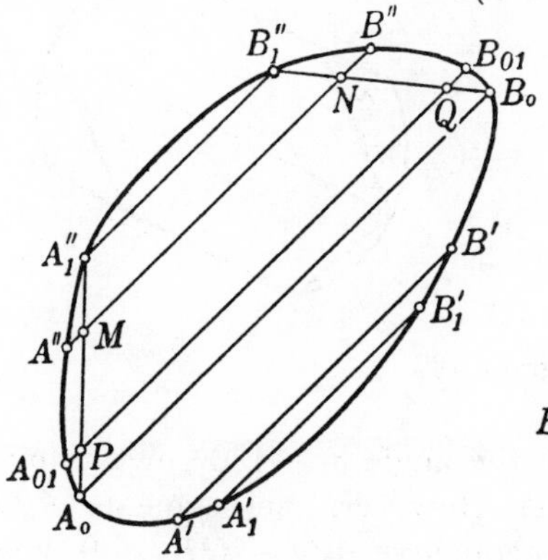

Diagram 185 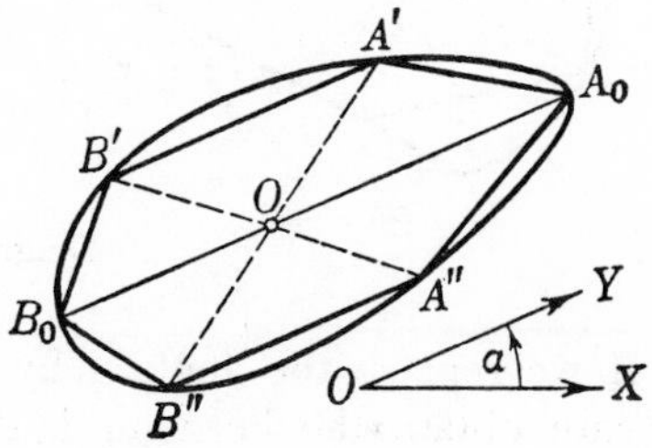   Diagram 186

However by the first inequality above, this implies the contradiction

$$A_0B_0 - PQ > 4(A_0B_0 - PQ).$$

The chords A_0B_0 and $A_{01}B_{01}$ are therefore identical. From this fact it follows without difficulty that the chords $A'B'$ and $A_1'B_1'$ (and also $A''B''$ and $A_1''B_1''$) lie on a single straight line.

(b) Let l be a line determined by the angle α which it is to form with an arbitrary fixed initial ray OX. For simplicity we select α so that the curve K contains no straight line segment parallel to l. Let $A'B'$, $A''B''$ and A_0B_0 denote chords of the curve K parallel to l and having the property that A_0B_0 is equidistant from $A'B'$ and $A''B''$ and $A'B' = A''B'' = A_0B_0/2$ (see Exercise 3-6 a, especially the remark at the end of the solution to that exercise). The hexagon $A'B'B_0B''A''A_0$ will be denoted by $L(\alpha)$. The diagonals $A'B''$ and $A''B'$ of the hexagon $L(\alpha)$ obviously intersect in the point O of the diagonal A_0B_0 and are bisected by this point (Diagram 186).

We now suppose that A_0O is not equal to OB_0 in our hexagon, say $A_0O > OB_0$, and hence $A_0O - OB_0 > 0$.

Under continuous increase of the angle α, the hexagon $L(\alpha)$ also changes continuously. If for some angle α there is no unique corresponding hexagon $L(\alpha)$—which can occur if the curve K contains line segments parallel to l—then, as the hexagon changes, we pass from hexagons corresponding to angles less than α to the hexagon $L_2(\alpha)$ shown in Diagram 187 b. We then transform $L_2(\alpha)$ continuously into the hexagon $L_1(\alpha)$ shown in Diagram 187 a, and pass on to consideration of angles greater than α.

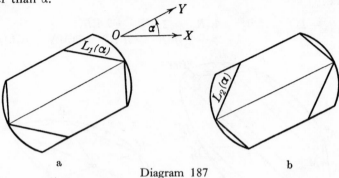

Diagram 187

If we replace the angle α by the angle $\alpha + 180°$ in this manner, we again obtain the hexagon $L(\alpha)$. However, the segments A_0O and OB_0 exchange roles, and the inequality $A_0O - OB_0 > 0$ becomes $B_0O - OA_0 < 0$; thus the difference changes sign. Hence there must exist a hexagon $L(\alpha_0)$ such that

$$A_0O = OB_0 = A'B' = A''B''$$

and

$$B'O = OA'', \quad A'O = OB''.$$

It follows that $A'B'OA_0$ is a parallelogram (since $A'B'$ equals and is parallel to A_0O), and similarly $OB_0B''A''$ is a parallelogram (since OB_0 equals and is parallel to $A''B''$). Thus

$$A_0A' \,||\, A''B' \,||\, B''B_0;$$

likewise one proves

$$B'B_0 \,||\, A'B'' \,||\, A_0A''.$$

3-7. (a) S. S. Kovner's Theorem. Prove that in each convex figure Φ, we can construct a centrally symmetric convex figure whose area is greater than or equal to 2/3 the area of the figure Φ.

(b) Prove that it is impossible to construct within a general triangle a centrally symmetric figure whose area is greater than 2/3 the area of the triangle.

(a) In the convex curve K bounding the figure Φ we inscribe a hexagon $A'B'B_0B''A''A_0$ which satisfies the premises of Exercise 3-6 b (Diagram 188). This hexagon has central symmetry and is enclosed by the figure Φ. We assert that the area of this hexagon is at least $\frac{2}{3}$ the area of the figure Φ.

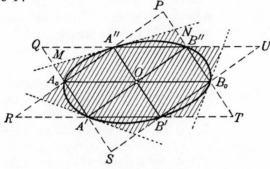

Diagram 188

Denote the area of the triangle $A'B'O$ by σ. The diagonals $A'B''$, $B'A''$, and A_0B_0 divide the hexagon $A'B'B_0B''A''A_0$ into six congruent triangles, one of which is the triangle $A'B'O$. The area of the hexagon is thus equal to 6σ. If we extend the sides $A'B'$, B_0B'', $A''A_0$ to form a triangle and similarly extend the sides $B'B_0$, $B''A''$, A_0A' of the hexagon $A'B'B_0B''A''A_0$ until they intersect, we obtain the star-shaped figure $PA''QA_0RA'SB'TB_0UB''$ shown in Diagram 188, which clearly consists of twelve triangles congruent to the triangle $A'B'O$. The area of this 12-sided polygon is therefore equal to 12σ. Obviously, since the figure Φ lies in the interior of this star-shaped, 12-sided polygon, the area of Φ is less than 12σ. Hence the area of the hexagon $A'B'B_0B''A''A_0$ is at least $\frac{1}{2}$ the area of the figure Φ. This estimate, however, can be considerably improved.

We draw supporting lines to the figure Φ through the vertices A', B_0, and A''. These lines cut off from the first star-shaped, 12-sided polygon a smaller star-shaped, 9-sided polygon (shaded in Diagram 188). The area of this 9-sided figure is 9σ, as can easily be seen. For example, suppose that the supporting line through A'' of the figure Φ cuts the trangles $A''MQ$ and $A''NP$ out of the triangles $A_0A''Q$ and $A''B''P$, belonging to the 12-sided polygon (Diagram 188). Then

$$\triangle A_0A''Q = \triangle A''B''P = \triangle OA''B''$$

and hence

$$S(\triangle A_0A''Q) + S(\triangle A''B''P) = 2\sigma,$$

where S denotes area. Moreover $\triangle A''MQ = \triangle A''B''N$ (since $A''Q = A''B'$, and the angles adjacent to these sides are respectively equal). Similarly, $\triangle A''NP = \triangle A_0A''M$ and hence

$$S(\triangle A''MQ) + S(\triangle A''NP) = \tfrac{1}{2}[S(\triangle AA''Q) + S(\triangle A''B''P)] = \sigma.$$

Likewise the supporting lines of Φ at the points B_0 and A' cut out from the 12-sided polygon a pair of triangles having the combined area σ. The area of the 9-sided figure is therefore equal to $12\sigma - 3\sigma = 9\sigma$. However, the figure Φ is enclosed by this 9-sided polygon; hence the area of Φ is less than or equal to 9σ and the area of the hexagon $A'B'B_0 B''A''A_0$ which equals 6σ cannot be less than $\tfrac{2}{3}$ the area of Φ.

(b) Let O be the center of a centrally symmetric figure Φ inscribed in the triangle ABC. When we reflect Φ in the point O, the figure Φ is

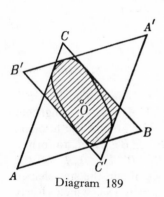

Diagram 189

transformed into itself, while the triangle ABC is converted into the triangle $A'B'C'$ symmetric to triangle ABC with respect to the point O (Diagram 189). Since the figure Φ is enclosed in the triangle ABC, the figure obtained from Φ by reflection in O, which is again Φ, must also lie inside the triangle $A'B'C'$. Thus we conclude that Φ is enclosed in the triangle $A'B'C'$ as well as in the triangle ABC; that is, Φ is contained in the intersection of the triangles ABC and $A'B'C'$. However this intersection is itself a centrally symmetric convex figure, for by reflection in the point O, the triangle ABC is carried into triangle $A'B'C'$, the triangle $A'B'C'$ into the triangle ABC, and the intersection of these triangles is carried into itself. Thus we see that the intersection of the triangles ABC and $A'B'C'$ is the largest centrally symmetric figure contained in the triangle ABC and having center O. Every other such figure is enclosed in this intersection.

In order to find the largest centrally symmetric figure enclosed in the triangle ABC, we must find in the interior of triangle ABC a point O such that the area of the intersection of triangle ABC with triangle $A'B'C'$ is maximal, where the latter triangle is obtained by reflection of triangle ABC in O.

Depending on the position of the point O, this intersection is a parallelogram (Diagram 190 a) or a hexagon (Diagram 190 b). However, t is at once clear that when the intersection is a parallelogram the position of the point O can always be changed so that the intersection of the triangles ABC and $A'B'C'$ becomes a hexagon and its area increases (Diagram 190 a). Hence the largest centrally symmetric figure that can be inscribed in a given triangle ABC must necessarily be a hexagon.

If the intersection is a hexagon, then the triangle $A'B'C'$ cuts away from the triangle ABC three smaller triangles which are similar to the

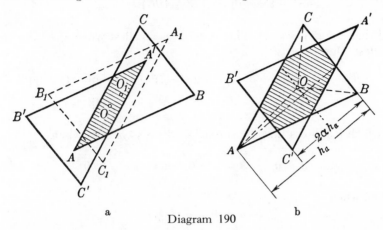

a   Diagram 190   b

triangle ABC (the sides of each of these triangles are parallel to the sides of triangle ABC). Denote the sides of the triangle ABC by a, b, and c, the corresponding altitudes by h_a, h_b, h_c, and let the distances of the point O from the sides a, b, c have the ratios α, β, γ to the corresponding altitudes h_a, h_b, and h_c. In this notation, the distances of the point O from the sides of triangle ABC are respectively equal to αh_a, βh_b, γh_c. The equalities

$$ah_a = bh_b = ch_c = 2S(\triangle ABC)$$

and

$$a \cdot \alpha h_a + b \cdot \beta h_b + c \cdot \gamma h_c = 2S(\triangle BCO) + 2S(\triangle ACO) + 2S(\triangle ABO)$$
$$= 2S(\triangle ABC)$$

imply that

$$\alpha + \beta + \gamma = 1.$$

From Diagram 190 b it is easy to see that the triangle cut off from triangle ABC by the side $B'C'$ has a similarity ratio to the entire triangle ABC equal to $(h_a - 2\alpha h_a)/h_a = 1 - 2\alpha$ (since the distance from O to BC is αh_a, the distance between BC and $B'C'$ must be $2\alpha h_a$). Likewise the sides $A'C'$ and $A'B'$ cut away from triangle ABC triangles similar to it in the ratios $1 - 2\beta$ and $1 - 2\gamma$ respectively.

Hence the sum of the areas of the three triangles cut off from triangle ABC by the sides of triangle $A'B'C'$ is equal to

$$[(1 - 2\alpha)^2 + (1 - 2\beta)^2 + (1 - 2\gamma)^2] \, S(\triangle ABC)$$
$$= [3 - 4\alpha - 4\beta - 4\gamma + 4\alpha^2 + 4\beta^2 + 4\gamma^2] \, S(\triangle ABC)$$
$$= [4(\alpha^2 + \beta^2 + \gamma^2) - 1] \, S(\triangle ABC)$$

(recall that $\alpha + \beta + \gamma = 1$). This product is smallest when $\alpha^2 + \beta^2 + \gamma^2$ is smallest. But

$$\alpha^2 + \beta^2 + \gamma^2 = \tfrac{1}{3}[(\alpha + \beta + \gamma)^2 + (\alpha - \beta)^2 + (\beta - \gamma)^2 + (\alpha - \gamma)^2]$$
$$= \tfrac{1}{3}[1 + (\alpha - \beta)^2 + (\beta - \gamma)^2 + (\alpha - \gamma)^2],$$

from which it follows that the sum $\alpha^2 + \beta^2 + \gamma^2$ is least when

$$\alpha - \beta = 0, \qquad \beta - \gamma = 0, \quad \text{and} \quad \alpha - \gamma = 0$$

and thus when

$$\alpha = \beta = \gamma = \tfrac{1}{3}.$$

In this case (which, it is evident, occurs when the point O is the intersection of the medians of triangle ABC) we have

$$[4(\alpha^2 + \beta^2 + \gamma^2) - 1] = \tfrac{1}{3}.$$

Thus the sum of the areas of the three triangles that are cut off from the triangle ABC is equal to $\tfrac{1}{3} S(\triangle ABC)$, and the area of the intersection of triangles ABC and $A'B'C'$ (the area of the largest centrally symmetric figure that can' be inscribed in the triangle ABC) is equal to $\tfrac{2}{3} S(\triangle ABC)$.

3-8. (a) Prove that every convex figure Φ can be contained in a centrally symmetric convex figure whose area is less than or equal to twice that of the figure Φ. (b) Prove that a general triangle cannot be contained in a centrally symmetric convex figure whose area is less than twice that of the triangle.

(a) Draw any pair of parallel supporting lines l and l' to the figure Φ. Let the points of contact of these lines with Φ be A and B (A and B need not be unique; see Diagram 191). Draw supporting lines m and m' of the figure Φ parallel to the line AB, intersecting Φ in the points C and D (which also need not be unique). The four lines l, l', m, m' form a parallelogram $PQRS$ circumscribed about Φ. The segment AB

subdivides this parallelogram into two smaller parallelograms. Obviously the area of one of these parallelograms is double the area of triangle ABC and the area of the other is double the area of the triangle ABD. Hence the area of the parallelogram $PQRS$ is twice that of the quadrilateral $ABCD$. Since the figure Φ is convex, it encloses the entire quadrilateral $ABCD$. Hence it follows that the area of parallelogram $PQRS$ (which is a centrally symmetric convex figure enclosing Φ) is less than or equal to twice the area of Φ, as we wished to prove.

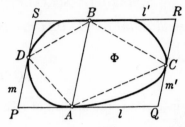

Diagram 191

(b) In analogy with the solution of Exercise 3-7 b, we conclude that every centrally symmetric figure whose center of symmetry is O and which is enclosed in a triangle ABC also contains the triangle $A'B'C'$ formed from triangle ABC by reflection in O. Hence a *convex* centrally symmetric figure which contains the triangle ABC must also contain the convex hull of the pair of triangles ABC and $A'B'C'$ (see page 32).

The intersection of the triangles ABC and $A'B'C'$ is a parallelogram or a centrally symmetric hexagon (see Diagrams 190 a and b). In the first case, the convex hull of triangles ABC and $A'B'C'$ forms a parallelogram $ABA'B'$ (Diagram 192 a) whose area is at least twice the area of triangle ABC. In fact,

$$S(\square ABA'B') = 4S(\triangle AOB)$$

and $S(\triangle AOB) \geq \frac{1}{2} S(\triangle ABC)$; for if the altitude of triangle AOB were less than half the altitude of triangle ABC, then the point C' would lie outside triangle ABC below the side AB, and the intersection of triangles ABC and $A'B'C'$ would not be a parallelogram.

In the second case, the convex hull is a centrally symmetric hexagon $AC'BA'CB'$ (Diagram 192 b) whose area is exactly twice that of triangle ABC.

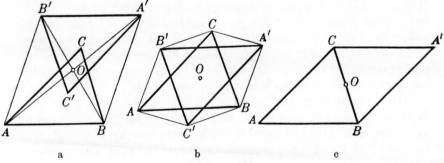

a   b   c

Diagram 192

In fact

$$S(AC'BA'CB') = S(\triangle OAB') + S(\triangle OA'B) + S(\triangle OCA') + S(\triangle OC'A)$$
$$+ S(\triangle OBC') + S(\triangle OB'C) = 2S(\triangle OAB') + 2S(\triangle OCA') + 2S(\triangle OBC').$$

Also

$$S(\triangle OAB') = S(\triangle OAB),$$

since AO is the median of triangle $AB'B$. Similarly

$$S(\triangle OCA') = S(\triangle OCA), \qquad S(\triangle OBC') = S(\triangle OBC)$$

and consequently

$$S(AC'BA'CB') = 2S(\triangle OAB) + 2S(\triangle OCA) + 2S(\triangle OBC) = 2S(\triangle ABC).$$

> *Note.* The simplest example of a centrally symmetric convex figure whose area equals $2S(\triangle ABC)$ and which encloses the triangle ABC is the parallelogram shown in Diagram 192 c.

3-9. (a) Prove that the center of gravity of a convex figure Φ of width 1 (see page 18) has a distance of at least $1/3$ from each supporting line of the figure Φ. (b) Let a convex figure Φ be given whose area is S; let a segment AB of length 1 form part of its boundary. Prove that the center of gravity of the figure Φ has a distance of at most $2S/3$ from the line AB.

(a) Let l be any supporting line of the figure Φ and let l' be another supporting line parallel to l. Since the width of the figure is 1, the distance d between l and l' is greater than or equal to 1. Assume that the line l touches the boundary of the figure Φ along the segment CD, and that the line l' touches the boundary of Φ along the segment AB (D may coincide with C, and B with A). The boundary of the figure Φ consists of four parts, the segments AB and CD and two curves DA and BC (Diagram 193 a). Suppose that the part AD of the boundary of Φ is not a straight line segment. We join the points A and D by the line AD and rotate it about the point A. Let E be the variable intersection point of the rotating line with the supporting line l (E moves on l in the direction to the left of the point D), and let F be the corresponding point of intersection of the rotating line with the curve AD.

Upon rotation of the line AE, the area of the sector AGF of Φ decreases from its greatest value, which is the area of the sector cut off by the line AD, to the value zero. The area of the curvilinear triangle DEF increases from 0 and finally becomes larger than any preassigned amount.

The difference $S(AGF) - S(DEF)$ of these two areas varies continuously. For the initial position of the segment this difference is positive (and equals the area of the sector cut off by AD); subsequently it becomes negative. Therefore, there is a point F on the curve AD such that

$$S(AGF) - S(DEF) = 0,$$

and hence the area of the sector AGF is equal to the area of the curvilinear triangle DEF.

Next we replace the figure Φ by the figure $ABCEA$, whose area is equal to that of Φ. Let M_1 be the center of gravity of the part $ABCDFA$ of Φ (omitting the sector AGF), M_2 be the center of gravity of the sector AGF, and M_3 be the center of gravity of the curvilinear triangle DEF.

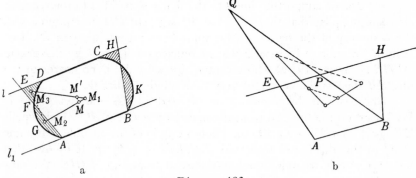

Diagram 193

The figure Φ consists of the part $ABCDFA$ and the sector AGF. The center of gravity M of Φ lies on the line M_1M_2. The figure $ABCEFA$ consists of the part $ABCDFA$ and the curvilinear triangle DEF. The center of gravity M' of this figure lies on the line M_1M_3. Also $M_1M'/M_1M_3 = M_1M/MM_2$ and hence $MM' \parallel M_2M_3$. Thus the center of gravity M' of the figure $ABCEFA$ is no further from the line l than the center of gravity M of the figure Φ.

Following the same procedure as above, we replace the curve BC of Φ by a straight line segment BH, and obtain a trapezoid $ABHE$ whose area equals that of the figure Φ and whose center of gravity is no further from the line l than is the center of gravity of Φ.

If the segment AB has length zero (if B coincides with A), then the trapezoid becomes a triangle. If A coincides with B, then the center of gravity M' of triangle EAH is a trisection point of the median through A (the median AR of triangle AEH is divided by M' in the ratio $RM'/RA = 1/3$). Thus the distance of M' from l is not less than $1/3$ of d (the altitude of the triangle), and is therefore not less than $1/3$. Hence the distance of the point M from l is also certainly not less than $1/3$. If

EABH is a trapezoid, then its center of gravity M' lies on the line segment connecting the centers of gravity of the triangles *AEH* and *ABH*. The center of gravity of the first of these triangles is at distance $d/3$ from l. The center of gravity of the second triangle is the same distance from l' and thus at distance $2d/3$ from l. Hence the distance of the point M' from l is greater than $d/3 \geq 1/3$. This implies that the distance of the point M from l is certainly greater than $1/3$.

(b) We investigate any convex figure Φ with area S whose boundary contains a line segment (Diagram 193 a) and prove that if this figure is replaced by a triangle *ABQ* with the same area and with base *AB*, then the distance from the line *AB* to the center of gravity of the figure is only increased by the replacement.

We draw a supporting line l to the figure Φ parallel to the segment *AB*, and suppose that the line l has the segment *CD* in common with the boundary of the figure Φ (the point *C* may coincide with *D*). Just as in the solution of Exercise 3-9 a, we replace the figure Φ by a trapezoid *ABHE* (Diagram 193 a) whose center of gravity M' is no nearer to the line *AB* than is the center of gravity M of the figure Φ.

The bases of the trapezoid are denoted by $AB = a$ and $EH = b$. We lay off on the line *AE* from the point *A* a segment *AQ* which equals $AE \cdot (a + b)/a$ (Diagram 193 b). Then the ratio of the altitude of triangle *ABQ* to the altitude of trapezoid *ABHE* is $(a + b) : a$. It follows that the area of this triangle equals the area of trapezoid *ABHE*. We now replace trapezoid *ABHE* by triangle *ABQ*, which has the same area. The trapezoid *ABHE* consists of the quadrilateral *ABPE* and the triangle *BHP*. Its center of gravity lies on the line segment joining the centers of gravity of these two parts. The triangle *ABQ* consists of the quadrilateral *ABPE* and the triangle *PEQ*. The center of gravity of triangle *ABQ* lies on the line segment joining the centers of gravity of these parts. It follows without difficulty that the center of gravity of triangle *ABQ* is at a greater distance from the segment *AB* than is the center of gravity of trapezoid *ABHE*.

Thus the distance of the center of gravity of the triangle *ABQ* from the line *AB* is at least equal to the distance of the center of gravity of the original figure Φ from that line. The distance of the center of gravity of the triangle *ABQ* from the segment *AB* is $1/3$ of the altitude. The altitude of a triangle *ABQ* with base 1 and area S is obviously equal to $2S$; this completes the proof.

3-10. Winternitz's Theorem. A convex figure is divided into two parts by a line l that passes through its center of gravity. Prove that the ratio of the areas of the two parts always lies between the bounds $4/5$ and $5/4$.

Let Φ be any convex figure with center of gravity M. Consider the pencil of lines through M and compare the ratios of the areas of the parts into which the lines of the pencil subdivide Φ. These ratios lie between certain bounds. We shall prove that we can find a triangle T such that the ratio of the subareas into which the triangle is divided by a line through the center of gravity is less than the analogous ratio for the figure Φ. This proof will be carried out in several steps.

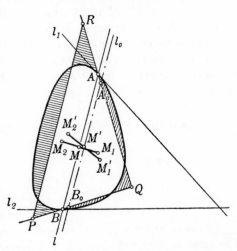

Diagram 194

Let l be a line through the center of gravity M of the figure Φ (Diagram 194). The line l divides the figure Φ into two parts, Φ_1 and Φ_2, with areas S_1 and S_2, respectively. Next we replace Φ_1 by a triangle ABQ with the same area S_1 as Φ_1 (A and B are the points of intersection of the line l with the boundary of Φ). We select the vertex Q of this triangle so that both it and Φ_1 lie in the region bounded by the line l and the two supporting lines l_1 and l_2 to Φ_1 through A and B respectively. (If A and B are corner points, then l_1 and l_2 are any supporting lines through A and B respectively.) It is clear that we can always select the point Q in this manner. (In Diagram 194, the case is shown where the lines l_1 and l_2 intersect on the side of l in which the part Φ_1 lies; in the contrary case the possibility for such a choice of Q is even more obvious.) In this case, the figure Φ_2 is situated entirely inside the angle AQB (and, in fact, on the other side of the segment AB from the triangle AQB); however, this fact is immaterial. We now replace the part Φ_2 of the figure by a trapezoid $BARP$, with the same area S_2 as Φ_2, whose smaller base is the segment AB and whose sides AR and BP lie on the lines QA and QB (Diagram 194). Thus we replace the figure Φ by the triangle PQR having the same area as Φ.

Let M' be the center of gravity of the triangle PQR. We claim that the point M' belongs to the triangle ABQ. Let M_1 be the center of gravity of the figure Φ_1, M_2 the center of gravity of the figure Φ_2, M_1' the center of gravity of the triangle ABQ, and M_2' the center of gravity of the trapezoid $BARP$. The point M lies on the segment M_1M_2 and divides it in the ratio $M_1M : MM_2 = S_2 : S_1$. The point M' lies on the segment $M_1'M_2'$ and divides it in the same ratio. However, the point M_1' is no nearer to the line AB than the point M_1 (Exercise 3-9 b);

on the other hand, the center of gravity M_2' of the trapezoid $BARP$ is no further from the line AB than is the center of gravity M_2 of the figure Φ_2 (of all figures with the area S_2 which lie within the angle AQB on the same side of the segment AB as Φ_2, the trapezoid $BARP$ obviously has its center of gravity nearest to the segment AB; a rigorous proof of this can easily be given by examining the separate pieces making up the trapezoid $BARP$ and the figure Φ_2). From this it follows that the center M' of the triangle PQR lies on the same side of the segment AB as the triangle ABQ.

Through the center of gravity M' of the triangle PQR draw a line l_0 parallel to l (and hence parallel to the base RP); let A_0 and B_0, respectively, denote the intersections of this line with the sides QR and QP of the triangle. It is now obvious that

$$S(A_0B_0Q) \leq S(ABQ) = S_1, \qquad S(B_0A_0RP) \geq S(BARP) = S_2,$$

and consequently

$$\frac{S(A_0B_0Q)}{S(B_0A_0RP)} \leq \frac{S_1}{S_2}.$$

This is the result we wished to obtain. It means the following: *The ratio of the areas into which a convex figure Φ is divided by a line l through its center of gravity is least when Φ is a triangle and l is parallel to a base of the triangle Φ.* In this case, however, the ratio of the areas $S(A_0B_0Q)/S(B_0A_0RP)$ is obviously 4/5, for the triangle A_0QB_0 is similar to the triangle RQP and the similarity ratio is 2/3 (a median of a triangle is divided in the ratio $2/3 : 1/3$ by the center of gravity). Hence

$$S(A_0B_0Q) = \frac{4}{9} S, \qquad S(B_0A_0RP) = \frac{5}{9} S.$$

(S is the area of the figure Φ.) From this it follows that

$$\frac{S_1}{S_2} \geq \frac{S(A_0B_0Q)}{S(B_0A_0RP)} = \frac{4}{5},$$

which we wished to prove.

Note. If the figure Φ is not a triangle, then, as follows from the above solution, the ratio of the areas into which a line through its center of gravity divides it always lies within narrower bounds than 4/5 and 5/4.

3-11. (a) Prove that if Φ is a convex figure, then for any point P not in Φ there exists exactly one point of Φ which is nearest to P. (b) Conversely, if the figure Ψ is bounded by a simple, closed curve L so that for every point P not in Ψ there exists exactly one point of the figure Ψ which is nearest to P, then the figure Ψ is convex.

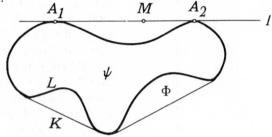

Diagram 195

(a) Assume that the convex figure Φ contains two points A and B which are nearest to a point P not belonging to Φ. Consider the isosceles triangle PAB and let M be the midpoint of the side AB. The point M also belongs to the figure Φ (since Φ is *convex*); on the other hand, $PM < PA$ (the altitude of an equilateral triangle is smaller than the lateral sides); hence the point A is not a nearest point. This contradiction proves the theorem.

(b) Assume that a figure Ψ, with the property stipulated in the hypothesis of the exercise, is not convex; let Φ be the convex hull of the figure Ψ (see page 32), and let K be the boundary of Φ. Since Ψ is nonconvex, it does not coincide with Φ, and this means that K is not coincident with L. Let M be a point of the curve K not belonging to the curve L; let l be a supporting line of the figure Φ passing through the point M. The line l is also a supporting line for the figure Ψ; it also contains points A_1 and A_2 of the curve L such that the point M lies between them (compare Diagram 195 with Diagram 44 a); we suppose that A_1 and A_2 are the points of the line l nearest to M having the property just described. Draw two circles with centers A_1 and A_2

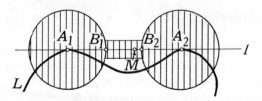

Diagram 196

and with radii $\frac{1}{3} A_1A_2$; let B_1 and B_2 be the points of intersection of these circles with the segment A_1A_2. No point of the segment B_1B_2 belongs to the figure Ψ; hence there is a distance h so small that the two segments parallel to l at distance h from it, and whose ends lie on the circles, are completely outside the figure Ψ. Let us denote by X the shaded figure in Diagram 196 (the "dumbbell"); it is clear that the "arm" of this dumbbell does not contain points of the figure Ψ, that is, all points of the figure Ψ inside the dumbbell X lie in one or the other of the nonintersecting circular areas C_1 and C_2 bounded by the circles with centers A_1 and A_2 respectively.

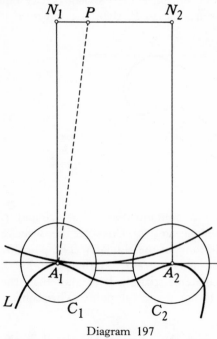

Diagram 197

We pass rays through the points A_1 and A_2 perpendicular to the segment A_1A_2, lying on the opposite side of the line l from the figure Ψ. On these rays we lay off segments A_1N_1 and A_2N_2 of length $d^2/2h$, where d is the length of the segment A_1A_2. We now consider any circle passing through either A_1 or A_2 with center P on the segment N_1N_2 and with radius R. On such a circle, the arc containing A_1 (or A_2) which lies between the lines A_1N_1 and A_2N_2, does not pass outside the dumbbell (Diagram 197). This follows from the fact that the radius R is bounded between the two distances of the segment N_1N_2 from the segments that bound the dumbbell arm. For it is clear that

$$R \geq N_1A_2 = d^2/2h > (d^2/2h) - h.$$

But also,

$$R \leq N_2A_2 = \sqrt{\left(\frac{d^2}{2h}\right)^2 + d^2} < \sqrt{\left(\frac{d^2}{2h} + h\right)^2} = \left(\frac{d^2}{2h}\right) + h.$$

It follows that for any point P of the segment N_1N_2, the nearest point to it in Ψ (which is no further away than one of the points A_1 or A_2) must lie in one of the circular regions C_1 or C_2. As the point P moves continuously along the segment N_1N_2, there is, by hypothesis, a unique point of Ψ nearest to P, and clearly this nearest point moves continuously along the curve L. Thus the distance y from this point to A_1 is a continuous function of the distance x from P to N_1. But obviously when $x = 0$, that is, when P is N_1, the point nearest to P is A_1, that is, $y = 0$. When $x = d$, that is, when P is N_2, A_2 is the point nearest to P, that is, $y = d$. Thus the continuous function y of the variable x must assume all intermediate values between 0 and d when x varies from 0 to d; in particular it must assume the value $d/2$. But within the dumbbell there are no points of the figure Ψ at a distance $d/2$ from A_1, so y cannot assume this value. This contradiction proves the theorem.

3-12. (a) Let P be a point of the plane such that the distance d from P to the set of convex figures Φ_1, Φ_2, ..., Φ_n is a minimum (that is, for any point Q of the plane, the distance from Q to the set Φ_1, Φ_2, Φ_3, ..., Φ_n is not less than d). Prove that either there are three of the given figures Φ_i, Φ_j, Φ_k, for which the points A_i, A_j, A_k nearest to P are at a distance d from P and form a triangle containing the point P within itself, or else there are two figures Φ_i, Φ_j for which the points A_i, A_j, nearest to P and distance d from it, are the ends of a segment containing the point P. (b) Obtain from the theorem in Exercise 3-12 a new proof of Helly's Theorem.

(a) Obviously it is impossible for only *one* of the figures Φ_1, Φ_2, ..., Φ_n, say Φ_i, to be at distance d from the point P under consideration while the rest are at smaller distances; in this case it would be sufficient to move the point P slightly in the direction of Φ_i in order to find a point whose distance from the set of figures is less than d (Diagram 198 a). If only two of the figures, say Φ_i and Φ_j, are at a distance d from the point P, and the rest are at smaller distances, then the point P must lie on a segment connecting the points A_i and A_j of the figures Φ_i and Φ_j so that $PA_i = PA_j = d$. Then P must be the midpoint of this segment, since, in the contrary case, if we moved the point P slightly toward the segment A_iA_j, we would again find a point nearer to the system of figures than the point P (Diagram 198 b). Finally, if the point P is such that there are $k \geq 3$ figures Φ_{i_1}, Φ_{i_2}, ..., Φ_{i_k} at a distance d from P, then the point P must be inside (or on the longest side) of the convex polygon formed by the points A_{i_1}, A_{i_2}, ..., A_{i_k} of these figures nearest to P. Otherwise a slight displacement of P toward the longest side of this polygon would produce a point whose distance from the set of all the figures is less than d (Diagram 198 c). But in that event the point P either lies inside one of the triangles into which the polygon A_{i_1}, A_{i_2}, ..., A_{i_k} is subdivided by the diagonals from one vertex (Diagram 199 a), or else lies on one of the diagonals of this polygon (Diagram 199 b; note that when $k = 3$ the proof is somewhat simpler).

(b) Let Φ_1, Φ_2, ..., Φ_n be n convex figures in the plane each three of which have a common point, and let P be a point at a minimum distance d from the set Φ_1, Φ_2, ..., Φ_n. We must prove that all the figures Φ_1, Φ_2, ..., Φ_n have a common point, that is, that $d = 0$, so that the point P

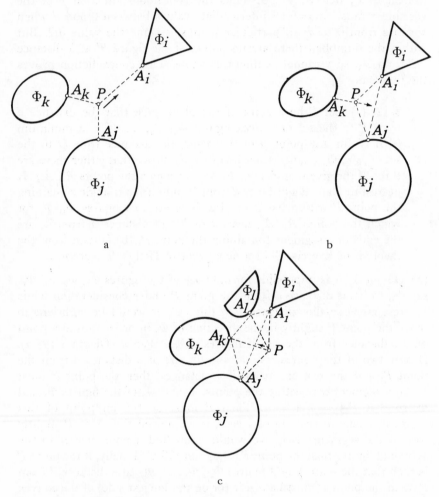

a

b

c

Diagram 198

belongs to all our figures. We prove our theorem by contradiction, that is, we assume that it is false. In this event, either the point P lies on a segment A_iA_j such that A_i and A_j are the points of the figures Φ_i and Φ_j nearest to the point P, and $PA_i = PA_j = d$, or else P lies inside the triangle $A_iA_jA_k$ where A_i, A_j, A_k are the points of the figures Φ_i, Φ_j, Φ_k nearest to P, and $PA_i = PA_j = PA_k = d$. Suppose that the first alternative occurs (Diagram 200 a). At the points A_i and A_j draw lines l_i and l_j perpendicular to the segment A_iA_j. The figures Φ_i and Φ_j lie entirely on opposite sides of the strip between the lines l_i and l_j (*cf.* the solution of Exercise 2-12, page 136); hence they are

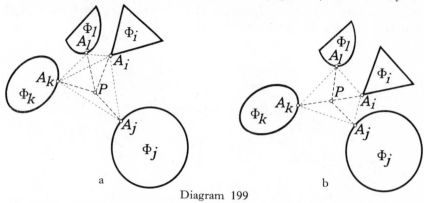

Diagram 199

separated by this region, contrary to the hypothesis that each three of the n figures has a common point. Suppose next that the second case occurs, and as before, at the points A_i, A_j and A_k, draw lines l_i, l_j, and l_k perpendicular respectively to PA_i, PA_j, PA_k (Diagram 200 b). Since the figures Φ_i, Φ_j, Φ_k lie respectively on the sides of the lines l_i, l_j, l_k not containing P, they cannot have a common point. This contradiction establishes the theorem.

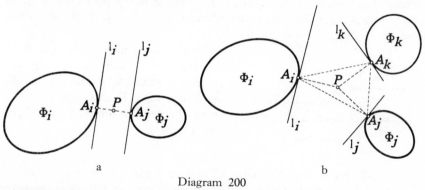

Diagram 200

4-1. If Φ_1 and Φ_2 are two nonparallel segments, prove that the sum $\Phi_1 + \Phi_2$ is a parallelogram. If, however, Φ_1 and Φ_2 are parallel segments, then $\Phi_1 + \Phi_2$ is a segment parallel to Φ_1 and Φ_2 whose length is the sum of the lengths of Φ_1 and Φ_2.

Let A_0 be any fixed point of the segment A_1A_2. It is easy to see that the sum $A_0 + B$, in which B ranges over all points of the segment B_1B_2, is a segment parallel and equal to B_1B_2 with end points $A_0 + B_1$ and $A_0 + B_2$. Since the triangles OB_1B_2 and $A_0(A_0 + B_1)(A_0 + B_2)$[†] are congruent and parallel to each other (Diagram 201), it follows that the figure $OBCA_0$, in which B and C are corresponding points of the segments B_1B_2 and $(A_0 + B_1)(A_0 + B_2)$, is a parallelogram $(OB = A_0C$ and $OB \parallel A_0C)$. Hence $C = A_0 + B$.

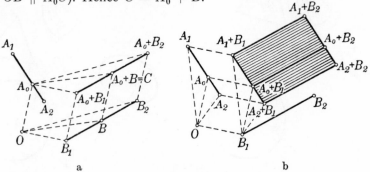

Diagram 201

If we now vary the position of the point A_0 on the segment A_1A_2, we obtain a sequence of parallel and equal segments (Diagram 201 b). The points $A_0 + B_1$, which are the left end points of these segments, form a segment with end points $A_1 + B_1$ and $A_2 + B_1$ which is parallel to A_1A_2 and equal to it. In this fashion, the set of all points $A + B$, where A is a point of the segment A_1A_2 and B is a point of the segment B_1B_2, forms a parallelogram with vertices $A_1 + B_1$, $A_1 + B_2$, $A_2 + B_2$, and $A_2 + B_1$ (Diagram 201 b).

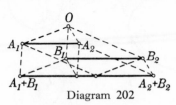

Diagram 202

If the segments A_1A_2 and B_1B_2 are parallel, the parallelogram degenerates into a segment parallel to A_1A_2 and B_1B_2 with length equal to the sum of the lengths of A_1A_2 and B_1B_2 (Diagram 202).

4-2. Prove that the sum of convex figures is also convex (or, what is the same thing, that the sum of convex curves is convex).

Let Φ_1 and Φ_2 be two convex figures and let C and D be two points of the figure $\Phi = \Phi_1 + \Phi_2$. By the definition of the sum of two figures, there are points A_1 and A_2 of the figure Φ_1 (which may coincide) and points B_1 and B_2 of figure Φ_2 (which may also coincide) such that

---

† We denote by $A_0(A_0 + B_1)(A_0 + B_2)$ the triangle with end points A_0, $A_0 + B_1$, and $A_0 + B_2$.

$C = A_1 + B_1$ and $D = A_2 + B_2$ (Diagram 203). Since the figures Φ_1 and Φ_2 are convex, the segment A_1A_2 belongs entirely to Φ_1 and the segment B_1B_2 belongs entirely to Φ_2. The parallelogram (or segment) which is the sum of the segments A_1A_2 and B_1B_2 (see Exercise 4-1) belongs entirely to the figure $\Phi = \Phi_1 + \Phi_2$. In particular the segment connecting $A_1 + B_1$ with $A_2 + B_2$ and thus C with D (it is a diagonal of the parallelogram) belongs to the figure Φ. Thus the figure contains the segment joining any two of its points and is therefore convex.

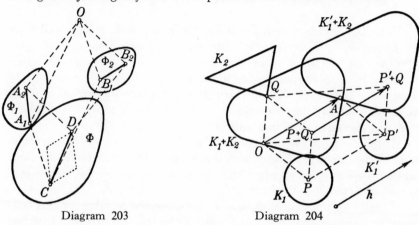

Diagram 203   Diagram 204

4-3. If the convex curve K_1 is entirely enclosed by the convex curve L_1 and if the convex curve K_2 is entirely enclosed by the convex curve L_2, prove that the curve $K_1 + K_2$ is entirely enclosed by the curve $L_1 + L_2$.

Let Φ_1 and Φ_2 denote the figures bounded by the curves K_1 and K_2 and let Ψ_1 and Ψ_2 be the figures bounded by the curves L_1 and L_2. The figures Φ_1 does not extend beyond the boundary of the figure Ψ_1; that is, all points of Φ_1 are also points of Ψ_1. Likewise all points of Φ_2 are points of Ψ_2. Hence all points of $\Phi_1 + \Phi_2$ are also points of $\Psi_1 + \Psi_2$. Thus the curve $K_1 + K_2$ does not extend beyond the boundaries of the curve $L_1 + L_2$.

4-4. Prove that the form of the sum $\Phi_1 + \Phi_2$ (the form of the sum curve $K_1 + K_2$) remains invariant under change of origin and parallel displacement of the summands. Under these circumstances the sum undergoes only a parallel displacement.

First subject only the curve K_1 to a parallel displacement, while the curve K_2 and the origin O remain unchanged. Let OA be a segment laid off from the origin, parallel and equal to the segment through which each point of the curve K_1 is moved by the parallel displacement. Let

K_1' be the curve into which the parallel displacement carries K_1; let Φ_1, Φ_2, and Φ_1' be the figures bounded respectively by the curves K_1, K_2, K_1' (Diagram 204). Let P be any point of the figure Φ_1, Q any point of the figure Φ_2, and P' be the point into which P is carried by the parallel displacement. From the definition of the addition of points and the properties of parallel displacements, we obviously obtain

$$P = P + A \text{ and } P' + Q = (P + A) + Q = (P + Q) + A.$$

The last equality means that the figure $\Phi_1' + \Phi_2$ is obtained from the figure $\Phi_1 + \Phi_2$ by parallel displacement (the points of the figure $\Phi_1' + \Phi_2$ are obtained from the corresponding points of the figure $\Phi_1 + \Phi_2$ by displacement along a segment parallel and equal to OA). If we leave the figure Φ_1 undisturbed, but displace Φ_2 parallel to itself, we prove similarly that the sum $\Phi_1 + \Phi_2$ undergoes a parallel displacement (in the same direction and of the same amount).

It follows from the definition of the addition of figures that displacement of the the origin O produces in the figure $\Phi_1 + \Phi_2$ exactly the same parallel displacement as when the figures Φ_1 and Φ_2 are both subjected to the same parallel displacement.

Finally let the figures Φ_1 and Φ_2 be subjected to different displacements and simultaneously let the origin O be transformed into a certain point O'. First displace the figures Φ_1 and Φ_2 and the origin O along the segment OO'. The figures Φ_1 and Φ_2 assume new positions Φ_1'' and Φ_2'', and $\Phi_1 + \Phi_2$ is displaced parallel to the segment OO'. Now we displace Φ_1'' parallel to itself into the position Φ_1' and finally Φ_2'' into Φ_2'. Each of these parallel displacements produces a parallel displacement of the sum $\Phi_1 + \Phi_2$. In this way the figure $\Phi_1 + \Phi_2$ formed by the addition of points with respect to the origin O is changed into the sum $\Phi_1' + \Phi_2'$ which is formed by the addition of points with respect to O', and this is accomplished by three successive parallel displacements, which can be replaced by a single resultant parallel displacement.

4-5. Let K_1 and K_2 be two convex curves. Prove that if A_1 and A_2 are corresponding points of the curves K_1 and K_2, then the curve $K_1 + K_2$ is the locus of all points $A_1 + A_2$, where the point $A_1 + A_2$ of the curve $K_1 + K_2$ corresponds to the points A_1 and A_2 of the curves K_1 and K_2. The curve $K_1 + K_2$ possesses, therefore, a supporting line through the point $A_1 + A_2$ which is parallel to the supporting lines of the curves K_1 and K_2 through the points A_1 and A_2.

Let A_1 and A_2 be corresponding points of the curves K_1 and K_2; let l_1 and l_2 be parallel and similarly directed supporting lines of K_1 and K_2

through A_1 and A_2 respectively; let Φ_1 and Φ_2 be the figures bounded by K_1 and K_2 (Diagram 205). Then the point $A = A_1 + A_2$ belongs to the figure $\Phi = \Phi_1 + \Phi_2$. We show that this point is a boundary point. To do this, we pass a line l through the point $A_1 + A_2$, parallel to l_1 and l_2 and similarly oriented, and show that since each point B of the figure $\Phi_1 + \Phi_2$ lies to the left of the line l, l must be a supporting line of the figure $\Phi = \Phi_1 + \Phi_2$.

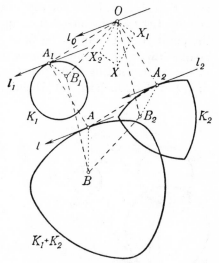

Diagram 205

Let B be a point of Φ and let B_1 and B_2 be points of Φ_1 and Φ_2, respectively, such that $B = B_1 + B_2$. Join the point A_1 to B_1, A_2 to B_2, A to B, and lay off from the origin O the segments OX_1, OX_2, and OX, which are equal and parallel respectively to A_1B_1, A_2B_2, and AB. By definition of addition of points, we then have

$$B_1 = A_1 + X_1, \qquad B_2 = A_2 + X_2, \qquad B = A + X.$$

Since

$$B = B_1 + B_2, \qquad A = A_1 + A_2,$$

we also have

$$X = X_1 + X_2.$$

The quadrilateral OX_1XX_2 is thus a parallelogram. We pass a line l_0 through the point O parallel to and having the same direction as the lines l_1, l_2, l. Since a convex figure always lies to the left of each oriented supporting line (see page 13), the segments OX_1 and OX_2 parallel to A_1B_1 and A_2B_2 also lie to the left of the line l_0 (Diagram 205). Hence the entire parallelogram OX_1XX_2 lies to the left of l_0; thus the segment OX is to the left of l_0. Since, l is parallel to l_0 and the segment AB is parallel to OX, it follows that B lies to the left of l.

Thus every point of Φ lies to the left of l; that is, l is a supporting line of Φ. This proves that the sum of two corresponding points of the curves K_1 and K_2 is a point of the curve K (and in fact corresponds to them). However in order to prove that K is the locus of sums of corresponding points of the curves K_1 and K_2, we must still show that every point of the curve K is the sum of corresponding points of K_1 and K_2, since it might be possible that the sum of corresponding points forms only an arc of the curve K, but not the entire curve.

Now let A be any point of the curve K. Let A_1 and A_2 be points of the figures Φ_1 and Φ_2, respectively, such that $A_1 + A_2 = A$. We show that A_1 and A_2 are corresponding boundary points of the figures Φ_1 and Φ_2. Let l be any one of the supporting lines of the figure Φ through the point A. Let l_1 and l_2 be lines through A_1 and A_2 parallel to l. We assume that at least one of these lines, say l_1, is not a supporting line of the corresponding figure; that is, there are points of Φ_1 to the right of l_1. Let B_1 be such a point (Diagram 206). Then the point $B_1 + A_2 = B$

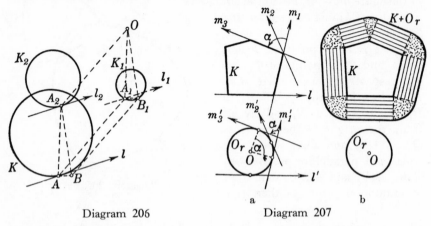

Diagram 206   Diagram 207

is a point of the figure Φ, by definition of the sum of figures. The segment A_1B_1 is, however, equal and parallel to the segment AB and therefore the point B lies to the right of the line l, just as B_1 lies to the right of l_1. This contradicts the fact that l is a supporting line of Φ. Thus l_1 and l_2 must be supporting lines of the figures Φ_1 and Φ_2 respectively. Hence A_1 and A_2 are corresponding points of the curves K_1 and K_2, as we wished to show.

4-6. Let K be any convex polygon with perimeter L and area S; let O_r be a circle of radius r. Prove that the length of the curve $K + O_r$ is $L + 2\pi r$ and that the area of the figure bounded by this curve is $S + Lr + \pi r^2$.

Obviously there corresponds to each side of the polygon K a single point of the circle O_r (the point at which a line parallel to the side under consideration is tangent to the circle). To each vertex of K there corresponds an entire arc of the circle O_r whose central angle is equal to the exterior angle of the polygon at the vertex in question (Diagram 207 a). For the sake of simplicity we choose the center of the circle O_r as the origin O. In this case the curve $K + O_r$ is made up of segments parallel and equal to the sides of K and at distance r from the sides of K, and also of circular arcs of radius r, about the vertices of the polygon, which subtend angles equal to the exterior angles of the polygon (Diagram 207 b). The sum of the lengths of all the segments is equal to the perimeter L of the polygon K. The sum of the lengths of all the arcs is equal to the perimeter of the circle of radius r, that is, $2\pi r$ (since the sum of all exterior angles of a polygon is $360°$ or 2π). Hence the length of the curve $K + O_r$ is equal to $L + 2\pi r$.

The figure Φ bounded by the curve $K + O_r$ obviously consists of the polygon K of area S, rectangles whose bases are the sides of the polygon K and with altitudes r (the sum of the areas of all these rectangles is equal to Lr) as well as circular sectors of radius r (the sum of all sectors equals πr^2; see Diagram 207 b). Hence the area of the region bounded by the curve $K + O_r$ is equal to $S + Lr + \pi r^2$.

4-7. Prove that the sum $K_1 + K_2$ of two convex polygons K_1 and K_2 is also a convex polygon. If the two convex polygons K_1 and K_2 have no parallel and similarly directed sides (see page 13), then the number of sides of the convex polygon $K_1 + K_2$ equals the sum of the number of sides of K_1 and K_2; the polygon $K_1 + K_2$ then consists of segments that are equal and parallel to the sides of K_1 and K_2. If the polygon K_1 has a side parallel in the same direction to a side of K_2, then the polygon $K_1 + K_2$ has a side parallel to these two parallel sides in the polygons K_1 and K_2, and whose length equals the sum of their lengths. In every case the perimeter of the polygon $K_1 + K_2$ equals the sum of the perimeters of K_1 and K_2.

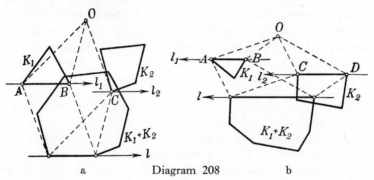

a   Diagram 208   b

Let K_1 and K_2 be two polygons having no pair of parallel and similarly directed sides (Diagram 208 a). By Exercise 4-5, the sum curve of these polygons is the locus of the sums of corresponding points. Let l_1 be a supporting line of the polygon K_1, the prolongation of one of the sides, say AB. Let l_2 be a supporting line of the second polygon which is similarly directed and parallel to l_1. Since the polygons have no parallel sides, the line l_2 has only one point C in common with the second polygon. The corresponding points of the polygons are then the point C and each point of the segment AB. The sum of the corresponding points in this case forms a segment parallel to the segment AB and having the same direction (see the solution of Exercise 4-1).

If we add all points of the n-sided polygon K_1 to the corresponding points of the m-sided polygon K_2 (to each side of the first polygon there corresponds a uniquely determined point of the second polygon, in fact a definite vertex; the vertices of the first polygon corresponds to the sides of the second polygon), then we obtain an $(m + n)$-sided polygon, each of whose sides is equal and parallel to some side of the polygon K_1 or to some side of the polygon K_2. The perimeter of this polygon is obviously equal to the sum of the perimeters of the polygons K_1 and K_2.

Suppose now that the polygons K_1 and K_2 have parallel and similarly directed sides. Suppose for example that the side AB of the polygon K_1 is parallel to the side CD of the polygon K_2 and has the same direction (Diagram 208 b). Then each point of the segment AB corresponds to each point of the segment CD; the sum of the corresponding points forms a segment that is parallel to the segments AB and CD, and whose length is equal to the sum of their lengths (see Exercise 4-1). The sum of the polygons K_1 and K_2 is a polygon with fewer than $m + n$ sides. Even in this case, the perimeter of the polygon $K_1 + K_2$ is obviously equal to the sum of the perimeters of the polygons K_1 and K_2.

4-8. If K_1 and K_2 are two convex curves and if L_1 and L_2 are two polygons which are circumscribed about these curves, and which have pairwise parallel and similarly oriented sides, prove that $L_1 + L_2$ is a polygon circumscribed about the curve $K_1 + K_2$. Does this statement remain true if the sides of the polygon L_1 and L_2 are not parallel and similarly oriented?

Let P_1Q_1 and P_2Q_2 be parallel and similarly directed sides of the polygons L_1 and L_2. Let A_1 and A_2 be their points of intersection with the curves K_1 and K_2 (Diagram 209). From the definition of addition of convex curves given in Exercise 4-5, it follows that the side PQ of the polygon $L_1 + L_2$ is parallel to the lines P_1Q_1 and P_2Q_2 (see Exercise 4-7) and passes through the point $A_1 + A_2$. That is, PQ is a supporting line of the curve $K_1 + K_2$.

The sides of the polygon $L_1 + L_2$ are thus segments of supporting lines of the curve $K_1 + K_2$. Moreover, the polygon $L_1 + L_2$ is convex (see Exercise 4-1) since it is the sum of two convex polygons, and it contains the curve $K_1 + K_2$ in its interior (see Exercise 4-2). Thus $L_1 + L_2$ is a polygon circumscribed about the curve $K_1 + K_2$.

If the circumscribed polygons L_1 and L_2 have no pair of parallel and similarly directed sides, the assertion of the exercise does not hold. For example, if K_1 and K_2 are equal circles and if L_1 and L_2 are equilateral triangles with parallel but oppositely directed sides, and if L_1 and L_2 are circumscribed about K_1 and K_2, then $K_1 + K_2$ is a circle; however $L_1 + L_2$ is a hexagon which is *not* circumscribed about the circle $K_1 + K_2$ (Diagram 210).

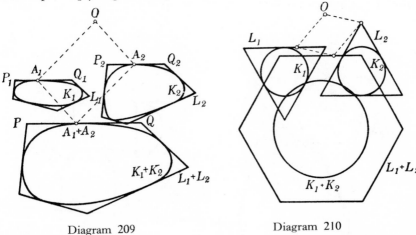

Diagram 209   Diagram 210

4-9. Let $K = K_1 + K_2$ be the sum of two convex curves K_1 and K_2, and suppose that this sum contains a line segment AB of length a. Prove that in this case either one of the curves K_1 and K_2 has a segment of length a which is parallel to AB, or else both curves K_1 and K_2 contain segments parallel to AB, the sum of whose lengths is a.

From the definition of the addition of convex curves given in Exercise 4-5, it follows that if the curve $K_1 + K_2$ contains a line segment AB, then this segment is the locus of all possible sums of points A_1 and A_2, where the points A_1 are those points of the curve K_1 corresponding to the points of the segment AB of the curve $K_1 + K_2$, while the points A_2 are points of the curve K_2 corresponding to the points of segment AB. From this consideration and from the definition of the points of a curve which correspond to one another (page 44), the assertion of the exercise follows at once. (See also Exercise 4-1.)

4-10. Let K_1 and K_2 be two convex curves, with sum $K_1 + K_2$ and let A_1 and A_2 be corresponding points of the curves K_1 and K_2. Prove that if $A_1 + A_2$ is a corner point of the curve $K_1 + K_2$, then both of the points A_1 and A_2 are corner points (however, A_1 and A_2 can be corner points of the curves K_1 and K_2 without the point $A_1 + A_2$ being a corner point of the curve $K_1 + K_2$).

Let K_1 and K_2 be two convex curves. Let A_1 and A_2 be mutually corresponding points of these curves, and let l_1 and l_2 be parallel supporting lines through A_1 and A_2 respectively. For definiteness, we shall assume that A_2, say, is not a corner point of the curve K_2 (Diagram 211) and then prove that the line l parallel to l_1 and l_2 is the only supporting line of the figure $K_1 + K_2$ through the point $A = A_1 + A_2$. Thus the point A is a regular point of the curve $K_1 + K_2$.

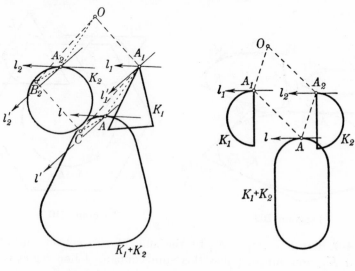

Diagram 211   Diagram 212

Let l' be any line through the point A distinct from the line l. Let l'_1 and l'_2 be lines through the points A_1 and A_2 respectively which are parallel to l'. Since A_2 is a regular point of the curve K_2, l'_2 cannot be a supporting line of the curve K_2. In other words, there is a point B_2 of the curve K_2 to the right of l'_2. Draw a segment AC equal and parallel to A_2B_2. The quadrilateral OA_1CB_2 is a parallelogram; that is, the point C is the sum of the points A_1 and B_2, and therefore C belongs to the figure bounded by the curve $K_1 + K_2$. The triangles AA_1C and A_2OB_2 are congruent and parallel. Hence the point C of the figure bounded by the curve $K_1 + K_2$ lies to the right of the line l'. Thus l' is not a supporting line of the figure $K_1 + K_2$, as we wished to prove.

From the fact that A_1 and A_2 are corners points, it does not follow that the point $A_1 + A_2$ is a corner point of the curve $K_1 + K_2$. For example, in Diagram 212 two semicircles are shown whose corner points correspond to each other; however, the sum of these semicircles has no corner point.

4-11. Prove that the width h of the curve $K_1 + K_2$ in any given direction is equal to the sum of the widths h_1 and h_2 of the curves K_1 and K_2 in the same direction.

Let K_1 be a convex curve; let l_1 and l_1' be two parallel supporting lines of the curve K_1, and let A_1 and A' be the points of contact of these lines with the curve. Likewise let K_2 be another convex curve with supporting lines l_2 and l_2' parallel to l_1 and l_1' and having contact points A_2 and A_2' with K_2 (Diagram 213). We shall investigate the sum $K = K_1 + K_2$ of these two curves. Denote by l and l' the supporting lines of $K_1 + K_2$ that are parallel to the lines l_1, l_2, l_1' and l_2'. The points of contact of l and l' with the curve $K_1 + K_2$ will be denoted by A and A', where $A = A_1 + A_2$, $A' = A_1' + A_2'$ (cf. Exercise 4-5). Draw a segment $A_1'M$ parallel and equal to OA_2, and through the point M pass a line l_0 parallel to all six supporting lines.

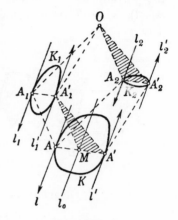

Diagram 213

The quadrilateral $A_1'A_1AM$ is a parallelogram (since the segment $A_1'M$ is equal and parallel to OA_2, which in turn is equal and parallel to the segment A_1A). This means that the segment AM is equal and parallel to the segment A_1A_1'. Hence the distance between the lines l and l_0 is equal to the distance between the lines l_1 and l_1' and therefore equals the width h_1 of the curve K_1 in the direction perpendicular to all the supporting lines drawn.

Analogously, the segment MA' is equal and parallel to the segment A_2A_2' (since the triangles $A_1'MA'$ and OA_2A_2' are congruent); hence the distance between the lines l_0 and l' is equal to the distance between the lines l_2 and l_2', which equals the width h_2 of the curve K_2 in the given direction. The width h of the curve $K_1 + K_2$ in the given direction is equal to the sum of the distance between the lines l and l_0 and the distance between the lines l_0 and l'; hence it is equal to $h_1 + h_2$.

4-12. Prove that every convex polygon can be represented as the sum of triangles and segments.

Let K be any polygon. Suppose that two of its sides, AB and CD, are parallel, and that CD is the larger of these sides (Diagram 214). On the segment CD draw a segment CE equal to AB and draw the connecting segments CA and BE. Then the polygon K is divided into the parallelogram $ABEC$ and two parts bounded by the sides AC and BE. From these last two parts we form a new polygon K_1 (by bringing them together with BE on AC). Let T_1 denote a segment parallel and equal to the segment AB. Using the definition of addition of convex curves given in Exercise 4-5, it is now easy to see that the sum of the polygon K_1 and the segment T_1 is the polygon K (*cf.* Exercise 4-7). Here the polygon K_1 is such that the number of its sides is one less than that of the polygon K (or, in fact, two less, if the segments AB and CD are equal), while T_1 is a segment.

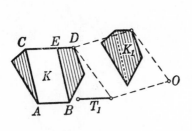
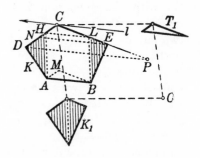

Diagram 214   Diagram 215

Next, suppose that the polygon K has no parallel sides. Select any side AB of K and draw a supporting line l parallel to AB. Denote the point of contact of the line l and the polygon K by C, and let the sides of K which meet at the vertex C be CD and CE (Diagram 215). Construct triangles ABM, CDP, and CNE such that each has its sides parallel respectively to the lines AB, CD, and CE. Suppose that the triangle ABM is the smallest of these triangles. Then the segment AM does not exceed the side CD and the segment BM does not exceed the side CE. On CD and CE we lay off segments CH and CL equal respectively to the sides AM and BM. Finally we join A to H and B to L. The triangles ABM and CHL are congruent and the quadrilateral $ABLH$ is a parallelogram.

Thus we have divided the polygon into the triangle CHL (congruent to triangle ABM), the parallelogram $ABLH$, and the triangles ADH and BEL which are shaded in Diagram 215. We combine the shaded triangles into a polygon K_1 and denote by T_1 a triangle congruent to the triangle CHL. It is easy to see that the sum of polygons K_1 and T_1 is the polygon K. Here T_1 is a triangle and K_1 has at least one side less than K, since K_1 had no sides parallel to AB.

We leave it to the reader to investigate for himself the case where ABM is not the smallest of the triangles ABM, CDP, and CNE (it is advisable to draw a diagram).

If we compare the two cases considered above, we conclude that every polygon K can be represented as a sum $K_1 + T_1$, where T_1 is a segment or a triangle and K_1 is a polygon with fewer sides than K. If K_1 is a triangle or a segment, there is nothing to prove. If not, then we continue the procedure with K_1; that is, we represent K_1 as a sum $K_2 + T_2$, where T_2 is a triangle or a segment and K_2 has fewer sides than K_1. If we repeat this operation a finite number of times, we achieve our purpose, since the number of sides of the polygon which is the first summand grows smaller and smaller.

4-13. Prove that every convex quadrilateral can be uniquely represented as the sum of two triangles (or a triangle and a segment, or two segments). However, there are pentagons which can be represented in several ways as the sums of triangles.

Let $ABCD$ be a convex quadrilateral that is neither a parallelogram nor a trapezoid. Denote the points of intersection of the opposite sides by P and Q, where P is the intersection of DA and BC produced (Diagram 216). It is easy to see that a triangle can be constructed whose

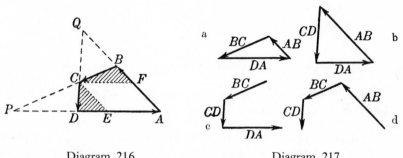

Diagram 216   Diagram 217

sides are parallel and have the same orientations as the sides DA, AB, and BC, or as the sides DA, AB, and CD (Diagram 217 a and b), but that no triangle can be constructed with sides parallel and similarly oriented to the sides BC, CD and DA, or to AB, BC, and CD, since segments having the orientations of these sides do not form a closed curve (Diagram 217 c and d). Since the sides of the two triangles whose sum equals the quadrilateral $ABCD$ must be parallel and have the same direction as the sides of the quadrilateral (*cf.* Exercise 4-7), $ABCD$ can only be the sum of triangles of the sort shown in Diagrams 217 a and b. It is readily evident that the sum of triangles of this sort is equal to the quadrilateral $ABCD$ only if one of the triangles has a side equal to BC and the other a side equal to CD. Only the shaded triangles BCF and CDE in Diagram 216 satisfy all these conditions, when C is chosen as the origin, and have a sum that is actually equal to the quadrilateral $ABCD$. Thus we have proved that the quadrilateral $ABCD$ can be uniquely represented as the sum of two triangles.

Analogously we show that every trapezoid can be represented in only one way as the sum of a triangle and a segment and that a parallelogram can be uniquely represented as the sum of two segments.

For pentagons and polygons with a larger number of sides, the situation is quite different. In Diagrams 218 a and b, two quite different possible constructions are shown for representing the same pentagon as the sum of two triangles.

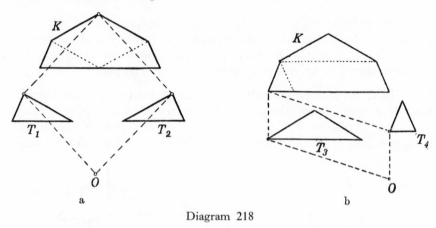

Diagram 218

4-14. If there exists an inner boundary curve of the r-neighborhood of a convex curve K, then it is also a convex curve.

Let A and B be two points which lie interior to the inner boundary curve of the r-neighborhood of a curve K; that is, points that are interior points of the figure bounded by the curve K and do not lie in the r-neighborhood of the curve K. Draw circles of radius r about the points A and B and construct their common external tangents (Diagram 219). There is no point of the curve K within the circles; indeed, if there were a point P of the curve K, within the circle of radius r about the point A for example, then the distance AP would be less than r and the point A would lie within the circle of radius r about the point P. It would therefore lie inside the r-neighborhood of the curve K.

Thus our two circles lie entirely in the interior of the convex curve; hence the segment joining any two points of these circles lies entirely inside the curve K. From this it follows that the figure bounded by the given circles and their external tangents lies within K (this figure is shaded in Diagram 219).

Now if C is any point of the segment AB, then the circle of radius r about C lies within the shaded figure and thus completely within the curve K. Hence the point C cannot belong to the r-neighborhood of K; that is, it lies within the inner boundary curve of the r-neighborhood.

All segments joining pairs of points lying inside the given curve likewise lie within this curve; that is, the curve is convex.

4-15. Let A, B, and C be three convex curves. We denote the distance between the curves A and B by $\overline{AB}$, the distance between the curves B and C by $\overline{BC}$, and that between the curves A and C by $\overline{AC}$. Prove that the inequalities $\overline{AB} + \overline{BC} \geq \overline{AC}$, $\overline{AC} + \overline{BC} \geq \overline{AB}$, and $\overline{AB} + \overline{AC} \geq \overline{BC}$ hold.

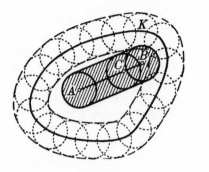

Diagram 219

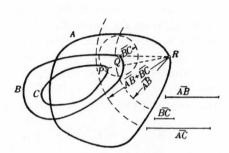

Diagram 220

Let P be any point of the curve C (Diagram 220). Since the distance of the curve C from the curve B cannot exceed the value $\overline{BC}$ (we recall that $\overline{BC}$ is the largest of the distances of the curve C from the curve B and of the curve B from the curve C), the point P lies in the $\overline{BC}$-neighborhood of the curve B; that is, there is a point Q on the curve B such that the circle of radius $\overline{BC}$ about the point Q contains the point P. The distance PQ does not exceed the value $\overline{BC}$.

Analogously there is a point R on the curve A such that the distance QR does not exceed the value $\overline{AB}$ (Diagram 220). From examination of the triangle PQR it follows immediately that

$$PR \leq PQ + QR,$$

and therefore that

$$PR \leq \overline{AB} + \overline{BC}.$$

The circle of radius $\overline{AB} + \overline{BC}$ with center at R thus contains the point P. Each point P of the curve C is therefore in the $(\overline{AB} + \overline{BC})$-neighborhood of the curve A; that is, the distance of the curve C from the curve A does not exceed the value $\overline{AB} + \overline{BC}$.

Similarly we prove that the distance of the curve A from the curve C does not exceed the value $\overline{AB} + \overline{BC}$. Thus the distance $\overline{AC}$

between the curves A and C is not greater than $\overline{AB} + \overline{BC}$. This establishes the first of the inequalities to be proved. The others are proved similarly.

4-16. Let K_1 and K_2 be two convex curves whose distance apart is not greater than r. Prove that the difference of the lengths of these curves is not greater than $2\pi r$ and the difference of the areas of the figures bounded by them does not exceed the value $Lr + \pi r^2$, where L is the greater of the lengths of the two curves.

Let K_2 be the longer of the two given curves. Since the distance of the curve K_2 from the curve K_1 is less than r, the curve K_2 must lie entirely in the r-neighborhood of the curve K_1. Therefore K_2 has no points outside the curve $K_1 + O_r$, which is the external boundary of the r-neighborhood of the curve K_1. Hence the length of the curve K_2 is not greater than the length of the curve $K_1 + O_r$. Therefore (if L_1 is the length of the curve K_1 and L_2 the length of the curve K_2)

$$L_2 \leq L_1 + 2\pi r, \qquad L_2 - L_1 \leq 2\pi r$$

(see page 45), as we wished to show.

Similarly, if the area S_2 of the region bounded by the curve K_2 is greater than the area S_1 of the region bounded by the curve K_1, then S_2 is not greater than the area of the region bounded by the curve $K_1 + O_r$; that is,

$$S_2 \leq S_1 + L_1 r + \pi r^2$$

(see page 45); hence

$$S_2 - S_1 \leq L_1 r + \pi r^2 \leq Lr + \pi r^2,$$

where L is the greater of the lengths L_1 and L_2.

4-17. Prove that if a sequence of circles has a limit curve, then this limit curve is a circle or a point.

Let K be any convex curve different from a circle (the region bounded by K is shaded in Diagram 221). We will prove that there exists a number r such that every circle is at a distance greater than r from the curve K. This will prove that the curve K is not the limit of a sequence of circles (and hence that a curve which is the limit of a sequence of circles must be a circle, possibly of radius zero).

Pass a circle through any three noncollinear points A, B, C of the curve K. Since K is not a circle, there is a point D on the curve K not belonging to the above circle. Suppose that the point D is outside the circle through A, B, C (the proof is essentially the same if the point D

is inside this circle). Let us assume that A, B, C, D is the cyclic succession of our four points on the curve K. Since K is convex, the quadrilateral $ABCD$ must be convex (*cf*. Exercise 1-10, page 13).

Through the point B draw a tangent l to our circle, and then construct a circle with greater radius which also is tangent to the line l at B but is such that the point D still remains outside this circle. The points A and C lie within this larger circle (Diagram 221). Now we

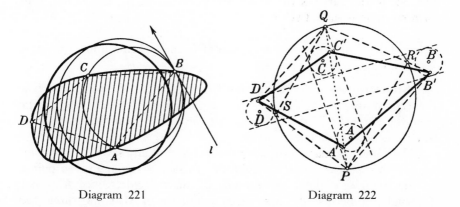

Diagram 221   Diagram 222

displace this circle, in a direction perpendicular to l, by an amount so small that the point D still is outside the circle, but the points A and C remain inside. The point B is then outside the displaced circle.

Thus we have found a circle such that of the four points A, B, C, D on the curve K, two—A and C—lie inside the circle and the other two—B and D—lie outside. Now, about the points A, B, C, and D draw circles with equal radii so small that the following conditions are satisfied: 1) They do not intersect the given circle; 2) The circles about the points A and C do not intersect the parallel external tangents to the circles about the points B and D; 3) The circles about the points B and D do not cut the parallel external tangents to the circles about the points A and C (Diagram 222). We assert that there is no circle that cuts all four small circles. In other words, there are no four points A', B', C', D' which lie respectively within the four circles in question and which also lie on a common circle.

Consider the quadrilateral $A'B'C'D'$. Because of conditions 2) and 3), which govern the construction of our small circles, this quadrilateral is convex; its diagonals intersect in its interior. We claim that this quadrilateral cannot be inscribed in a circle. Produce the segment $A'C'$ to intersect the large circle in the points P and Q; furthermore let the segment $B'Q$ intersect the large circle in the point R and let $D'P$ cut this circle in the point S. The angles at the vertices B' and D' of the quadrilateral $A'B'C'D'$ are less than the angles $PB'Q$ and $PD'Q$; the sum of the angles $PB'Q$ and $PD'Q$ is itself less than the sum of the angles PRQ and PSQ, which is equal to 180° (see Diagram 222). The sum of the opposite angles at B' and D' of the quadrilateral is therefore less than 180°; hence this quadrilateral cannot be inscribed in a circle.

We have thus shown that no circle can cut all four of the circles of radius r about the points A, B, C, D; that is, the four points A, B, C, D cannot lie in the r-neighborhood of any circle. This means that the distance of the curve K (on which the points $A, B, C,$ and D lie) from each circle is greater than r.

4-18. Prove that if a sequence of triangles has a limit, then this limit is a triangle, a segment, or a point.

Let K be any convex curve different from a triangle. We will prove that there is a number r such that every triangle is at a distance greater than r from the curve K. This will prove that the curve K cannot be the limit of a sequence of triangles.

A triangle is characterized by the fact that of any seven points lying on its sides, at least three are collinear. In fact, given any seven points on the triangle, at least three must lie on one side. Since K is not a triangle, it necessarily has seven points such that no three are collinear. If K is a convex polygon, then K must have at least four segments which lie on four different lines; if we take only two points from each of these segments, we obtain eight points, no three of which are collinear. If K has a curvilinear arc AB, any seven points of the arc AB satisfy our condition, since by Exercise 1-4, no line cuts a convex curve in more than two points.

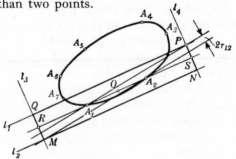

Diagram 223

Let $A_1, A_2, ..., A_7$ be seven points of the curve K, no three of which are collinear (Diagram 223). We will show that there is a number r for which there exists no triangle whose r-neighborhood contains all seven points $A_1, A_2, ..., A_7$. For this purpose, we choose two of the seven points, say A_1 and A_2, and pass a line A_1A_2 through them. By hypothesis, none of the points $A_3, A_4, ..., A_7$ lies on this line.

Draw two lines l_1 and l_2 parallel to A_1A_2 whose common distance from A_1A_2 is so small that the strip between the lines l_1 and l_2 contains none of our seven points except A_1 and A_2. Next draw two lines l_3 and l_4 perpendicular to l_1 and l_2 whose (equal) distances from the midpoint point O of the segment A_1A_2 are so large that all seven of the points A_1, ..., A_7 lie between the lines l_3 and l_4. The lines l_1, l_2, l_3, and l_4 form a rectangle whose vertices we denote by the letters M, N, P, and Q (the point A_1 is nearer to the side MQ and the point A_2 is nearer to the side NP; see Diagram 223).

Finally we draw the lines A_1P and A_2M. It is easy to see that they are parallel. Since the triangle A_1PS is congruent to the triangle A_2MR, where R and S are the intersections of the line A_1A_2 with the lines MQ and NP, it follows that the lines A_1P and A_2M form equal alternate interior angles with the line A_1A_2.

We denote the distance between the parallel lines A_1P and A_2M by $2r_{12}$. We observe that *every strip between two parallel lines whose width is not greater than $2r_{12}$ and in whose interior the points A_1 and A_2 lie contains no other points of our original seven*. This is so because the part of this strip between the lines l_3 and l_4 lies entirely inside the rectangle $MNPQ$ (Diagram 224 a) and thus can contain none of the seven points

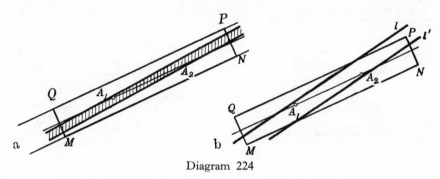

Diagram 224

except A_1 and A_2. In any event, none of the seven points lies outside the strip between l_3 and l_4. In fact, if a strip whose width is not greater than $2r_{12}$ contains the points A_1 and A_2, then the inclination of the lines l and l' (which bound the strip) to the line A_1A_2 is not greater than the angle PA_1A_2 (Diagram 223), since the sine of this angle (which equals the ratio of the width of the strip to the segment that the strip cuts out of the line A_1A_2) is less than the sine of the angle $PA_1\ A_2$. Assume now that one of the lines l and l' cuts the side MN or the side PQ of the rectangle $MNPQ$ (Diagram 224 b); for example, suppose that the line l cuts the side PQ. If we displace the strip parallel to A_1A_2 so that the line l' passes through the point A_2, then the line l cuts the side PQ. If we now rotate the displaced strip about the point A_2 so that the inclination of its boundary line to the line A_1A_2 equals the angle PA_1A_2 (counterclockwise rotation), then both before and after the rotation the line l cuts the segment PQ between the points P and Q. However, in its new position the line l' coincides with the segment A_2M (Diagram 223). Since the distance between l and l' is not greater than that between A_2M and A_1P, the line l cannot cut the side PQ.

Let us carry out a similar construction for every pair of our chosen seven points (all told we obtain 21 pairs of points). In this way we obtain 21 strips, whose widths we denote by $2r_{12}$, $2r_{13}$, ..., $2r_{17}$, $2r_{23}$, ..., $2t_{67}$. Denote the smallest of these by $2r$. This distance has the following property: *If the distance between two parallel lines is $2r$, then no more than two of the seven given points can lie in the strip between them.* Now it is easy to see that the r-neighborhood of any triangle T cannot contain the seven points A_1, ..., A_7. The r-neighborhood of the triangle T is, in fact, contained in three strips of width $2r$, one about each side of the triangle (Diagram 225). In each of these strips there are no more than two of the given seven points. This means that in all three strips there are at most six of the given points. In other words, the entire curve K (to which the points A_1, A_2, ..., A_7 belong) cannot be in the r-neighborhood of a triangle T; that is, the distance of any triangle T from the curve K is greater than r, as we wished to show.

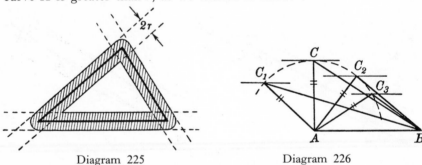

Diagram 225   Diagram 226

5-1. (a) Prove that of all triangles with two given sides, the triangle in which the sides are mutually perpendicular has the greatest area. (b) Prove that if two triangles are incongruent but have equal bases and equal angles opposite the equal bases, then the greater area and the greater perimeter belong to that triangle in which the difference of the base angles (or what is the same thing, the difference of the other two sides) is the smaller; of all triangles with given base and given angle opposite the given base, the isosceles triangle has the greatest area and the greatest perimeter. (c) Prove that of all parallelograms with a given acute angle and given perimeter, the rhombus has the greatest area. (d) Prove that of two incongruent triangles with equal bases and perimeters, the triangle for which the difference of the base angles (or what is the same thing, the difference of the other two sides) is least has the greatest area; among all triangles with given base and perimeter the isosceles triangle has the greatest area. (e) Prove that of all trapezoids with given base and given perimeter, the isosceles trapezoid has the greatest area.

(a) The assertion of the exercise is completely evident (Diagram 226).

(b) We place two triangles satisfying the conditions of the exercise exercise upon each another so that their bases coincide and the vertices C and C' lie on the same side of the common base AB and simultaneously

$$\angle CAB < \angle CBA, \qquad \angle C'AB < \angle C'BA$$

(Diagram 227 a). Then the vertices C and C' of the triangles lie on a circular arc $BC''CA$, and the inscribed angle ACB equals the inscribed angle $AC'B$. It is at once obvious from Diagram 227 a that the vertex C of the triangle ABC, in which the difference of the base angles is less than that for the triangle ABC', is nearer to the midpoint of the arc $BC'CA$. Thus it follows that the altitude of the triangle ABC is greater than that of the triangle ABC'. Hence we have $S(\triangle ABC) > S(\triangle ABC')$.

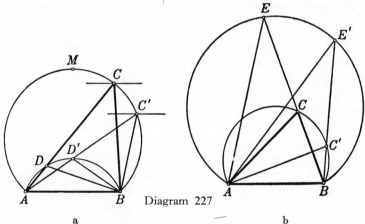

Diagram 227

a   b

It remains to show that

$$CA - CB < C'A - C'B$$

and that

$$CA + CB > C'A + C'B.$$

We lay off the segment $CD = CB$ on the side CA, and the segment $C'D' = C'B$ on the side $C'A$, and join D and D' to B (Diagram 227 a).

Since the angles ADB and $AD'B$ are exterior angles of the isosceles triangles BCD and $BC'D'$, we have

$$\angle ADB = 180^\circ - \frac{180^\circ - \angle ACB}{2} = 90^\circ + \frac{\angle ACB}{2},$$

$$\angle AD'B = 90^\circ + \frac{\angle AC'B}{2}.$$

Since $\angle ADB = \angle AD'B$, D and D' lie on a circular arc $BD'DA$. Since $\angle DBA < \angle D'BA < 180^\circ$, we have

$$CA - CB = DA < D'A = C'A - C'B.$$

If we lay off the segments $CE = CA$ and $C'E' = C'A$ (Diagram 227 b) on the prolongations of the sides BC and BC' respectively, we obtain analogously

$$CA + CB = BE > BE' = C'A + C'B,$$

since

$$\angle AEB = \frac{\angle ACB}{2} = \frac{\angle AC'B}{2} = \angle AE'B.$$

The second assertion of the exercise follows at once from what has been proved.

(c) A parellelogram with given acute angles α and given perimeter is divided by a diagonal into two triangles. Hence, in order to solve the exercise, it is sufficient to prove that of all triangles with a given angle α, and with a given length p for the sum of the sides including α, the isosceles triangle has the greatest area.

Let ABC be a nonisosceles triangle such that $\angle BAC = \alpha$ and $AB + AC = p$. Let us assume for example that $AB > AC$ (the proof is analogous otherwise). We construct an isosceles triangle $AB'C'$ such that $\angle B'AC' = \alpha$ and $AB' + AC' = p$ as shown in Diagram 228. The point of intersection of sides BC and $B'C'$ will be denoted by M.

We now show that $S(\triangle CC'M) > S(\triangle BB'M)$.

The triangles $CC'M$ and $BB'M$ have, in fact, equal vertical angles at the point M, and they have equal bases CC' and BB' because

$$CC' - BB' = (AC' - AC) - (AB - AB') = (AB' + AC') - (AB + AC)$$
$$= p - p = 0.$$

Moreover among the angles $BB'M$, $B'BM$, $CC'M$, and $C'CM$, the first is the largest and hence the second is the least (since the sum of the first two angles equals the sum of the last two). Hence the difference of the base angles of the triangle $BB'M$ is greater than the difference of the base angles of the triangle $CC'M$. Hence $S(\triangle C'CM) >$ $S(\triangle B'BM)$ (see Exercise 5-1b). Thus $S(\triangle AB'C') > S(\triangle ABC')$, as we wished to prove.

   Note. This exercise can also be worked very easily by algebra. The area of a parallelogram with sides a and b and angle α is equal to $ab \sin \alpha = \frac{1}{4}[(a+b)^2 - (a-b)^2] \sin \alpha = \frac{1}{4}[p^2 - (a-b)^2] \sin \alpha$, where $p = a + b$, the semiperimeter of the given parallelogram. Thus it follows at once that, when the perimeter $2p$ and the acute angle α are given, the area is largest if $a - b = 0$; that is, $a = b$, so that the parallelogram is a rhombus.

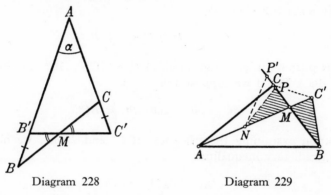

Diagram 228   Diagram 229

   (d) Let triangles ABC and ABC' satisfy the conditions of the exercise, and place one upon the other so that their bases coincide and the vertices C and C' lie on the same side of the common base AB. We suppose that

$$\sphericalangle CAB < \sphericalangle CBA, \quad \text{and} \quad \sphericalangle C'AB < \sphericalangle C'BA$$

(Diagram 229), and also that $\sphericalangle CAB > \sphericalangle C'AB$. Then if $\sphericalangle CBA$ were greater than $\sphericalangle C'BA$, the triangle ABC' would be enclosed in the triangle ABC and they would not have the same perimeter. Hence the triangles are situated as shown in Diagram 229. It follows from this and the above inequalities for the angles that the difference of the base angles is greatest in triangle $AC'B$.

   Denote the point of intersection of the sides AC' and BC by M. Lay off on the line MA the segment $MN = MB$ and on the line MC the segment $MP = MC'$. Then the point N lies between A and M, since the inequalities

$$\sphericalangle MBA > \sphericalangle CAB > \sphericalangle MAB,$$

imply that $MA > MB$. On the other hand, the point P lies between M and C; for if it coincided with any point P' on the extension of MC, then from the equality of the perimeters of the two triangles, which implies that $AC + CB = AC' + C'B$, we would have

$$AC + P'M - CP' + MB = AN + NM + MC' + C'B.$$

Since $P'M = MC'$, $MB = MN$, and $C'B = P'N$, we would obtain

$$AC = AN + NP' + P'C,$$

which is impossible.

If we now remove from the triangles ABC and ABC' respectively the congruent triangles NMP and MBC' (shaded in Diagram 229), we see at once that the triangle ABC has the larger area.

We must still prove that

$$CA - CB < C'A - C'B.$$

For this purpose it is enough to check that $AC < AC'$ (and hence that $BC > BC'$). But if we suppose that

$$AC > AC' \quad \text{and} \quad BC < BC',$$

then, upon examining the triangles ACC' and BCC', we obtain the two contradictory inequalities

$$\sphericalangle ACC' < \sphericalangle AC'C \quad \text{and} \quad \sphericalangle BCC' > \sphericalangle BC'C.$$

The equality $AC = AC'$ cannot hold since the triangles ABC and ABC' are incongruent.

We remark, moreover, that still another formulation of the exercise results from the solution: *Given two triangles with a common base and equal perimeter, that triangle with the greatest of the four base angles has the smaller area.*

The second assertion of the exercise follows immediately from what has been proved.

(e) In order that the area of a trapezoid $ABCD$ with given bases shall be a maximum, its altitude must be a maximum. If we draw the line BD' parallel to CD (Diagram 230) the following results: The greatest altitude of the trapezoid $ABCD$ corresponds to the greatest area of the triangle ABD' with given base (equal to the difference of the bases of the trapezoid) and

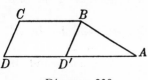

Diagram 230

given perimeter (equal to the perimeter of the trapezoid less twice the smaller base line). It remains only to apply the conclusion of Exercise 5-1 d to the triangle ABD'.

5-2. (a) Prove that among all triangles of equal perimeter, the equilateral triangle has the greatest area. (b) Prove that among all quadrilaterals with given perimeter, the square has the greatest area.

(a) Let ABC be a nonequilateral triangle and let AB be its greatest side (or one of the two greatest sides).

By Exercise 5-1 d, the isosceles triangle ABC', having the same perimeter as the triangle ABC and sharing a common base with it (Diagram 231 a), has an area not less than that of triangle ABC. Now

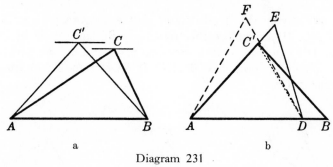

Diagram 231

we construct a triangle ADE whose side AD is exactly equal to $\frac{1}{3}$ the perimeter of triangle ABC', such that $\sphericalangle DAE = \sphericalangle BAC'$, and whose perimeter equals that of the triangle ABC'. The triangle ADE is placed as shown in Diagram 231 b. Since AB is the largest side of triangle ABC' and AD is $\frac{1}{3}$ the perimeter of this triangle, we have $AB > AD$. Hence $AE > AC'$ (otherwise triangle ADE would be enclosed in the triangle ABC' and could not have the same perimeter). Because AB is the largest side of the isosceles triangle ABC',

$$AC' = BC' < \frac{AB + BC' + C'A}{3} = AD.$$

It follows from this inequality that $\sphericalangle AC'D > \sphericalangle ADC'$, that is, that $\sphericalangle EC'D < \sphericalangle BDC'$. Moreover, since it is obvious that $\sphericalangle BDC' > \sphericalangle EDC'$, Exercise 5-1 d implies that of the two triangles $C'DE$ and $BC'D$, which have a common base and the same perimeter, the second has the smaller area (*cf.* the last remark in the solution of Exercise 5-1 d). Hence we have

$$S(\triangle C'DE) > S(\triangle BC'D), \qquad S(\triangle ADE) > S(\triangle ABC').$$

Now we construct on the base AD an isosceles triangle ADF having the same perimeter as the triangle ADE (this triangle, shown by dotted lines in Diagram 231 b, must obviously be equilateral). By

Exercise 5-1 d, we have $S(\triangle ADF) > S(\triangle ADE)$ (the triangle ADE does not coincide with the equilateral triangle ADF since $\sphericalangle EAD \neq 60°$). The inequalities

$$S(\triangle ABC) \le S(\triangle ABC') < S(\triangle ADE) < S(\triangle ADF)$$

prove the theorem (in this chain of inequalities we must write "$\le$" in place of "$<$" at the beginning, since it is not certain that the triangle ABC is distinct from the triangle ABC'; that is, the triangle ABC may already be isosceles).

(b) We divide the quadrilateral $ABCD$ into two triangles by its diagonal AC. If we replace the triangles ABC and ACD by isosceles triangles $AB'C$ and ACD' with the same bases and the same perimeters, then we obtain a quadrilateral $AB'CD'$ (Diagram 232 a) for which, by Exercise 5-1 d,

$$S(AB'CD') \ge S(ABCD).$$

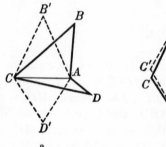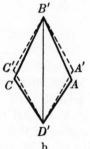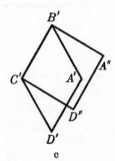

a   b   c

Diagram 232

Next we replace the congruent triangles $AB'D'$ and $B'CD'$ by isosceles triangles $A'B'D'$ and $B'C'D'$ with the same bases and the same perimeters. We obtain a rhombus $A'B'C'D'$ such that

$$S(A'B'C'D') \ge S(AB'CD')$$

(Diagram 232 b). Finally, the rhombus $A'B'C'D'$ has an area which is not greater than that of the square $A''B'C'D''$ having the same sides (Diagram 232 c). If the quadrilateral $ABCD$ is not a square, then in the chain of inequalities

$$S(ABCD) \le S(AB'CD') \le S(A'B'C'D') \le S(A''B'C'D'')$$

a strict inequality must appear in at least one place.

5-3. (a) Prove that among all n-sided polygons inscribed in a given circle, the regular n-sided polygon has the greatest area.
(b) Prove that among all n-sided polygons inscribed in a circle, the regular n-sided polygon has the greatest perimeter.

(**a**) If an n-sided polygon inscribed in a circle is not regular, then it has a side that is smaller than a side of the corresponding regular n-sided polygon. Furthermore, we may suppose that our inscribed, irregular, n-sided polygon has a side greater than a side of the regular n-sided polygon (if this were not so, then the entire n-sided polygon could be inscribed in a circular arc smaller than the nth part of the circle; we can exlude this case at once, however, since then the polygon could be entirely included in the regular n-sided polygon and would certainly have a smaller area; Diagram 233).

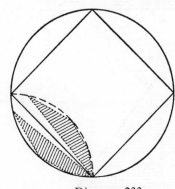
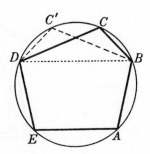

Diagram 233   Diagram 234

Without changing the area of a polygon inscribed in a circle we can exchange the location of its sides so that a side greater than the side of the regular n-sided polygon and a side smaller than the side of the regular n-sided polygon are adjacent (if we exchange the position of two neighboring sides of a polygon inscribed in a circle, the area of the polygon obviously remains unchanged; see Diagram 234. By repeating the process, we can make any two sides adjacent). If we now change the lengths of these two adjacent sides so that one of them is equal to a side of the regular polygon, and the remaining sides are unaltered, then the polygon remains inscribed in the circle, and by Exercise 5-1 b the area is increased. Continuation of this process gives us finally a regular n-sided polygon. Areas can only *increase* through this process of replacement of sides.

(**b**) The proof is similar to that of Exercise 5-3 a.

5-4. Prove that among all convex quadrilaterals with given side lengths, the one with greatest area can be inscribed in a circle.

First Solution. We subject the convex quadrilateral $ABCD$ ($AB = a$, $BC = b$, $CD = c$, $DA = d$) to a similitude with coefficient $k = c/a$ (see translators' note, page 111). The side $A'B'$ of the transformed quadrilateral $A'B'C'D'$ is then equal to the side CD of the

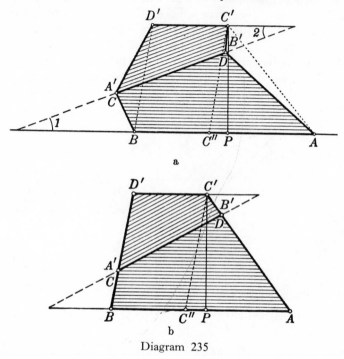

Diagram 235

quadrilateral $ABCD$. Now we join the quadrilaterals $ABCD$ and $A'B'C'D'$ with their equal sides together as shown in Diagram 235 a. The area of the total figure $ADC'D'CB$ is obviously

$$S(ABCD) + S(A'B'C'D') = (1 + k^2)\, S(ABCD).$$

From the similarity of the quadrilaterals $A'B'C'D'$ and $ABCD$, it follows that

$$\sphericalangle ADC' = \sphericalangle BCD'.$$

In fact,

$$\sphericalangle BCD' = \sphericalangle C + \sphericalangle A,$$

and

$$\sphericalangle ADC' = 2\pi - \sphericalangle D - \sphericalangle B = \sphericalangle C + \sphericalangle A.$$

The product of the sides $AD \cdot DC'$ in triangle DAC' equals the product of the sides $BC \cdot CD'$ in triangle BCD' since $d \cdot kb = b \cdot kd$. Thus

$$S(\triangle CBD') = S(\triangle DAC')$$

and hence

$$S(ABD'C') = S(ABCD'C'D) = (1 + k^2)\, S(ABCD) = \frac{a^2 + c^2}{a^2}\, S(ABCD).$$

The quadrilateral $ABD'C$ is a trapezoid, for the sides AB and $C'D'$ are parallel (the alternate interior angles which they form with the secant CD are equal; that is, angles 1 and 2 in Diagram 235 a). We must determine when the area of the trapezoid $ABD'C'$ with given bases $AB = a$ and $C'D' = kc = c^2/a$ is largest; that is, when the altitude of this trapezoid is largest.

For this purpose, we draw $C'C''$ parallel to $D'B$ and examine the triangle $AC'C''$ having the same altitude as the trapezoid $ABD'C'$ and base

$$AC'' = a - kc = (a^2 - c^2)/a.$$

We can show that the difference of the squares of the sides of this triangle is constant when the sides of the quadrilateral $ABCD$ are fixed. By the law of cosines we have, in fact,

$$C'C''^2 = D'B^2 = b^2 + k^2d^2 - 2kbd \cos \sphericalangle BCD',$$
$$AC'^2 = d^2 + k^2b^2 - 2kbd \cos \sphericalangle ADC',$$

and since $\sphericalangle BCD' = \sphericalangle ADC'$, it follows that

$$C'C''^2 - AC'^2 = b^2 + k^2d^2 - (d^2 + k^2b^2)$$
$$= (b^2 - d^2)(1 - k^2) = \frac{(b^2 - d^2)(a^2 - c^2)}{a^2}.$$

We denote by P the foot of the altitude from the vertex C' of the triangle $AC'C''$. Then

$$AC'^2 = AP^2 + C'P^2, \qquad C'C''^2 = C''P^2 + C'P^2,$$
$$C'C''^2 - AC'^2 = C''P^2 - AP^2 = (C''P + AP)(C''P - AP).$$

Suppose that the point P lies between the points A and C''. Then

$$C''P + AP = AC'' = a - kc = (a^2 - c^2)/a$$

and hence[†]

$$C''P - AP = (b^2 - d^2)/a.$$

[†] From this it is clear that our assumption that the point P lies between A and C'' is correct only if $a^2 - c^2 \geq b^2 - d^2$. If $a^2 - c^2 < b^2 - d^2$, then the point C'' lies between A and P, and the rest of the argument remains unchanged. (In this case we have $C''P + AP = (b^2 - d^2)/a$ and $C''P - AP = (a^2 - c^2)/a$.)

Therefore

$$AP = (a^2 - b^2 - c^2 + d^2)/2a, \qquad C''P = (a^2 + b^2 - c^2 - d^2)/2a,$$

so that the position of the point P is uniquely determined.

Thus the foot of the altitude from the vertex C' onto the side AB of the trapezoid $ABD'C'$ does not depend upon the angles of the quadrilateral $ABCD$. Consequently the altitude $C'P$ of the trapezoid is greatest when the angles of the quadrilateral satisfy the relation $\sphericalangle C + \sphericalangle A = 180°$ (in this case the side AC' of the triangle $AC'C''$ has the maximum value $d + kb = d + (bc/a)$; see Diagram 235b); that is, when the quadrilateral $ABCD$ can be inscribed in a circle. This completes the proof.

> *Note.* The hypothesis of the exercise is significant, since a unique quadrilateral exists which can be inscribed in a circle and whose sides in prescribed order have given lengths a, b, c, and d. In fact it is not hard to construct such a quadrilateral by using the arguments set forth above. To begin with, we can easily construct a right triangle APC' with sides
>
> $$AP = (a^2 - b^2 - c^2 + d^2)/2a$$
>
> and
>
> $$AC' = d + (bc/a)$$
>
> (Diagram 235 b). On the sides AP and AC' of this triangle we lay of the segments $AB = a$ and $AD = b$, and thus find the vertices B and D of the quadrilateral $ABCD$. The final vertex C is easily constructed, since $BC = b$ and $DC = c$.

In the hypothesis of the present exercise it is unnecessary to require that the order of the sides of the quadrilateral be specified (an hypothesis which we used in our solution). If in an arbitrary quadrilateral $PQRS$ the sides are arranged in the order $PQ=a$, $QR=b$, $RS=c$, $SP=d$, then its area is less than that of the quadrilateral $P'R'Q'S'$ inscribed in a circle, in which the sides appear in the same order ($P'Q'=a$, $Q'R'=b$, $R'S'=c$, $S'P' = d$). The area of the latter quadrilateral is, as can easily be seen from Diagram 236, equal to that of the quadrilateral $P'Q'R'S''$ inscribed in a

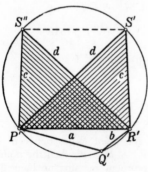

Diagram 236

circle and having sides $P'Q' = a$, $Q'R' = b$, $R'S'' = c$, $S''P' = d$, which are arranged in different order.[†]

Second Solution. (*cf.* the first solution of Exercise 5-5 a.) We consider two quadrilaterals with corresponding equal sides: the quadrilateral $ABCD$, which is inscribed in a circle S with radius R and center O, and the quadrilateral $A_1B_1C_1D_1$ (Diagram 237 a, b). Now

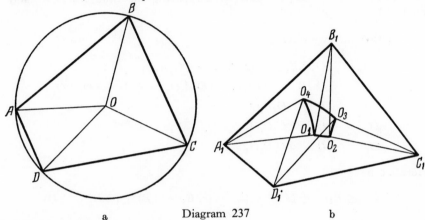

a   Diagram 237   b

we imagine that the quadrilateral $ABCD$ is movable and deform it by changing the angles so that it is transformed into the quadrilateral $A_1B_1C_1D_1$. Under this transformation, the isosceles triangles ABO, BCO, CDO, and DAO which bound the sides of the quadrilateral $ABCD$ change their position and go over finally into the triangles $A_1B_1O_1$, $B_1C_1O_2$, $C_1D_1O_3$, and $D_1A_1O_4$ (Diagram 237 b). Now compare the area of $ABCD$ and $A_1B_1C_1D_1$. We have

$$S(\triangle ABO) = S(\triangle A_1B_1O_1), \quad S(\triangle BCO) = S(\triangle B_1C_1O_2),$$
$$S(\triangle CDO) = S(\triangle C_1D_1O_3), \quad S(\triangle DAO) = S(\triangle D_1A_1O_4).$$

We join the points O_1 and O_2, O_2 and O_3, O_3 and O_4, O_4 and O_1 by circular arcs of radius R and centers at B_1, C_1, D_1, and A_1 respectively. Now we show that two of the opposite angles of the quadrilateral $A_1B_1C_1D_1$ are less than the corresponding angles of the quadrilateral $ABCD$ and that the other two angles are greater than the corresponding angles in $ABCD$. Suppose that $\sphericalangle A_1 < \sphericalangle A$; in this case we see, by comparing triangles ABD and $A_1B_1D_1$ (where $AB = A_1B_1$, and

[†]We can show that the area of a quadrilateral with sides a, b, c, d, inscribed in a circle, is $\sqrt{(p - a)(p - b)(p - c)(p - d)}$ where $p = (a + b + c + d)/2$ (generalized formula of Heron). From this it is immediately evident that the area does not depend on the order of the sides. However, we do not need this formula.

$AD = A_1D_1$), that $B_1D_1 < BD$. Comparing triangles CBD and $C_1B_1D_1$, we then observe that $\angle C_1 < \angle C$. Furthermore, not all the angles of the quadrilateral $A_1B_1C_1D_1$ can be less than the corresponding angles of the quadrilateral $ABCD$ (since the sum of the angles in a quadrilateral is always 360°). If we assume, for example, that $\angle B_1$ is less than $\angle B$, we then have $A_1C_1 < AC$ (by comparing the triangles BAC and $B_1A_1C_1$) and $\angle D_1 < \angle D$ (by comparing the triangles DAC and $D_1A_1C_1$).

In this way we obtain

$$\angle A_1 = \angle O_1A_1B_1 + \angle O_4A_1D_1 - \angle O_1A_1O_4$$
$$= \angle OAB + \angle OAD - \angle O_1A_1O_4 = \angle A - \angle O_1A_1O_4$$
$$\angle B_1 = \angle B + \angle O_1B_1O_2$$
$$\angle C_1 = \angle C - \angle O_2C_1O_3$$
$$\angle D_1 = \angle D + \angle O_3D_1O_4.$$

Here we have

$$(\angle A - \angle A_1) + (\angle C - \angle C_1) = (\angle B_1 - \angle B) + (\angle D_1 - \angle D)$$

(since $\angle A + \angle B + \angle C + \angle D = \angle A_1 + \angle B_1 + \angle C_1 + \angle D_1 = 360°$); thus

$$\angle O_1A_1O_4 + \angle O_2C_1O_3 = \angle O_1B_1O_2 + \angle O_3D_1O_4$$

and hence

$$S(\text{sect. } A_1O_1O_4) + S(\text{sect.} C_1O_2O_3) = S(\text{sect. } B_1O_1O_2) + S(\text{sect. } D_1O_3O_4).$$

Since

$$S(ABCD) = S(\triangle A_1B_1O_1) + S(\triangle B_1C_1O_2) + S(\triangle C_1D_1O_3) + S(\triangle A_1D_1O_4)$$

and

$$S(A_1B_1C_1D_1) = S(\triangle A_1B_1O_1) + S(\text{sect. } B_1O_1O_2) + S(\triangle B_1C_1O_2)$$
$$+ S(\triangle C_1D_1O_3) + S(\text{sect. } D_1O_3O_4) + S(\triangle A_1D_1O_4)$$
$$- [S(\text{sect. } A_1O_1O_4) + S(O_1O_2O_3O_4) + S(\text{sect. } C_1O_2O_3)],$$

where $O_1O_2O_3O_4$ is the curvilinear quadrilateral, then

$$S(ABCD) - S(A_1B_1C_1D_1) = S(O_1O_2O_3O_4)$$
$$+ [S(\text{sect. } A_1O_1O_4) + S(\text{sect. } C_1O_2O_3)]$$
$$- [S(\text{sect. } B_1O_1O_2) + S(\text{sect. } D_1O_3O_4)]$$
$$= S(O_1O_2O_3O_4).$$

Thus, to establish the inequality

$$S(ABCD) > S(A_1B_1C_1D_1)$$

(and this is the content of the exercise), it suffices to show that the area of the curvilinear quadrilateral $O_1O_2O_3O_4$ is always positive. This assertion has the following meaning.
It is not *a priori* certain that the arcs O_1O_4 and O_2O_3 do not intersect; that is, that our curvilinear quadrilateral does not have the form shown in Diagram 238. In this case the lens PQ (shaded in Diagram 238) must be subtracted from the total area, since it projects into the sectors $A_1O_1O_4$ and $C_1O_2O_3$. We must prove that the area of this lens cannot exceed the sum of the areas of the curvilinear triangles O_1O_2P and O_3O_4Q. This is what is meant when we speak of the positivity of the area of the curvilinear quadrilateral $O_1O_2O_3O_4$ (if the quadrilateral has the form shown in Diagram 238, we must use the formula $S(O_1O_2P) + S(O_3O_4Q) - S(PQ)$ in determining its area).

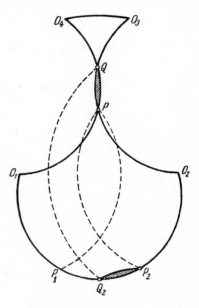

Diagram 238

We note that all the arcs $\overset{\frown}{O_1O_2}$, $\overset{\frown}{O_2O_3}$, $\overset{\frown}{O_3O_4}$, and $\overset{\frown}{O_4O_1}$ have the same radius R and that the following relation holds:

$$\overset{\frown}{O_1O_2} + \overset{\frown}{O_3O_4} = \overset{\frown}{O_1O_4} + \overset{\frown}{O_2O_3}$$

(since $\sphericalangle O_1B_1O_2 + \sphericalangle O_3D_1O_4 = \sphericalangle O_1A_1O_4 + \sphericalangle O_2C_1O_3$). Hence

$$(\overset{\frown}{O_1O_2} + \overset{\frown}{O_3O_4}) - (\overset{\frown}{O_1O_4} + \overset{\frown}{O_2O_3}) = (\overset{\frown}{O_1O_2} - \overset{\frown}{O_1P} - \overset{\frown}{O_2Q})$$

$$+ (\overset{\frown}{O_3O_4} - \overset{\frown}{O_4P} - \overset{\frown}{O_3Q}) = 0,$$

and therefore at least one of the expression $\overset{\frown}{O_1O_2} - \overset{\frown}{O_1P} - \overset{\frown}{O_2Q}$ and $\overset{\frown}{O_3O_4} - \overset{\frown}{O_4P} - \overset{\frown}{O_3Q}$ is nonnegative. Suppose that the first of these expressions is nonnegative. We rotate the arc O_1P about O_1 into the position O_1P_1, and the arc O_2Q, together with the lens PQ, about O_2 into the position $O_2P_2Q_2$ (Diagram 238). Thus we have

$$\overset{\frown}{O_{11}P} + \overset{\frown}{O_2Q_2} = \overset{\frown}{O_1P} + \overset{\frown}{O_2Q} \leq \overset{\frown}{O_1O_2}.$$

It therefore follows that the lens P_2Q_2 cannot intersect the arcs O_1P and O_2P (for it intersects neither the curvilinear sector O_1P_1P nor the curvilinear sector O_2P_2P). Hence

$$S(PQ) = S(P_2Q_2) < S(O_1O_2P)$$

and

$$S(PQ) < S(O_1OP_2) + S(O_3O_4Q)$$

both hold. This completes the proof.

5-5. (a) Prove that among all convex quadrilaterals with given angles and perimeter, that one in which a circle can be inscribed has the largest area. (b) Prove that among all convex n-sided polygons with given angles and perimeter, that one in which a circle can be inscribed has the largest area.

(a) *First Solution.* (Compare with the second solution of Exercise 5-4.) We consider a quadrilateral $ABCD$ circumscribed about a circle ρ with radius r and another quadrilateral $A_1B_1C_1D_1$ which has the same angles and perimeter as $ABCD$ (Diagram 239 a, b). From the center O

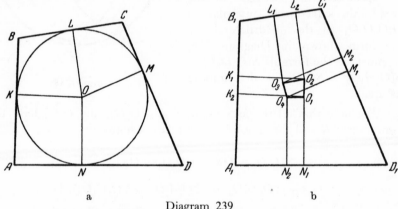

a   b

Diagram 239

we drop perpendiculars OK, OL, OM, and ON onto the sides of the quadrilateral $ABCD$ and consider the quadrilaterals $A_1N_1O_1K_2 = ANOK$, $B_1K_1O_2L_2 = BKOL$, $C_1L_1O_3M_2 = CLOM$, and $D_1M_1O_4N_2 = DMON$ whose angles at A_1, B_1, C_1, and D_1 agree with the angles of the quadrilateral $A_1B_1C_1D_1$. If $A_1B_1 > AB$, then obviously $C_1D_1 > CD$ (to prove this it is sufficient to place the quadrilaterals $ABCD$ and $A_1B_1C_1D_1$ upon one another so that the vertices A and A_1 coincide and the sides A_1D_1 and A_1B_1 fall along the sides AD and AB respectively). In this case we also obtain $B_1C_1 < BC$ and $D_1A_1 < DA$. Now, since the perimeters of the quadrilaterals $ABCD$ and $A_1B_1C_1D_1$ are equal, it follows that

$$AB + BC + CD + DA = A_1B_1 + B_1C_1 + C_1D_1 + D_1A_1,$$
$$(A_1B_1 - AB) + (C_1D_1 - CD) = (BC - B_1C_1) + (DA - D_1A_1)$$

or, in other words,

$$(A_1B_1 - A_1K_2 - B_1K_1) + (C_1D_1 - C_1M_2 - D_1M_1)$$
$$= (B_1L_2 + C_1L_1 - B_1C_1) + (D_1N_2 + A_1N_1 - D_1A_1),$$

that is,

$$K_1K_2 + M_1M_2 = L_1L_2 + N_2N_1.$$

This means that

$$S(K_1K_2O_1O_2) + S(M_1M_2O_3O_4) = S(L_2L_1O_3O_2) + S(N_2N_1O_1O_4),$$

since all these quadrilaterals are rectangles with the same altitude r. Now

$$S(ABCD) = S(A_1N_1O_1K_2) + S(B_1K_1O_2L_2) + S(C_1L_1O_3M_2) + S(D_1M_1O_4N_2);$$

and from Diagram 239 it is clear that

$$S(A_1B_1C_1D_1) = S(A_1N_1O_1K_2) + S(K_1K_2O_1O_2) + S(B_1K_1O_2L_2)$$
$$+ S(C_1L_1O_3M_2) + S(M_1M_2O_3O_4) + S(D_1M_1O_4N_2)$$
$$- [S(L_1L_2O_2O_3) + S(N_1N_2O_4O_1) + S(O_1O_2O_3O_4)].$$

Then

$$S(ABCD) - S(A_1B_1C_1D_1) = S(O_1O_2O_3O_4) + [S(L_1L_2O_2O_3) + S(N_1N_2O_4O_1)]$$
$$- [S(K_1K_2O_1O_2) + S(M_1M_2O_3O_4)] = S(O_1O_2O_3O_4),$$

from which it follows that

$$S(ABCD) > S(A_1B_1C_1D_1).$$

Second Solution. We drop the requirement that the perimeter of the quadrilateral be given and, among all quadrilaterals with given angles, look for that one in which the ratio of the area to the square of the perimeter is a maximum (see page 52). Suppose that the sum of the angles at the vertices A and B of the quadrilateral is less than 180° (if $\angle A + \angle B > 180°$ then $\angle C + \angle D = 360° - \angle A - \angle B < 180°$), and we need only replace the angles at A and B by the angles at C and D).[†]

[†] We exclude the case in which the sum of any two adjacent angles of the quadrilateral is 180°. Then the quadrilateral is a parallelogram. In this case the statement of the present exercise agrees with that of Exercise 5-1c.

We construct a triangle ABT in which two angles are equal to the angles

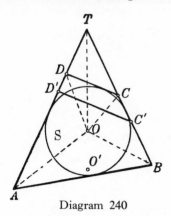

Diagram 240

at the vertices A and B of the desired quadrilateral (Diagram 240). We must cut this triangle with a line CD having a given direction so that for the resulting quadrilateral the ratio of the area to the square of the perimeter is a maximum.

Let the circle S inscribed in the triangle ATB have radius R and center O. Let $C'D'$ be any line with the preassigned direction and let CD be a line with the same direction which touches S (Diagram 240). We must prove the following inequality:

$$\frac{S(ABCD)}{(AB + BC + CD + DA)^2} > \frac{S(ABC'D')}{(AB + BC' + C'D' + D'A)^2}$$

Let the perimeter $AB + BT + TA$ of the triangle ATB be $2P$, and let the expression $CT + TD - CD$ equal $2p$. Further, let k be the similarity coefficient of the triangles $TC'D'$ and TCD (k can be greater than or less than 1). Then we have

$$C'T + TD' - C'D' = 2kp$$

and hence

$$AB + BC + CD + DA = (AB + BT + TA) - (CT + TD - CD)$$
$$= 2(P - p),$$
$$AB + BC' + C'D' + D'A = (AB + BT + TA) - (C'T + TD' - C'D')$$
$$= 2(P - kp).$$

Furthermore we have

$$S(\triangle ABT) = S(\triangle AOT) + S(\triangle BOT) + S(\triangle BOA)$$
$$= \tfrac{1}{2}R \cdot AT + \tfrac{1}{2}R \cdot BT + \tfrac{1}{2}R \cdot BA = P \cdot R$$
$$S(\triangle CDT) = S(\triangle COT) + S(\triangle DOT) - S(\triangle COD)$$
$$= \tfrac{1}{2}R \cdot CT + \tfrac{1}{2}R \cdot DT - \tfrac{1}{2}R \cdot CD = p \cdot R,$$

which shows, since the triangle $C'D'T$ and the triangle CDT are similar, that

$$S(\triangle C'D'T) = k^2 pR.$$

Hence we have

$$S(ABCD) = S(\triangle ABT) - S(\triangle CDT) = (P - p) \cdot R,$$
$$S(ABC'D') = S(\triangle ABT) - S(\triangle C'D'T) = (P - k^2 p) \cdot R.$$

Thus the inequality to be proved assumes the following form

$$\frac{(P-p)\,R}{4(P-p)^2} > \frac{(P-k^2p)\,R}{4(P-kp)^2}$$

or

$$\frac{1}{P-p} > \frac{P-k^2p}{(P-kp)^2}.$$

If we multiply the last inequality by the positive expression $(P-p)\,(P-kp)^2$ the result is

$$(P-kp)^2 > (P-p)\,(P-k^2p),$$

which is clearly correct since

$$(P-kp)^2 - (P-p)\,(P-k^2p) = P^2 - 2kpP + k^2p^2 - p^2 + k^2pP + pP - k^2p^2$$
$$= k^2pP - 2kpP + pP = pP(1-k)^2 > 0.$$

We call attention to the fact that in the last inequality the sign ">" and not "≥" appears, since p and P are positive and $k \neq 1$ ($k = 1$ would mean that the triangles CTD and $C'TD'$ were not only similar, but also congruent; then $C'D'$ would coincide with CD).

(b) The solution is very like the second solution of Exercise 5-5 a.

For simplicity we will solve the problem first for the case of a pentagon. We consider two equiangular pentagons $ABCDE$ and $A'B'C'D'E'$, the first of which is circumscribed about a circle, while the second is dissimilar to the first (Diagram 241). In order to prove

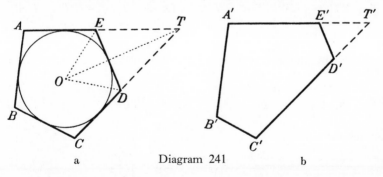

a   Diagram 241   b

that the ratio of the area to the square of the perimeter is greater for the pentagon $ABCDE$ than for the pentagon $A'B'C'D'E'$, we delete the sides DE and $D'E'$ of these pentagons (for which $\sphericalangle D + \sphericalangle E > 180°$) and prolong the sides adjacent to DE and to $D'E'$, respectively, to their respective intersections. We thus obtain two quadrilaterals

ABCT and *A'B'C'T'* with corresponding angles equal, the first of which is circumscribed about a circle. To simplify the proof let us assume that the size of the pentagon *A'B'C'D'E'* has been chosen so that the perimeter of the quadrilateral *A'B'C'T'* equals the perimeter $2P$ of the quadrilateral *ABCT* (by a similarity transformation of the pentagon *A'B'C'D'E'* with a suitable ratio we can always insure the fulfillment of this condition. See Translators' Note, page 111). The area of the quadrilateral *ABCT* is $R \cdot P$, where R is the radius of the circle inscribed in this quadrilateral. Let $\alpha R \cdot P$ denote the area of the quadrilateral *A'B'C'T'*. By the result if the previous exercise, since the quadrilateral *A'B'C'T'* has the same angles and the same perimeter as the quadrilateral *ABCT*, it cannot have a greater area, and therefore we have $\alpha \leq 1$. Here $\alpha = 1$ only if the quadrilateral *A'B'C'T'* can be circumscribed about a circle; that is, if it is congruent with *ABCT*. We now denote the expression $DT + TE - DE$ by $2p$ and the expression $D'T' + T'E' - D'E'$ by $2kp$; here k is the similarity ratio of the triangles *D'T'E'* and *DTE*. The area of the triangle *DTE* is Rp (where R is the radius of the escribed circle of this triangle); hence the area of the triangle *D'T'E'*, which is similar to the triangle *DTE* in the ratio k, must be $k^2 Rp$.

We have

$$S(ABCDE) = S(ABCT) - S(\triangle DET),$$

$$AB + BC + CD + DE + EA = (AB + BC + CT + TA)$$
$$- (DT + TE - ED),$$

$$S(A'B'C'D'E') = S(A'B'C'T') - S(\triangle D'E'T'),$$

$$A'B' + B'C' + C'D' + D'E' + E'A' = (A'B' + B'D' + C'T' + T'A')$$
$$- (D'T' + T'E' - E'D').$$

Hence the inequality to be proved,

$$\frac{S(ABCDE)}{(AB + BC + CD + DE + EA)^2} > \frac{S(A'B'C'D'E')}{(A'B' + B'C' + C'D' + D'E' + E'A')^2}$$

assumes the form

$$\frac{R \cdot P - Rp}{(2P - 2p)^2} > \frac{\alpha R \cdot P - k^2 Rp}{(2P - 2kp)^2} \qquad ✳$$

or

$$\frac{1}{P - p} > \frac{\alpha P - k^2 p}{(P - kp)^2},$$

or

$$(P - kp)^2 > (P - p)(\alpha P - k^2 p).$$

This last inequality holds, since

$$(P - pk)^2 - (P - p)(\alpha P - k^2 p) = (P - kp)^2 - (P - p)(P - k^2 p)$$
$$+ (1 - \alpha)(P - p)P = Pp(1 - k)^2 + (1 - \alpha)(P - p)P > 0$$

(see the solution to Exercise 5-5 a), because $1 - \alpha \geq 0$ and $P > p$ by the definitions of these quantities. In the last inequality the sign ">" and not "$\geq$" appears, since for $1 - \alpha = 0$, that is for $\alpha = 1$, the quadrilateral $A'B'C'T'$ would equal the quadrilateral $ABCT$. In order for the pentagon $A'B'C'D'E'$ to be incongruent to the pentagon $ABCDE$, the triangle $D'E'T'$ must be incongruent to the triangle DET, that is, $k \neq 1$; if, however, $(1 - \alpha)(P - p)P = 0$, then $Pp(1 - k)^2$ is clearly > 0.

The solution of the exercise for n-sided polygons can now be carried out by induction. It is in no way different from the proof given above and all of the calculations have exactly the same form, except that instead of "pentagon" we speak always of n-sided polygon, and in place of "quadrilateral" we speak of $(n - 1)$-sided polygon for which, by the induction hypothesis, the theorem is already proved (which permits us to assert that $\alpha \leq 1$).

Note. We observe that not only the inequality $*$ holds, but also the stronger inequality

$$\frac{R \cdot P - Rp}{(2P - 2p)^2} : \frac{R \cdot P}{p^2} > \frac{\alpha R \cdot P - k^2 Rp}{(2P - 2kp)^2} : \frac{\alpha R \cdot P}{P^2} . \qquad **$$

The inequality $**$ can be transformed as follows:

$$\frac{1}{P - p} > \frac{\alpha P - k^2 p}{\alpha(P - kp)^2} ,$$

$$\alpha(P - kp)^2 - (P - p)(\alpha P - k^2 p) > 0,$$
$$- 2\alpha k Pp + \alpha k^2 p^2 + k^2 Pp + \alpha Pp - k^2 p^2 > 0,$$
$$\alpha Pp(1 - k)^2 + k^2 p(1 - \alpha)(P - p) > 0,$$

and the last inequality is obviously correct.

The inequality $**$ indicates that in passing from the quadrilateral to the pentagon (in the general case from the $(n - 1)$-sided polygon to the n-sided polygon), the ratio of the area to the square of the perimeter increases more rapidly for polygons circumscribed about a circle than for any other polygons. We shall make use of this fact later.

5-6. If a chord of a convex figure Φ bisects the perimeter but divides the area in two unequal parts, prove that there is a figure $\overline{\Phi}$ with the same perimeter as Φ but a larger area.

If a chord AB of the figure Φ divides the perimeter of Φ into two equal parts and the area into two unequal parts, and of we replace the smaller part by the image of the larger under a reflection in the chord AB, we obtain a figure $\overline{\Phi}$ with the same perimeter as Φ but greater area (Diagram 242). The figure $\overline{\Phi}$ thus obtained need not be convex; in this case its area can be further increased without increasing the perimeter (*cf.* p. 51).

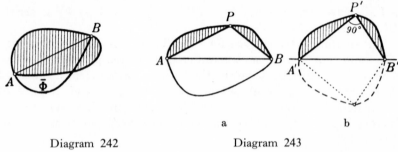

Diagram 242   Diagram 243

5-7. Using the results of Exercises 5-6 and 5-1 a, prove that for each convex figure Φ which is not a circle there exists a figure $\overline{\Phi}$ with the same perimeter but greater area.

Let the perimeter of Φ be bisected by a chord AB. If the chord AB divides the area of the figure Φ into two unequal parts, then there is a figure $\overline{\Phi}$ with the same perimeter as Φ and having a greater area (*cf.* Exercise 5-6). If the chord AB bisects both the perimeter and the area of the figure Φ and if Φ is not a circle, then at least one of the two parts into which AB divides Φ must be different from a semicircle with diameter AB. From this it follows that on the boundary of the figure there is a point P such that $\sphericalangle APB$ is not a right angle (Diagram 243a; otherwise the boundary of Φ would be a circular arc of diameter AB and the figure Φ would be a circular region). We now replace the half of Φ containing the arc APB by a new figure bounded by a segment $A'B'$ and an arc $A'P'B'$ (Diagram 243 b). In doing this, we leave unchanged the segments separated from the chords AP and PB and replace the triangle APB by a right triangle whose legs have the same length as the sides of the triangle APB ($AP = A'P'$, $PB = P'B'$); hence the relation $S(\triangle A'P'B') > S(\triangle APB)$ holds by Exercise 5-1 a. If we now reflect the new figure in the chord $A'B'$, we obtain a figure $\overline{\Phi}$ with the same perimeter as Φ (the perimeter of each of the two figures is twice the length of the curve APB); $\overline{\Phi}$ has a greater area (since $\overline{\Phi}$ was constructed so that half its area is greater than half the area of Φ).

> *Note.* The argument presented here originated with the Swiss geometer Steiner who assumed that it completely solves the isoperimetric problem. In reality, however, this argument offers no rigorous proof of the isoperimetric property of the circle (see pages 54 and 55).

5-8. Prove, by using the result of Exercise 5-5, that the circle has a greater area than any other figure with the same perimeter.

Let Φ be any convex figure and let K be a circle. We must prove that the ratio of the area of the circle K to the square of its perimeter is greater than the ratio of the area of the figure Φ to the square of its perimeter. Here the area and the perimeter of K and Φ are defined as the limit of the areas and the limit of the perimeters respectively of polygons circumscribed about these convex figures and forming a sequence in which all exterior angles approach zero (see page 12).

We shall examine polygons which are circumscribed about the figure Φ and the circle K and whose corresponding angles are equal (for example, polygons circumscribed about the figure Φ or the circle K and having parallel sides; Diagram 244). By Exercise 5-5 b, the ratio of the area to the square of the perimeter for

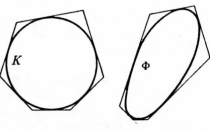

Diagram 244

each polygon circumscribed about the circle K is not less than that for a corresponding polygon which is circumscribed about the figure Φ. Thus, on passing to the limit, we have

$$\frac{\text{Area of } K}{(\text{Perimeter of } K)^2} \geq \frac{\text{Area of } \Phi}{(\text{Perimeter of } \Phi)^2} \qquad \text{\Large *}$$

from which it follows at once that a circle has an area at least as great as that of any other convex figure of equal perimeter.

We next suppose that the figure Φ is *not* a circle; thus it is different from K. Obviously, then, not all polygons circumscribed about the circle K are similar to the corresponding polygons circumscribed about the figure Φ. Suppose that M is the first of the polygons circumscribed about the circle K which is not similar to the corresponding polygon M circumscribed about the figure Φ. Then the ratio of the area to the square of the perimeter in the case of the polygon M must be *greater* (not merely "not less than") than the value of the same ratio in the case of the polygon $\overline{M}$ (see the solutions of Exercises 5-5 a and b). Since in the sequel the ratio of the area to the square of the perimeter for the circumscribed polygons of the circle K will be greater each time (on passing from the circumscribed n-sided polygon to the circumscribed $(n + 1)$-sided polygon) than for the polygons circumscribed about the figure Φ (see note at the end of the solution of Exercise 5-5b), we can conclude finally:

$$\frac{\text{Area of } K}{(\text{Perimeter of } K)^2} > \frac{\text{Area of } \Phi}{(\text{Perimeter of } \Phi)^2}. \qquad \text{✱✱}$$

> *Note.* If we have already proved that the area of the circle K of perimeter 1 is *not less than* the area of any other figure of the same perimeter (as asserted by the inequality ✱), it follows immediately from the result of Exercise 5-7 (for each figure Φ not a circle, a figure $\overline{\Phi}$ of equal perimeter and greater area can be found) that the area of K (which cannot be less than the area of Φ) is greater than the area of Φ (see inequality ✱✱).

5-9. Prove that a polygon that can be inscribed in a circle has a greater area than any other polygon with corresponding sides of equal length.

Consider a polygon M inscribed in a circle, and also an arbitrary polygon N whose sides have the same lengths as those of M. We transform N into a figure Φ by replacing its sides by the corresponding circular segments of the circle K circumscribed about the polygon M

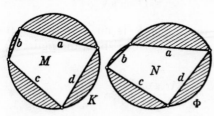

Diagram 245

(Diagram 245). The area of K is the area of the polygon M plus the sum of the areas of the segments shaded in Diagram 245; the area of the figure Φ is equal to the area of the polygon N plus the sum of the same segment areas. The figure Φ has the same perimeter as the circle K; hence its area is less than the area of K (see Exercise 5-8). It follows that the area of N is less than the area of M.

> *Note.* In the hypothesis of the present exercise it is unnecessary to require that a definite sequence of sides be defined for the polygon (the hypothesis used in our solution). The proof for this is the same as that for the analogous assertion made in the solution of Exercise 5-4 (Diagram 236).

5-10. Prove that of all convex n-sided polygons with the same perimeter, the regular n-sided polygon has the greatest area.

We first establish that of two regular polygons of perimeter $2p$, the one with the greater number of sides has the greater area. The area of a regular n-sided polygon is, in fact, equal to the product of its semi-perimeter and the radius of the incircle. The radius of the incircle of a regular n-sided polygon of perimeter $2p$ is equal to $(p/n)/\tan(\pi/n)$ and increases with n.

To prove this we write $(p/n)/\tan(\pi/n)$ in the form $(p/\pi)[(\pi/n)/\tan(\pi/n)]$. We then note that two radii at angle α in a unit circle cut out a circular sector of area 2α, while a triangle of area $2\tan\alpha$ is formed by the radii and a tangent line at the end point of one radius. We see geometrically that $(\tan\alpha)/\alpha$ (the ratio of the area of the triangle to the area of the sector) decreases with α (and increases with α).[†] It follows that $(\pi/n)/\tan(\pi/n)$ *increases with* n.

We give a proof by induction. Suppose that it has been proved that the area of every convex n-sided polygon of perimeter $2p$ is less than that of a regular n-sided polygon of the same perimeter. We will prove that the same statement holds for $(n + 1)$-sided polygons. The use of induction is justified since the assertion is true for $n = 3$ and $n = 4$ (see Exercises 5-2 a and b).

First we will show that the area of any $(n + 1)$-sided polygon of perimeter $2p$ is either less than or equal to that of some n-sided polygon of perimeter $2p$ or else is less than or equal to that of an $(n + 1)$-sided polygon with perimeter $2p$ and equal sides [each of which has length $2p/(n + 1)$].

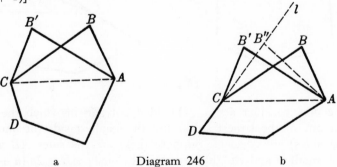

a   Diagram 246   b

Let $ABCD\ldots$ be any $(n + 1)$-sided polygon of perimeter $2p$ and let AB and BC be two adjoining sides. Draw the diagonal AC and construct a triangle $AB'C$ congruent to triangle ABC (Diagram 246 a).

[†] See D. O. Šklyarskiĭ et al.: *Izbrannye zadači i teoremy èlementarnoi matematiki* (Selected problems and theorems of elementary mathematics). vol. 1, Gostehizdat, Moscow-Leningrad, 1950, page 25, Exercises 102c.

The polygon $AB'CD...$, which is obtained by replacing the triangle ABC by the triangle $AB'C$, may be nonconvex (Diagram 246 b). Then the extension of a side which adjoins AB or BC intersects the triangle $AB'C$. Suppose that this occurs for the extension l of the segment CD. We select on the line l a point B'' such that $AB'' + B''C = AB + BC$ (the existence of such a point follows from considerations of continuity; see Section 3). Then the triangles ABC and $AB''C$ have equal perimeters and equal bases, but in the latter triangle the difference of the base angles is smaller; hence (*cf.* Exercise 5-1 d) $S(\triangle AB''C) > S(\triangle ABC)$ and the n-sided polygon $AB''D...$ has the perimeter $2p$, but its area is greater than that of the original polygon $ABCD...$.

If we carry out the above construction for the triangle $AB'C$ we either pass to a *convex* polygon $AB'CD...$ (Diagram 246 a) with the same perimeter and area but with the sides AB and BC interchanged, or we see that the area of the original polygon is less than that of some n-sided polygon with the same perimeter as the original $(n + 1)$-sided polygon. By application of this process (through sufficiently many interchanges of two adjacent sides of the polygon) we either can arrange that the largest and the smallest side are adjacent or else we find that the $(n + 1)$-sided polygon under consideration has a smaller area than an n-sided polygon with the same perimeter.

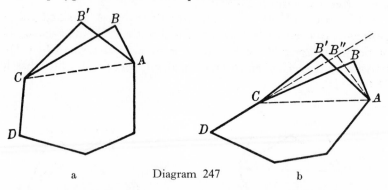

a   Diagram 247   b

We now consider an $(n + 1)$-sided polygon in which the largest side (or one of the largest sides) and the smallest side (or one of the smallest sides) are adjacent. Suppose these are the sides AB and BC (AB the smallest and BC the largest). Obviously $AB < 2p/(n + 1)$ and $BC > 2p/(n+1)$; if the smallest side AB were greater than $2p/(n+1)$, then the perimeter of the polygon would be greater than $(n + 1) \cdot 2p/(n+1) = 2p$, which is impossible. We construct a triangle $AB'C$ with the same base AC and perimeter (and hence the same sum for the sides abutting on the base) as in triangle ABC and such that one of these new sides is equal to $2p/(n + 1)$ and $AB' \leq B'C$ (Diagram 247a). The difference of the sides of the triangle $AB'C$ is less than the difference of the sides of the triangle ABC so $S(\triangle AB'C) > S(\triangle ABC)$ (*cf.* Exercise 5-1 d), and the polygon $AB'CD\ldots$ has the same perimeter but greater area than the original polygon. If it should turn out that the polygon $AB'CD\ldots$ is nonconvex, then we proceed as before to show that the area of the original polygon is less than the area of an n-sided polygon with the same perimeter (Diagram 247 b).

With the aid of the procedure just described we can therefore construct either a convex polygon $AB'C\ldots$ one of whose sides equals $2p/(n+1)$ and with the same perimeter but greater area than the polygon $ABCD\ldots$, or a convex n-sided polygon with the same perimeter and greater area than the polygon $ABCD\ldots$.

In the former case, if the polygon thus obtained still has sides not equal to $2p/(n+1)$, then it necessarily has sides that are less than $2p/(n+1)$ as well as sides that are greater than $2p/(n+1)$, and we can apply the same process to construct either an $(n+1)$-sided polygon of the same perimeter and greater area which has *two* sides of length $2p/(n+1)$ or an n-sided polygon of perimeter $2p$ with greater area. Continuing this process, we see that the area of any $(n+1)$-sided polygon of perimeter $2p$ is either not greater than the area of an $(n+1)$-sided polygon, all of whose sides are of length $2p/(n+1)$, or else is not greater than the area of some n-sided polygon.

The area of a convex $(n+1)$-sided polygon all of whose sides are equal is not greater than the area of a regular $(n+1)$-sided polygon of the same perimeter (*cf.* Exercise 5-9). The area of an n-sided polygon of perimeter $2p$ is, by our induction hypothesis, less than the area of a regular n-sided polygon of perimeter $2p$ and hence is also less than the area of a regular $(n+1)$-sided polygon of the same perimeter (see the note at the beginning of the solution of this exercise). Thus the assertion is completely proved.

5-11. (a) Prove that of all convex figures Φ that are bounded by a segment of length a and by an arc of length l, where $l > a$, a circular segment has the greatest area. (b) Prove that of all convex figures Φ that are bounded by a segment of arbitrary length and by an arc of length l, the semicircle of radius l/π has the greatest area.

(a) We consider a circular segment S of chord length a and arc length l and any other figure Φ with perimeter $a + l$ whose boundary has a line segment of length a. We enlarge the segment S into a circular region K. We adjoin a second segment, of the kind required to expand S into a circular region, to the chord of the line segment in the boundary of the figure Φ in such a fashion that it is situated on the other side of the line segment from the figure Φ (Diagram 248 a). The figure Φ' thus formed has the same circumference as the circle K and hence has a smaller area (Exercise 5-8). By subtracting from the area of K and the area of Φ' the equal shaded segments in Diagram 248 a, we see that the area of the segment S is greater than the area of the figure Φ.

(b) We consider a semicircle S of radius l/π and any figure Φ which is bounded by a line segment and an arc of length l. We reflect

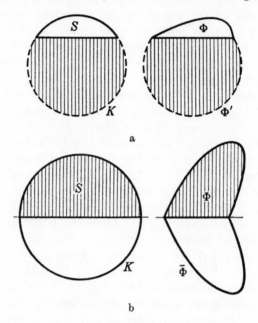

Diagram 248

the figures Φ and S in the lines on which the line segments in their boundaries lie (Diagram 248 b). In this way we obtain a circular region K (whose area is twice that of S) and a figure $\bar{\Phi}$ (whose area is twice that of Φ). The perimeter of $\bar{\Phi}$ is equal to the perimeter of K; hence the area of $\bar{\Phi}$ is less than the area of K (see Exercise 5-8), and the area of Φ is less than the area of S.

5-12. Find a convex curve of length 1 having a corner of angle α (see page 12) and which bounds a figure of maximum area.

The figure we seek is the convex figure bounded by the sides of the angle α and by an arc of a circle inscribed in this angle (Diagram 249). The solution can be obtained in a manner analogous to the solution of Exercise 5-8. We leave it to the reader to carry it out for himself.

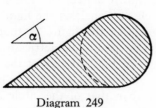

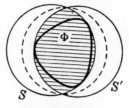

Diagram 249   Diagram 250

6-1. Prove that a plane figure Φ cannot have two distinct circum-circles. Moreover prove that of necessity the circumcircle of a plane figure Φ contains two boundary points of Φ which are the ends of a diameter of the circle, or else it contains three boundary points of Φ which form an acute-angled triangle. Deduce from this that if Φ has diameter 1, then the radius R of the circumcircle of Φ satisfies the inequalities

$$0.5 \le R \le 1/\sqrt{3} = 0.577\ldots.$$

A figure Φ cannot have two different circumcircles. If Φ is contained in both of two circles S and S' with the same radius R, then Φ lies in the two-angled curvilinear figure (shaded in Diagram 250) which is the intersection of the circular regions S and S'; hence Φ also lies within the circle which circumscribes this two-angled figure. This latter circular region has, however, a smaller radius than the circles S and S', so that neither of the circles S and S' is circumscribed about the figure Φ.

Moreover, if S encloses the plane figure Φ and passes through no boundary point of Φ, then there is a circle of smaller radius which also encloses Φ. To obtain this circle, we decrease the radius of the circle S without changing its center until the shrinking circle touches the boundary of the figure Φ at some point A (Diagram 251 a).

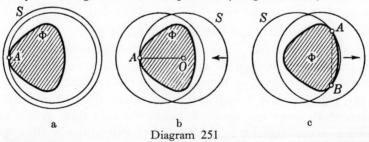

a   b   c

Diagram 251

If the circle S, which encloses the figure Φ, touches the figure at only one boundary point A, then there is a circle of smaller radius which encompasses Φ. To prove this, we displace the circle S in the direction of the radius OA (where O is the center of the circle S) so that the point A lies within the circle (Diagram 251 b). We thus obtain a circle with the same radius as S which encloses Φ and touches no boundary point of Φ. By what was shown above, the radius of this circle can be decreased so that the circle still encloses the figure Φ.

Finally if the circle S which encloses the figure Φ touches the figure at two boundary points A and B that are not diametrically opposite points of the circle S, and if the larger of the two arcs of the circle S through the points A and B contains no other points of the figure Φ, then there is a circle with radius less than that of the circle S which also encloses the figure Φ. To prove this, we displace the circle S in the direction perpendicular to the chord AB so that the points A and B are within the circle (Diagram 251 c). Thus we again obtain a circle of the same radius as the circle S which contains the figure Φ but passes through no boundary point of the figure. The radius of this circle can be decreased so that the figure Φ still lies within the diminished circle.

The smallest of all circles containing Φ must therefore necessarily pass through two diametrically opposite points (Diagram 252 a), or it must pass through three points of the figure Φ such that the circular arc between any two of these three points which does not contain the third is not greater than a semicircle; that is, the three points form an acute-angled triangle (Diagram 252 a).

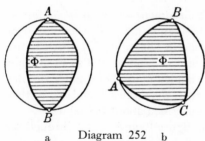

a   Diagram 252   b

It follows at once that the radius R of the circumcircle S of the figure Φ with diameter 1 lies within the boundaries established in the statement of the exercise. In fact, the greatest distance between points of the figure Φ is $2R$, since Φ is enclosed in the circle S of radius R. Since the diameter of the figure is 1, it follows that $2R \geq 1$ and hence $R \geq 1/2$. It only remains to prove that $R \leq 1/\sqrt{3}$.

If the circumcircle passes through two diametrically opposite points of the figure Φ, then the radius R of the circle cannot exceed $1/2$, since the distance between these points is not greater than 1. In this case the radius R is $1/2$ and is thus less than $1/\sqrt{3}$. If the circle S circumscribed about the figure Φ passes through three points of Φ, forming an acute-angled triangle ABC, then at least one of the angles α of this triangle is not less than 60° (the sum of the three angles of the triangle is 180°). The sine of this angle is then not less than $\sqrt{3}/2$, and since the side a opposite this angle is not greater than 1, the diameter $2R = a/\sin \alpha$ of the circumcircle S of the triangle ABC is not greater than $2/\sqrt{3}$.

Note. Both bounds for the radius of the circumcircle which we obtained in this exercise are attained, as is shown by the example of a rectangle on the one hand and an equilateral triangle on the other.

6-2. Prove that a circle inscribed in a convex figure Φ must either contain two boundary points of Φ which are ends of a diameter of the circle, or else it contains three boundary points of Φ which form an acute-angled triangle; in the latter case there is a unique circle inscribed in Φ. Prove also that the radius r of a circle inscribed in a convex figure of width 1 satisfies the inequalities $1/3 \leq r \leq 1/2$.

The solution is very similar to that of Exercise 6-1. If a circle S which is entirely enclosed in a convex figure Φ contains no boundary points of Φ, then there is another circle S' enclosed in Φ whose radius is greater than that of S. To find this circle, we enlarge the radius of S without changing the center until the increasing circle touches the boundary of Φ in some point A (Diagram 253 a).

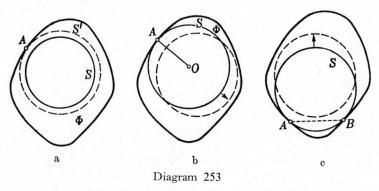

a   b   c

Diagram 253

If a circle S enclosed in a convex figure Φ contains just one boundary point A of the figure Φ, there is a circle enclosed in the figure Φ whose radius is greater than that of S. To prove this, we displace the circle S in the direction of the radius OA (where O is the center of S) so that the point A passes outside the circle (Diagram 253 b). Thus we obtain a circle with the same radius as S which lies inside Φ and does not touch the boundary of Φ. By what was shown above, the radius of the circle can be increased so that the enlarged circle remains inside Φ.

Finally, if a circle S enclosed in the figure Φ contains two boundary points A and B of Φ such that the arc $AB > 180°$ contains no other boundary point of Φ, then there is a circle contained in Φ with radius greater than that of S. We displace S perpendicular to the chord AB so that the points A and B pass outside the circle (Diagram 253 c).

Then we obtain a circle with the same radius as S which is enclosed in Φ and contains no boundary point of Φ. We can increase the radius of this circle so that the larger circle remains inside Φ.

Therefore the largest circle contained in Φ must either pass through two diametrically opposite boundary points of Φ (Diagram 254 a) or through three boundary points of Φ such that any arc of the circle between two of them always contains the third if it is greater than a semi-circle; that is, the three points form an acute-angled triangle (Diagram 254 b).

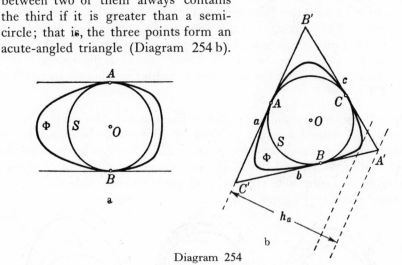

Diagram 254

Now it is easy to conclude that for a convex figure of width 1 the radius r of an inscribed circle lies within the bounds given in the statement of the exercise. Since the circle S is inside Φ and hence lies inside every strip formed by a pair of parallel supporting lines of the figure, the diameter of S cannot exceed 1, and hence the radius r of the circle S cannot exceed $1/2$. Hence we need only show that r cannot be less than $1/3$.

If a circle S inscribed in a convex figure Φ touches the boundary of the figure at a point A, then the supporting line of the figure at A must also be a supporting line of the circle S. Since only one supporting line can be passed through a boundary point of a circle, it follows that the figure Φ can have only one supporting line at A tangent to the circle (that is, the point A cannot be a corner point of the figure Φ). Hence, if an inscribed circle S passes through diametrically opposite boundary points A and B of the figure Φ, then the radius of S is $1/2$ the distance between the parallel supporting lines of Φ at A and B respectively; the radius can therefore not be less than $1/2$ and must in this case equal $1/2$ (Diagram 254 a).

If an inscribed circle S passes through three boundary points A, B, and C of the figure Φ which form an acute-angled triangle, then the supporting lines if the figure Φ at A, B, C must form a triangle $A'B'C'$

which is circumscribed about both the figure Φ and the circle S (Diagram 254 b). We denote the sides of this triangle by a, b, c (a being the largest side) and the corresponding altitudes by h_a, h_b, h_c. The area of the triangle $A'B'C'$ is equal on the one hand to $(a + b + c)r/2$, and on the other to $ah_a/2$. Since $a \geq b$, $a \geq c$, it follows from the equality

$$\frac{(a + b + c)r}{2} = \frac{a}{2} \cdot h_a$$

that

$$h_a = \left(1 + \frac{b}{a} + \frac{c}{a}\right) \cdot r \leq 3r,$$

and thus

$$r \geq \frac{1}{3} h_a.$$

The altitude h_a of the triangle $A'B'C'$ cannot be less than the width of Φ (Diagram 254 b), from which it follows that $r \geq 1/3$, as we wished to show.

If a circle S inscribed in the convex figure Φ passes through three boundary points of Φ which form an acute-angled triangle, then there is a triangle $A'B'C'$ which is circumscribed about both the figure Φ and the circle S. It follows that in this case the inscribed circle S is unique, since every other circle in Φ must also be contained in the triangle $A'B'C'$ and is therefore smaller than the circle S inscribed in the triangle $A'B'C'$. However, if the inscribed circle touches the boundary of Φ in two diametrically opposite points, then the circle need not be unique (see Diagram 77, page 59).

> *Note.* The two bounds for the value of the radius of an inscribed circle of a convex figure of width 1 are attained, as is shown by the example of a rectangle on the one hand and an equilateral triangle on the other. From the solution of the exercise it is easy to see that the equilateral triangle is the sole convex figure for which the radius of the inscribed circle is $\frac{1}{3}$ the width of the figure.

6-3. Prove that if Φ is a convex figure with center O and centralness coefficient λ, then at least three chords, A_1B_1, A_2B_2, A_3B_3, through O have the property that $A_1O/OB_1 = A_2O/OB_2 = A_3O/OB_3 = \lambda$. Deduce from this that the centralness coefficient of a convex figure cannot be less than $1/2$.

Let Φ be a convex figure with center O and centralness coefficient λ. Each chord AB of the figure Φ which passes through the point O is divided by this point in the ratio AO/OB, which is not smaller than λ. In other words, we have $OA \geq \lambda \cdot OB$. If we lay off on the segment OA

the segment $OA' = \lambda \cdot OB$, then the point A' also belongs to the figure Φ (Diagram 255). The set of all such points A' which can be marked on chords AB through O forms the boundary of a certain figure Φ' which is similar to the figure Φ in the ratio λ, with the center of similitude at the point O (see translators' note, page 111). The figure Φ' is enclosed by the figure Φ and must touch its boundary, since there

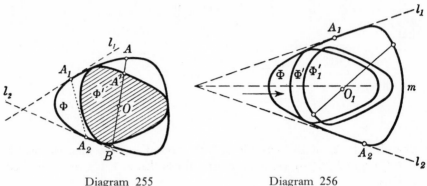

Diagram 255   Diagram 256

exist chords of the figure Φ passing through the point O which are divided at the point O in a ratio AO/OB exactly equal to λ.

Now let A_1mA_2 be any arc of the boundary curve of Φ which contains no points of the figure Φ'. We assert that the supporting lines of the figure Φ passing through the points A_1 and A_2 (these supporting lines need not be unique) intersect in a point lying on the same side of the chord A_1A_2 as the arc A_1mA_2 (in case these lines are not parallel).

We shall assume the contrary, and hence that the case shown in Diagram 256 arises. Then we can displace the figure Φ' parallel to the angle bisector between the lines l_1 and l_2 by a small amount so that the resulting figure Φ_1' is contained in Φ and has no boundary point in common with Φ. We shall denote the center of similitude of the figures Φ and Φ_2' by O_1 (we readily see that the figures Φ and Φ_1' are, indeed, in a position of similarity).[†] Since the ratio of similitude of Φ and Φ_1' is λ and the figure Φ_1' lies entirely inside of Φ and does not touch the boundary of Φ, all chords of Φ passing through O must necessarily be divided at the point O in a ratio greater than λ. This contradicts the fact that the point O is the center of Φ.

We denote the boundary of Φ by K and the boundary of Φ' by K'. If some arc of the curve K does not touch the curve K', then, as we readily discover, the supporting lines of the curve K at the end points of this arc necessarily intersect on the same side of the chord (belonging

---

[†] We readily prove that two similar figures are in a position of similarity (have a center of similarity) if corresponding segments of these figures are parallel. From this it also follows that the figures Φ and Φ_1' are in a position of similarity.

to the arc) as that on which the arc itself lies. This can occur only in the following cases: a) the boundary of the figure Φ contains three points of Φ', A_1, A_2, and A_3, such that the supporting lines l_1, l_2, and l_3 at these points form a triangle circumscribed about the figure Φ; b) the boundary of Φ contains two points A and B such that the supporting lines l_1 and l_2 of Φ at these points are parallel. As we easily prove, the latter case can only occur when the centralness coefficient of Φ is 1; that is, when Φ is centrally symmetric (and Φ coincides with Φ'). We leave it to the reader to carry out for himself this simple proof.

We now consider the first case. Let A_1, A_2, and A_3 be three common points of the boundary of Φ with the boundary of Φ'; that is, let A_1B_1, A_2B_2, and A_3B_3 be three chords of the figure Φ passing through the point O such that $A_1O/OB_1 = A_2O/OB_2 = A_3O/OB_3 = \lambda$. Since the supporting lines l_1, l_2, and l_3 at the points A_1, A_2, and A_3 form a triangle circumscribed about the figure Φ, we can easily see that the point O lies within the triangle $A_1A_2A_3$.

Let us assume that this is not the case. If the point O lies on the side A_1A_2 of the triangle $A_1A_2A_3$, then $A_1O/OA_2 = A_2O/OA_1 = \lambda$; hence, we have $\lambda = 1/\lambda$, $\lambda = 1$, and the figure Φ is centrally symmetric. Assume next that the point O lies outside the triangle $A_1A_2A_3$ and therefore within one of the three triangles obtained from the triangle with sides l_1, l_2, and l_3 by removing the triangle $A_1A_2A_3$. Suppose that the point O lies in that one of these three triangles (we designate it by T) which borders on the side A_1A_2 (the triangle T is shaded in Diagram 257 a). We denote the intersection of the lines A_1O and l_2 by D_1 and the intersection of the lines A_2O and l_1 by D_2. Then we have

$$A_1O/OB_1 \geq A_1O/OD_1$$

and

$$A_2O/OB_2 \geq A_2O/OD_2.$$

a   Diagram 257   b

At least one of the ratios A_1O/OD_1 and A_2O/OD_2 is greater than 1 (otherwise there would be a parallelogram within the triangle T with side A_1A_2 and center O, and the lines l_1 and l_2 could not intersect on the side of A_1A_2 on which the arc A_1A_2 lies; see Diagram 257 b). Suppose that $A_1O/OD_1 > 1$. Then we would have $\lambda = A_1O/OB_1 \geq A_1O/OD_1 > 1$, which is not possible, however, since for $\lambda > 1$ the figure Φ' would not be completely enclosed in Φ.

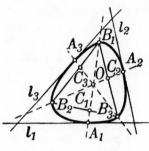

Diagram 258

Therefore O lies in the triangle $A_1A_2A_3$. Hence the points A_1, B_3, A_2, B_1, A_3, B_2 occur in cyclic succession on the boundary of Φ, and the point O also lies inside the triangle $B_1B_2B_3$ (Diagram 258). From this we can show that $\lambda \geq 1/2$.

To obtain this result, denote the intersections of the lines A_1B_1, A_2B_2, and A_3B_3 with the sides of the triangle $B_1B_2B_3$ by C_1, C_2, and C_3 respectively. Then we have

$$B_1O/OC_1 \geq B_1O/OA_1 = 1/\lambda, \qquad B_2O/OC_2 \geq 1/\lambda, \qquad B_3O/OC_3 > 1/\lambda;$$

from this it follows that

$$B_1C_1/OC_1 = (B_1O + OC_1)/OC_1 \geq 1 + (1/\lambda) = (1 + \lambda)/\lambda,$$
$$OC_1/B_1C_1 \leq \lambda/(\lambda + 1);$$

similarly

$$OC_2/B_2C_2 \leq \lambda/(1 + \lambda), \qquad OC_3/B_3C_3 \leq \lambda/(1 + \lambda).$$

However, we have

$$(OC_1/B_1C_1) + (OC_2/B_2C_2) + (OC_3/B_3C_3) = [S(\triangle OB_2B_3)/S(\triangle B_1B_2B_3)]$$
$$+ [S(\triangle OB_3B_1)/S(\triangle B_2B_3B_1)] + [S(\triangle OB_1B_2)/(S(\triangle B_3B_1B_2)]$$
$$= [S(\triangle OB_2B_3) + S(\triangle OB_3B_1) + S(\triangle OB_1B_2)]/S(\triangle B_1B_2B_3) = 1.$$

Hence we obtain

$$3 \cdot \lambda/(1 + \lambda) \geq 1, \qquad 3\lambda \geq 1 + \lambda, \qquad 2\lambda \geq 1$$

and finally

$$\lambda \geq 1/2.$$

Note. It is easy to see from the foregoing that the centralness coefficient of the figure Φ is $1/2$ if and only if Φ is a triangle.

6-4. Prove that of all convex curves of width 1, the equilateral triangle with altitude 1 has the smallest area.

We first note that, in view of Exercise 6-2, the radius r of a circle S inscribed in a figure Φ of width 1 cannot be greater than $1/2$ or less than $1/3$.

If $r = 1/2$, then the area of the figure Φ certainly cannot be less than $\pi(1/2)^2 = \pi/4 = 0.78 \ldots$, and is therefore greater than $\sqrt{3}/3 = 0.57 \ldots$, which is the area of an equilateral triangle with altitude 1. If $r = 1/3$, then Φ is an equilateral triangle with altitude 1.

Now let the radius of the circle S inscribed in the figure be r (where $1/3 \leq r \leq 1/2$). Then there is a triangle T circumscribed about both the figure Φ and the circle S (see the solution of Exercise 6-2, Diagram 254 b). We now draw three supporting lines to the figure Φ, parallel to the sides of the triangle T; we denote by A', B', and C' the points of contact of these supporting lines with the boundary of Φ (arbitrary points of contact if the line has an entire segment in common with Φ; Diagram 259). We denote the center of the circle S by O.

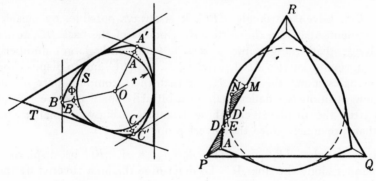

Diagram 259   Diagram 260

Since the distance between a pair of parallel supporting lines of the figure cannot be less than 1 and since the point O is at distance r from each side of the triangle, the distance of each of the points A', B', C' from the point O is at least $1 - r$. On the segments OA', OB', and OC' we determine points A, B, and C at distance $1 - r$ from O. If we draw tangents to the circle S at the points A, B, and C, we obtain a figure Φ_r which consists of a circle of radius r and mutually equal parts bounded by the circle and by two tangents to the circle (Diagram 259). This figure lies inside our figure Φ. If $r = 1/3$, then $\Phi_r = \Phi_{1/3}$ is an equilateral triangle of altitude 1.

We need only show that of all figures Φ_r, corresponding to different values of r $(1/3 \leq r < 1/2)$, the equilateral triangle $\Phi_{1/3}$ has the smallest area. In Diagram 260 there is an equilateral triangle PQR and a figure Φ_r

$(1/3 < r < 1/2)$. It is easy to see that the entire area of the parts of the equilateral triangle which extend beyond the boundary of the figure Φ_r is less than the area of the parts of Φ_r lying outside the triangle $\Phi_{1/3}$. The parts of the triangle outside the figure Φ_r consists of six triangles like the shaded triangle APD in Diagram 260. Let M be the midpoint of the side PR of the triangle PQR. From the point M we draw a segment MN parallel to and having the same length as PA. The point N is inside the circle that forms part of the figure Φ_r, since the smallest distance from the point M to the circle in a direction perpendicular to PR is PA (this also follows from the fact that the greatest distance from A to any point of the circle is the same as the altitude of the triangle and is therefore 1). We join N to A. Let NA cut the side PR in the point E. The triangle MNE is congruent to the triangle EAP. However, the triangle DAP forms only a part of the triangle EAP. Thus we can bring the triangle DAP within MNE, that is, within Φ_r (the new position of the triangle DAP is also shaded in Diagram 260). If in this manner we bring all six triangles like DAP inside Φ_r, we can see that the equilateral triangle $\Phi_{1/3}$ has a smaller area than Φ_r. This completes the proof.

6-5. Given a triangle ABC, it is always possible, by means of segments that join the vertex B to points of the base AC, to subdivide that triangle into a certain (sufficiently large) number of congruent triangles ABA_1, A_1BA_2, ..., $A_{n-1}BC$, and to displace these triangles along the line AC so that their common part in their new position is smaller than an arbitrarily small positive number. (After the displacement these triangles occupy a smaller space than previously since they overlap one another.)

Let the triangles ABA_1, A_1BA_2, A_2BA_3, ..., $A_{n-1}BC$ be displaced in any manner along the line AC. To determine the area covered by these triangles in their new positions, we draw through each point of intersection of the sides of any pair of triangles a line parallel to the common base AC. In this way we divide the set of all our triangles into a sequence of smaller triangles and trapezoids. The area of a triangle as well as

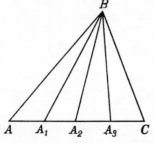
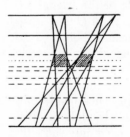

Diagram 261

that of a trapezoid is equal to the product of the midline and the altitude; hence the total area of all triangles and trapezoids lying between a consecutive pair of the constructed parallels is equal to the product of the width of the strip and the sum of the lengths of all the segments which the triangles cut out of the midline of the strip (that is, which are cut out of the line parallel to AC and equidistant from the boundary lines of the strip; see Diagram 261).

Therefore if we can insure that the total length of the segments cut out by the triangles ABA_1, A_1BA_2, ..., $A_{n-1}BC$ from each parallel to AC is less than σ/h, where h is the altitude of triangle ABC, then certainly the total area covered by all the triangles will be less than σ. In this case the area of the parts of the triangles enclosed between the ith and $(i + 1)$st parallels is less than $(\sigma/h) \cdot h_i$, where h_i is the distance between the ith and $(i + 1)$st parallel; the total area covered by all the triangles is then less than

$$(\sigma/h)(h_1 + h_2 + ...) = (\sigma/h) \cdot h = \sigma.$$

We now suppose that $n = 2^m$, where m is a sufficiently large integer, and displace the triangles ABA_1, A_1BA_2, ..., $A_{2^m-1}BC$ one after the other along the line AC as follows. We divide the altitude of triangle ABC into $m + 2$ equal parts, and through the points of division we draw lines l_0, l_1, ..., l_m parallel to AC (l_0 lies nearest to vertex B; l_1 is the immediate successor to l_0, etc.; Diagram 262 a). Each of these lines intersects all the triangles ABA_1, A_1BA_2, ..., $A_{2^m-1}BC$ in segments of equal length (since the triangles all have equal bases). We combine our 2^m triangles into 2^{m-1} pairs: $\{ABA_1, A_1BA_2\}$, $\{A_2BA_3, A_3BA_4\}$, ..., $\{A_{2^m-2}BA_{2^m-1}, A_{2^m-1}BC\}$ and displace the triangles so that different pairs do not cover each other, but in each pair the two triangles intersect in such a way that the segments in which these triangles intersect the line l_1 coincide (Diagram 262 b). Thus each parallel to AC nearer to AC than l_1 intersects each pair of displaced triangles in two segments with a common part whose length equals the length of the intersection of any one of the triangles with l_1 (we note that the two triangles of a pair have a pair of parallel lateral sides; these sides result from a lateral slit in the triangle ABC). It is thus obvious that the line l_1 cuts the displaced triangles in segments whose sum is half the length of the segment in which l_1 cuts triangle ABC; that is, $(1/2) \cdot 2a/(m+2) = a/(m + 2)$, where a is the length of the base AC of the triangle ABC. The displaced triangles now cut segments from each line, parallel to AC and nearer to AC than l_1, whose total length is less than the length of the intersection of such a line with the original triangle by the amount $a/(m + 2)$. Now we group the 2^{m-1} pairs of triangles together by pairing the first pair with the second pair, the third with the fourth, and so on until pair number $(2^{m-1} - 1)$ is grouped with pair number 2^{m-1}. In each quadruple of triangles we displace the individual pairs of triangles so that they coincide in the segments which were cut out of the pairs by the line l_2 (Diagram 262 c). It is easy to see that in the first displacement, the

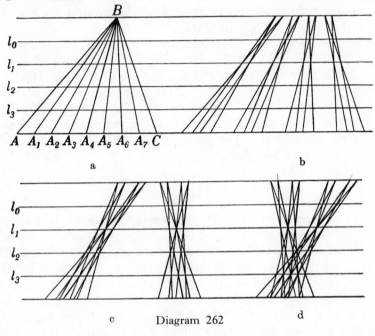

Diagram 262

paired triangles were all cut by l_2 in segments of the same length; for before any displacement, each two adjacent triangles regarded as a unit were cut by l_2 in segments of the same length [equal to $2 \cdot [3/(m+2)]$ $\cdot (a/2^m)]$. After the first displacement, the length of all these segments was decreased by the same amount (namely, by $2 \cdot [a/(m+2)] \cdot (1/2^m)$. The line l_2 cut the 2^{m-1} pairs of triangles in segments whose total length was equal to

$$\frac{3a}{m+2} - \frac{a}{m+2} = \frac{2a}{m+2};$$

the line l_2 cuts the displaced pairs in segments whose total length equals $1/2 \cdot 2a/(m + 2) = a/(m + 2)$. Thus, at the second stage, each of our parallels nearer than l_2 to AC is cut by the quadruples of triangles in segments whose total length is less by $a/(m + 2)$ than the total length of the segments in which this line was cut by the first 2^{m-1} pairs of triangles (note that each two neighboring pairs of displaced triangles likewise have pairs of parallel sides which arise by a cut across the triangle ABC). Hence after the second displacement, on each line parallel to AC and nearer to it than l_2, our 2^m triangles cut out segments whose total length is smaller by

$$\frac{a}{m+2} + \frac{a}{m+2} = \frac{2a}{m+2}$$

than the length of the segment this line cut from the original triangle ABC.

Now we combine the 2^{m-2} quadruples of triangles into 2^{m-3} pairs of quadruples and displace the two quadruples of each pair so that they intersect in the segment which was cut out of these quadruples by l_3 (Diagram 262 d). As before, we can establish that at stage two all quadruples cut out of l_3 segments of the same length. Before the displacement, the 2^{m-2} quadruples cut out of l_3 segments with total length $[4a/(m+2)] - [2a/(m+2)] = 2a/(m+2)$; after the displacement they cut out of l_3 a segment of length $1/2 \cdot 2a/(m+2) = a/(m+2)$. Each of the parallels nearer to AC than l_3 cuts the displaced quadruples in segments whose total length is smaller by $a/(m+2)$ than the total length of the segments in which this line cut the undisplaced quadruples of triangles. Thus, after the third displacement, the triangles cut segments out of every parallel nearer to AC than l_3 whose total length is less by

$$\frac{2a}{m+2} + \frac{a}{m+2} = \frac{3a}{m+2}$$

than the length of the intersection of this line with the triangle ABC. Now we group the 2^{m-3} octuples of triangles into 2^{m-4} pairs of octuples and displace each pair of octuples so that they coincide on the segment in which they were cut by the line l_4. We continue this process; at the last step we displace two sets of 2^{m-1} triangles so that they coincide in the segment in which they were cut by the line l_m at the previous stage.

Now we estimate the total length of all the segments which the triangles in their final position cut out of any line l parallel to AC. If l is nearer than l_1 to the vertices of the triangle, then the total length of all segments cut from it by the triangles is less than the length of the segment which is cut from it by the original triangle ABG, that is less than $2a/(m+2)$ (the length of the segment cut out of l_1 by triangle ABC). If l lies between l_1 and l_2, then initially the triangle ABC cut from it a segment of length less than the length $3a/(m+2)$ of the segment cut from l_2. After the first displacement, the sum of segments cut out on any parallel below l_1 was less by $a/(m+2)$ than the length of the segment that line cut from triangle ABC. At the first stage, then, the segments cut from l had length less than $[3a/(m+2)] - [a/(m+2)] = 2a/(m+2)$, and further displacements did not increase this total length.

If l lies between l_2 and l_3, then initially the triangle ABC cut from it a segment of length less than the length $4a/(m+2)$ which it cut from l_3. But after two displacements, the sum of the segments cut out on any parallel below l_2 was decreased by $2a/(m+2)$, so at the second stage the segments cut out of l had a total length less than $[4a/(m+2)] - [2a/(m+2)] = 2a/(m+2)$, and further displacements did not increase this total length. In this manner, we show that the length of the segment cut out of the line l parallel to AC by the displaced triangles does not exceed $2a/(m+2)$.[†] Thus it follows that the total area occupied by all 2^m triangles after the completed displacements does not exceed $2ah/(m+2) = 4S/(m+2)$, where S is the area of the triangle ABC.[§] Hence this area can be made smaller than an arbitrary, preassigned number σ (for this purpose one need only take the number m sufficiently large). This completes the proof.

6-6. Theorem of A. S. Besikovitch. Prove that a (nonconvex) plane figure of arbitrarily small area exists within which a segment of length 1 can be rotated through 360°.

Using Exercise 6-5, we can now easily construct a figure whose area is less than an arbitrarily small number σ and in which a segment of length 1 can be rotated through 360°. Let ABC be any triangle for which the radius of the inscribed circle is 1. We join the center O of this inscribed circle to the vertices of the triangle and consider the triangles AOB, BOC, and COA (Diagram 263). According to Exercise 6-5, we can

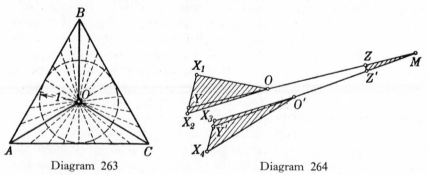

Diagram 263   Diagram 264

decompose each of these triangles into subtriangles by means of lines through O and then displace the pieces obtained so that the total area which the displaced triangles occupy is arbitrarily small. We carry out this construction in such a way that the space occupied by all triangles

---

[†] The rigorous proof of this fact can easily be carried out by means of induction.

[§] It can be proved that the area occupied by all the triangles ABA_1, A_1BA_2, ... $A_{2^{m}-1}BC$ after displacement equals $S/(m+2)$. However, we do not need this result.

(which result from the decomposition of the three triangles AOB, BOC, and COA) is not greater than $\sigma/2$. The triangles AOB, BOC, and COA each contain a segment of length 1 which can be turned in its triangle through an angle equal to $\sphericalangle AOB$, $\sphericalangle BOC$, $\sphericalangle COA$ respectively, since in each of these triangles there is a sector of the inscribed circle (with radius 1) whose center lies at vertex O.

Now let X_1OX_2 and $X_3O'X_4$ be two triangles from the decomposition of triangle ABC which were adjacent prior to their displacement; that is, which possessed a common side (for easier visualization, these triangles are shown displaced in Diagram 264 in such a way that they do not overlap, which in reality would not occur). Here the sides OX_2 and $O'X_3$, which arise by intersection with the triangle ABC, are parallel to one another. We draw the lines OY and $O'Y'$ in our triangles which form small angles with the sides OX_2 and $O'X_3$ respectively, and prolong these sides until they intersect in a point M. At the point M we construct a sector MZZ' of radius 1 with central angle OMO' (Diagram 264; in this diagram the sector does not cut the triangles X_1OX_2 and $X_3O'X_4$ which is, in reality, impossible).

At O we can rotate a segment of length 1 from a position on the line OX_1 into a position on the line OY and then displace it on the line YM into the position ZM, rotate it into the position $Z'M$, displace it on the line MY' so that it lies inside the triangle $X_3O'X_4$, and then rotate it into the position $O'X_4$.

If we now carry out the construction thus described for each pair of neighboring triangles in the decomposition of the triangle ABC, then in this manner we can turn a segment of length 1 through 360° within the figure formed from all triangles into which the triangle ABC is decomposed and from the lines of the form OM and MO' and from sectors of the form ZMZ' (Diagram 264). The area of each sector which is added to the figure can be made arbitrarily small (since we can make the central angle of the sector arbitrarily small). The added lines which we have also considered to be part of the figure have the area zero (we can replace these lines by strips of arbitrarily small width).

If the triangles in the decomposition of triangle ABC occupy an area less than $\sigma/2$ in their displaced positions (from Exercise 6-5 this is possible, however small σ may be), and the lines and sectors (strips and sectors respectively) are made to have a total area smaller than $\sigma/2$, then a figure of area less than σ is obtained in which a unit segment can be turned through 360°.

6-7. Prove that a triangle has a smaller area than any other convex figure with the same diameter and the same width.

Let Φ be a convex figure of diameter D and width Δ. We will prove that the area of Φ is not less than the area of a triangle with base D and altitude Δ, that is, $D\Delta/2$.

Let A and B be two boundary points of Φ at a maximal distance apart (that is, D). At A and B respectively we draw two supporting lines l_1 and l_2 perpendicular to AB (see Exercises 1-6 and 1-7); we draw two other supporting lines m_1 and m_2 perpendicular to l_1 and l_2 (parallel to AB; Diagram 265 a). According to the definition of the width of a

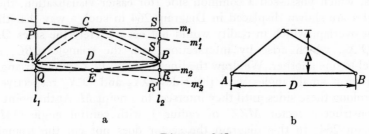

a   b

Diagram 265

convex figure, the distance between m_1 and m_2 cannot be less than Δ; hence the area of the rectangle $PQRS$ formed by the lines l_1, m_1, l_2, and m_2 is not less than $D\Delta$.

Let C be the point of contact of the line m_1 (of the side PS of the rectangle $PQRS$) with the figure Φ and E be the point of contact of the line m_2 with Φ. Since Φ is convex, it must contain the quadrilateral $BCAE$. The area of the triangle ABC is half the area of the rectangle $ABSP$, and the area of the triangle ABE is half the area of the rectangle $AQRB$. Hence the area of $BCAE$ is half the area of the rectangle $PQRS$ and thus cannot be less than $D\Delta/2$; hence the area of Φ cannot be less than $D\Delta/2$.

From this solution we see readily that the area of Φ is $D\Delta/2$ only if Φ is a triangle. Since a figure Φ of area $D\Delta/2$ must coincide with the quadrilateral $BCAE$ (Diagram 265 a), the diagonal AB must equal the diameter D of the quadrilateral $BCAE$ and the distance between the lines m_1 and m_2 must equal the width Δ. This can occur only if the segment AB coincides with one of the sides PS or QR of the rectangle $PQRS$. Otherwise it would always be possible to draw supporting lines m_1' and m_2' of the quadrilateral $BCAE$ at C and E respectively whose distance from each other was less than the distance between m_1 and m_2 (Diagram 265 a; if $CS \geq ER$, then $SS' \geq RR'$, $S'R' \leq SR$ and hence the distance between m_1' and m_2' is less than SR).

The area of a convex figure can therefore be $D\Delta/2$ only if the figure is a triangle with base D and altitude Δ (Diagram 265 b).

6-8. Prove that an isosceles triangle, each of whose equal sides is not less than its base, has an area which does not exceed that of any other convex figure of (a) the same perimeter and diameter; (b) the same perimeter and width.

(a) For any convex figure Φ of diameter D and perimeter L, we can always find a polygon whose diameter, perimeter, and area approximate those of Φ as closely as is desired.[†] Therefore we need only prove that an isosceles triangle T with perimeter L and diameter D equal to the length of its equal lateral sides[§] has a smaller area than any other convex polygon of the same perimeter L and diameter D. This will prove that no convex figure of diameter D and perimeter L has smaller area than the triangle T.[¶]

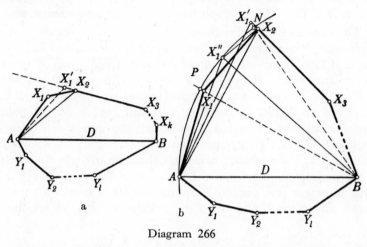

Diagram 266

Thus let M be a convex polygon of diameter D and perimeter L. We will show that the area of this polygon is greater than that of the triangle T. Let A and B be two points of M at distance D (it is obvious that A and B must be vertices of M); let $AX_1X_2 ... X_kB$ and $AY_1Y_2 ... Y_lB$ be the two polygons into which the segment AB divides M (Diagram 266 a). Since D is the diameter of M, none of the segments $BX_1, BX_2, ..., BX_k, BY_1, BY_2, ..., BY_l$ can exceed D.

[†] This property holds, for example, for a polygon inscribed in Φ and having sufficiently small sides, or for a polygon circumscribed about Φ, all of whose exterior angles are sufficiently small.

[§] A lateral side of T is thus not less in length than its base (it is clear that the diameter D of a triangle is its greatest side).

[¶] We can even prove that every other convex figure Φ with diameter D and circumference L has an area greater (and not merely not less) than that of the triangle T. We shall not give the proof.

Suppose that the diagonal BX_1 of the polygon $AX_1X_2 \ldots X_kB$ is less than D (if it were equal to D, we would replace AB by BX_1 and then consider the polygon $X_1X_2 \ldots X_kB$ in place of $AX_1X_2 \ldots X_kB$). Consider the triangle AX_1X_2. Suppose that $AX_1 \geq X_1X_2$; that is, $\angle X_1X_2A \geq \angle X_1AX_2$ (the rest of the construction would scarcely be altered if we had $\angle X_1X_2A < \angle X_1AX_2$; in this case we would make AX_1 a prolongation of the side Y_1A). We construct a triangle $AX_1'X_2$ so that its perimeter equals that of triangle AX_1X_2 and its side X_2X_1' is a prolongation of the side X_3X_2 (Diagram 266 a). By Exercise 5-1, the triangle AX_1X_2 has greater area than triangle $AX_1'X_2$. If the distance from X_1' to B does not exceed D, we replace the triangle X_2X_1A by the triangle $X_2X_1'A$ and in place of the polygon $AX_1X_2 \ldots X_kB$ we consider the polygon $AX_1'X_3 \ldots X_kB$, which has fewer sides and smaller area.

The case in which the distance from B to X_1' exceeds D is more complicated. We cannot as before replace the triangle AX_1X_2 by the triangle $AX_1'X_2$, since the resulting polygon $AX_1'X_3 \ldots X_kB$ has a diameter greater than D. Hence we draw a circle with radius D and center B. Let P and N be the points of intersection of this circle with BX_1 and BX_1' (Diagram 266 b). Since $BX_1 < D$ and $BX_1' > D$, the point X_1 lies on the segment BP and X_1' lies on the extension of BN. Hence the triangle APX_2 has a greater perimeter than triangle AX_1X_2, while the triangle ANX_2 has a smaller perimeter than the triangle AX_1X_2 (recall that the perimeters of triangles AX_1X_2 and $AX_1'X_2$ are equal). A continuity argument (see Section 3) shows that there must be a point X_1'' between the points P and N on the circular arc PN for which

$$AX_1'' + X_1''X_2 = AX_1 + X_1X_2.$$

Now replace the triangle AX_1X_2 by the triangle $AX_1''X_2$. The segment BX_1'' is equal to D. From now on, we consider BX_1'' in place of AB and in place of the polygon $AX_1X_2 \ldots X_kB$, the polygon $X_1''X_2X_3 \ldots X_kB$ with fewer sides.

If we now treat $AX_1''X_2 \ldots X_kB$ or $X_1''X_2X_3 \ldots X_kB$ in the same manner as we dealt with $AX_1X_2 \ldots X_kB$, we finally replace it by $AX_1''X_2'' \ldots X_{k_1}''B$ ($k_1 \leq k$), which has the same perimeter and smaller area, where

$$BA = BX_1'' = BX_2'' = \ldots = BX_{k_1}''.$$

Likewise we can replace $AY_1Y_2 \ldots Y_lB$ by a polygon $AY_1''Y_2'' \ldots Y_{l_1}''B$ ($l_1 \leq l$) of equal perimeter and smaller area such that

$$BA = BY_1'' = BY_2'' = \ldots = BY_{l_1}''.$$

Thus we obtain finally a polygon

$$AX_1''X_2'' \dots X_{k_1}''BY_{l_1}'' \dots Y_2''Y_1''$$

with perimeter L equal to that of the polygon M and with area less than the area of M. Denote this polygon by M_1.

We now need merely to compare the area of M_1 with that of the triangle T (Diagram 267). The polygon M_1 is subdivided into a number of

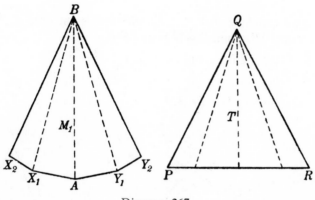

Diagram 267

isosceles triangles $BY_{l_1}Y_{l_1-1}$, $BY_{l_1-1}Y_{l-2}$, ..., BY_1A, BAX_1, BX_1X_2, ..., $BX_{k_1-1}X_{k_1}$, whose lateral sides equal D. The sum of the bases of all these triangles equals the base of T, since the perimeters of M_1 and T are equal. Hence each of these triangles has an altitude at least as large as that of triangle T (it is evident that when two isosceles triangles have equal lateral sides the triangle with the greater base has the smaller altitude). By means of lines through the vertex where the equal sides meet, we divide the triangle T into the same number of triangles as in the case of M_1 and with bases equal to the bases of the corresponding triangles of M_1. We conclude that the area of triangle T does not exceed the area of M_1. Hence the area of T does not exceed that of M. This complete the proof.

(b) The statement of Exercise 6-8 b is closely related to that of 6-8 a, and we can solve it with the method used to solve 6-8 a. However in this case the reasoning is significantly more difficult (transforming a polygon without increasing its width is more difficult than transforming it without increasing its diameter). Hence we take a different approach.

As in the solution of 6-8 a, we will show that the isosceles triangle T with width $\varDelta$ equal to the altitude dropped to one of the equal sides[†] has a smaller area than any other polygon M with the same width $\varDelta$ and the same perimeter L (here it is unessential for the proof that M is a polygon). Thus it will follow that there is no convex figure $\varPhi$ of width $\varDelta$ and circumference L with area less than that of the triangle T.[§]

Let σ denote the circle inscribed in M (see page 59) and $\bar{\sigma}$ the circle inscribed in T. Let r and $\bar{r}$ be the respective radii of these circles. Our main task is to prove that

$$r \geq \bar{r}.$$

From this we conclude that $S \geq \bar{S}$, where S is the area of M and $\bar{S}$ that of T. From Diagrams 268 a, b we have

$$S = \tfrac{1}{2}(\bar{r} \cdot AB + \bar{r} \cdot BC + \bar{r} \cdot CA) = \tfrac{1}{2}\bar{r} \cdot L$$

and

$$S = \tfrac{1}{2}(p_1 \cdot A_1A_2 + p_2 \cdot A_2A_3 + \ldots + p_n \cdot A_nA_1)$$
$$\geq \tfrac{1}{2}(r \cdot A_1A_2 + r \cdot A_2A_3 + \ldots + r \cdot A_nA_1) = \tfrac{1}{2}r \cdot L.$$

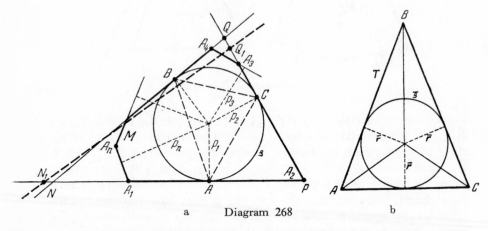

a   Diagram 268   b

In accordance with Exercise 6-2 the circle σ cuts the sides of M in two diametrically opposite points or in three points A, B, and C that are vertices of an acute-angled triangle. In the first case (cf. Diagram 77, page 59), it is obvious that $\varDelta = 2r$, and since $2\bar{r} < \varDelta$, we have $\bar{r} < r$. We thus have only the second case to consider.

Produce the sides of M that touch the circle σ in the points A, B, C (Diagram 268 a). They form a triangle NPQ with perimeter $L_1 \geq L$

[†] This means that a lateral side of the triangle is not less than the base. (It is evident that the width of the triangle equals the altitude dropped to the greatest side).

[§] In fact we can prove that every other convex figure $\varPhi$ of width $\triangle$ and perimeter L has a strictly greater area than the triangle T.

and no altitude less than the width Δ of M. Suppose that $\measuredangle N \leq P \leq \measuredangle Q$. Choose a point Q_1 on PQ at distance Δ from NP. Let N_1 be chosen on the prolongation of PN to the left of N so that the perimeter of the triangle N_1PQ_1 is also L_1 (the existence of such a point follows at once by continuity; *cf.* Section 3). Let R_1 be the radius of the circle inscribed in triangle N_1PQ_1. We must now prove that $r_1 \leq r$.

From Diagram 268 a, we have $\measuredangle N_1 \leq \measuredangle N \leq \measuredangle P \leq \measuredangle Q \leq \measuredangle Q_1$. Hence $\measuredangle N + \measuredangle Q = \measuredangle N_1 + \measuredangle Q_1 (= 180° - \measuredangle P)$ and

$$\measuredangle Q - \measuredangle N \leq \measuredangle Q_1 - \measuredangle N_1.$$

Let R and R_1 be the radii of the circles circumscribed about triangles NPQ and N_1PQ_1. The sides of the triangle NPQ are $2R \sin N$, $2R \sin P$, and $2R \sin Q$. Hence

$$2R \sin N + 2R \sin P + 2R \sin Q = L_1$$

and

$$2R = \frac{L_1}{\sin N + \sin P + \sin Q} = \frac{L_1}{\sin P + 2 \sin [(Q+N)/2] \cos [(Q-N)/2]}.$$

Similarly, we have

$$2R_1 = \frac{L_1}{\sin N_1 + \sin P + \sin Q_1} = \frac{L_1}{\sin P + 2 \sin [(Q_1+N_1)/2] \cos [(Q_1-N_1)/2]},$$

and thus

$$2R \leq 2R_1; \qquad NQ = 2R \sin P \leq 2R_1 \sin P = N_1Q_1.$$

It is also evident from Diagram 269 a that

$$PA = (PA + PC)/2 = (L_1 - 2NB - 2QB)/2 = (L_1 - 2NQ)/2;$$
$$r = PA \cdot \tan P/2 = (L_1 - 2NQ)(\tan P/2)/2,$$

and analogously

$$r_1 = (L_1 - 2N_1Q_1)(\tan P/2)/2.$$

Since $N_1Q_1 \geq NQ$, it follows that $r_1 \leq r$.

Now choose any point P_2 on PN_1. By reason of continuity (Section 3) it follows that there is a point N_2 on the extension of PN_1 beyond N_1 such that the perimeter of the triangle $N_2P_2Q_1$ equals L_1 as before (clearly there is exactly one such point). Again by reason of continuity, we can select a point P_2 such that $\measuredangle N_2P_2Q_1 = \measuredangle N_2Q_1P_2$; that is, such that the triangle $N_2P_2Q_1$ is isosceles. Let r_2 be the radius of the incircle of triangle $N_2P_2Q_1$. We now assert that $r_2 \leq r_1$ (Diagram 269 b).

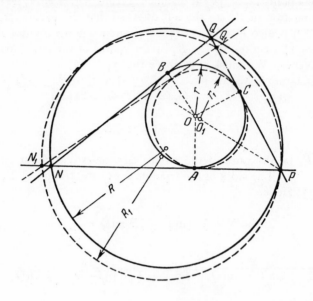

Diagram 269a

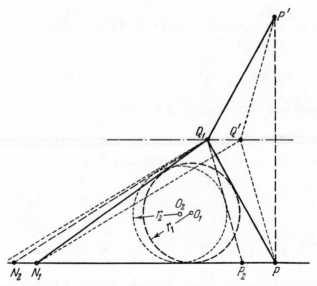

Diagram 269b

First we show that $N_2P_2 < N_1P$. Let $\overline{N}P_2 = N_1P$. Displace triangle $\overline{N}P_2Q_1$ so that $\overline{N}P_2$ coincides with N_1P. Then Q_1 goes into some point Q'. Let the point P' be symmetric with respect to the point P in the line Q_1Q'. In this case we obviously have

$$\overline{N}Q_1 + Q_1P_2 = N_1Q' + Q'P = N_1Q' + Q'P' \geq N_1Q_1 + Q_1P' = N_1Q_1 + Q_1P,$$

and furthermore

$$N_2Q_1 + Q_1P_2 + P_2N_2 = N_1Q_1 + Q_1P + PN_1 \leq \overline{N}Q_1 + Q_1P_2 + \overline{N}P_2.$$

Hence N_2 lies on $N_1\overline{N}$ and

$$N_2P_2 < \overline{N}P_2 = N_1P.$$

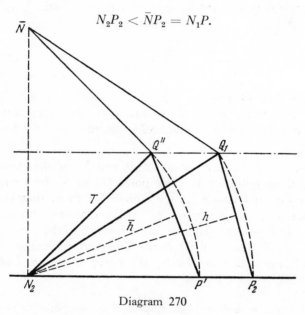

Diagram 270

Of the two triangles $N_2P_2Q_1$ and N_1PQ_1, which have equal altitudes, the first has the smaller base and therefore a smaller area. Hence

$$r_2 = \frac{2S(\Delta N_2P_2Q_1)}{L_1} \leq \frac{2S(\Delta N_1PQ_1)}{L_1} = r_1.$$

We now compare the isosceles triangles $N_2P_2Q_1$ and T. Both have two of their altitudes equal to Δ. We denote the third altitudes by h and $\overline{h}$ respectively. From Diagram 270 (in which $\overline{N}$ and N_2 are symmetric with respect to Q_1Q''), it follows that of the two isosceles triangles, the one with the greater pair of equal sides has the greater perimeter. In Diagram 270 we have

$$N_2P_2 + P_2Q_1 + Q_1N_2 = N_2P_2 + P_2Q_1 + Q_1\overline{N} > N_2P' + P'Q'' + Q''\overline{N}$$
$$= N_2P' + P'Q'' + Q''N_2.$$

Since $L_1 \geq L$, a lateral side of the triangle T does not exceed a lateral side of the triangle $N_2P_2Q_1$, and the base of triangle T is not less than that of triangle $N_2P_2Q_1$. Since the sides of a triangle are proportional to the altitudes (for example $S(\triangle N_2P_2Q_1) = (\varDelta/2) \cdot N_2P_2 = (h/2) \cdot P_2Q_1$ and $N_2P_2/P_2Q_1 = h/\varDelta$), it follows that $h \geq \bar{h}$.

Now we apply the formula

$$\frac{1}{r} = \frac{1}{h_1} + \frac{1}{h_2} + \frac{1}{h_3}.$$

Here r is the radius of the incircle of a triangle and h_1, h_2, h_3 are its altitudes.[†] It follows from this formula that:

$$\frac{1}{\bar{r}} = \frac{2}{\varDelta} + \frac{1}{\bar{h}} \geq \frac{2}{\varDelta} + \frac{1}{h} = \frac{1}{r_2},$$

and hence $\bar{r} \leq r_2$. Therefore $r \leq r_2 \leq r_1 \leq r$ and our proof is concluded.

Finally we note that we can easily show from the foregoing argument that $\bar{S} = S$ only when the polygon M coincides with the triangle T.

6-9. Let K be any convex curve and K' be the curve obtained from K by reflection in some point O; let K^* be a curve similar to the sum of K and K' in the ratio of $1/2$. Prove that: (a) the curve K^* has a center of symmetry; (b) the diameter and width of the curve K^* equal the diameter and the width of the curve K respectively; (c) the length of the curve K^* equals the length of the curve K; (d) the area bounded by the curve K^* is not less than that bounded by the curve K.

(a) From Exercise 4-4, we can assume that the point O is the origin. A rotation through 180° about O converts the curve K into K', K' into K, and the sum $K + K'$ into itself. This means that O is the center of symmetry of $K + K'$. Hence the curve K^*, which is similar to $K + K'$, also has a center of symmetry O.

(b) From the definition of the width of a curve with respect to a given direction (*cf.* Section 4, page 46, Diagram 68), it follows that the width of K' in any direction is equal to the width of K in the same direction (Diagram 271). Hence the width of $K + K'$ in every direction is twice as great as the width of the curve K or the curve K' in the same direction (*cf.* Exercise 4-11). This means that the curve K^* has in each direction the same width as the curves K and K'. Hence the diameter

---

[†] Let a, b, c be the sides of the triangle in question and let S be its area. Then $1/r = (a + b + c)/2S = (a/2S) + (b/2S) + (c/2S) = (1/h_1) + (1/h_2) + (1/h_3)$.

and the width of the curve K^* (see Exercise 1-7 and the definition on page 18) are the same respectively as those of K.

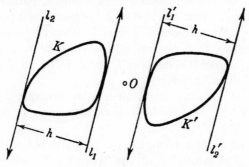

Diagram 271

(c) The length of the sum of convex curves is the sum of their lengths (*cf.* Section 4, page 46), and since the curves K and K' are congruent (each is obtained from the other by rotation through 180° about the point O) and thus have the same length, the length of $K + K'$ is twice the length of K. Thus the length of the curve K^* is equal to the length of K (and of K').

(d) About the curves K and K^* we circumscribe rectangles L_1 and L_1^* with parallel corresponding sides. Since K has the same width as K^* in every direction (see the solution to Exercise 6-9 b), these rectangles are congruent and thus have the same area. We draw supporting lines to the curves K and K^* perpendicular to the bisectors of the angles of L_1 and L_1^*. These lines together with the supporting lines already drawn form equiangular octagons L_2 and L_2^* (Diagram 272).

We now prove that the area of the octagon L_2 does not exceed that of the octagon L_2^*. Each pair of the parallel supporting lines just drawn cuts a pair of triangles from L_1 and L_1^*. Thus we obtain eight similar isosceles right triangles. The sum of the altitudes of the two triangles T_1 and T_2 cut from L_1 by the pair of parallel supporting lines l_1 and l_2

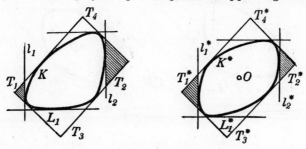

Diagram 272

equals the sum of the altitudes of the corresponding triangles T_1^* and T_2^* cut from L_1^* by the supporting lines l_1^* and l_2^* parallel to l_1 and l_2. To see this, observe that the distance between lines parallel to l_1, l_2, l_1^*, l_2^* and through the vertices of L_1 and L_1^* is correspondingly the same in the two figures, since L_1 and L_1^* are congruent, and the distance between l_1 and l_2 equals that between l_1^* and l_2^*. (The curve K has the same width as K^* in all directions).

Since K^* has a center of symmetry, the triangle T_1^* is congruent to the triangle T_2^* (T_1^* is symmetric with respect to T_2^* in the center of symmetry O of K^*).

The areas of similar triangles are proportional to the squares of their altitudes. The altitudes of the triangles T_1^* and T_2^* are equal. Hence the sum of the areas of triangles T_1 and T_2 cannot be less than the sum of the areas of triangles T_1^* and T_2^*.[†]

In the same way we prove that the sum of the areas of triangles T_3 and T_4 cut from the rectangle L_1 by the second pair of parallel supporting lines cannot be smaller than the sum of the areas of triangles T_3^* and T_4^* cut from L_1^* by supporting lines having the same direction. It follows that the area of the equiangular octagon L_2 circumscribed about K (equal to the difference between the area of L_1 and the sum of the areas of triangles T_1, T_2, T_3, and T_4) cannot exceed the area of the octagon L_2^* with corresponding parallel sides circumscribed about K^*.

Perpendicular to the angle bisectors of the octagons L_2 and L_2^*, we draw four pairs of parallel supporting lines to K and K^*. These lines cut four pairs of isosceles triangles from L_2 and L_2^* respectively (together with the sides of the octagons these lines form sixteen-sided polygons L_3 and L_3^* circumscribed about K and K^*).

The total area of each pair of triangles T_k and T_{k+1} cut from the octagon L_2 by a pair of parallel supporting lines cannot be less than the total area of the corresponding pair of triangles T_k^* and T_{k+1}^* formed from the octagon L_2^* (Diagram 273). The proof of this assertion is like

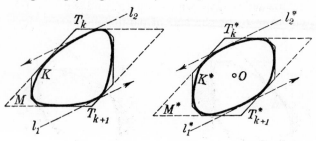

Diagram 273

[†] If a sum $h_1 + h_2$ is constant, then the sum of the squares $h_1{}^2 + h_2{}^2$ is least when $h_1 = h_2$. This follows directly from the formula
$$h_1{}^2 + h_2{}^2 = \tfrac{1}{2}\left[(h_1 + h_2)^2 + (h_1 - h_2)^2\right].$$

that given above; in place of the rectangles L_1 and L_1^*, we have only to consider the parallelograms M and M^* formed by pairs of sides of the octagons which meet in the vertices of triangles T_k and T_{k+1} or T_k^* and T_{k+1}^*; these parallelograms are circumscribed about K and K^* respectively (Diagram 273).

The parallelograms M and M^* are equal, since the two altitudes of the one are equal to the corresponding altitudes of the other (the curve K has the same width as K^* in all directions). Since the total area of all triangles cut from the octagon L_2 is not less than the area of all the triangles cut from the octagon L_2^*, the area of the sixteen-sided polygon L_3 does not exceed that of the sixteen-sided figure L_3^*.

In the same way, we prove that the area of an equiangular 2^n-sided polygon L_{n-1} circumscribed about K does not exceed the area of the 2^n-sided polygon L_{n-1}^* with corresponding parallel sides circumscribed about K^*. This proof is easily carried out by induction. Suppose it is known that the area of an equiangular 2^{n-1}-sided polygon L_{n-2} circumscribed about K does not exceed the area of the 2^{n-1}-sided polygon L_{n-2}^* with corresponding parallel sides circumscribed about K^*. We show easily that the sum of the areas of all the triangles cut from the 2^{n-1}-sided polygon L_{n-2} by 2^{n-1} supporting lines of the curve K perpendicular to the bisectors of the angles of L_{n-2} is not less than the sum of the areas of all the triangles formed from the 2^{n-1}-sided polygon L_{n-2}^* by supporting lines of K^* parallel to the supporting lines of the curve K mentioned above. Hence the area of L_{n-1} does not exceed that of L_{n-1}^*.

Passing to the limit, we conclude that the area of K does not exceed that of K^*.[†]

6-10. (a) Prove that of all convex curves of diameter 1, the circle bounds the greatest area. (b) Prove that of all convex figures of diameter D and width Δ, the figure shown in Diagram 88 (page 66) has the greatest area. This figure is cut from a circle of radius $D/2$ by two parallel lines equidistant from the center of the circle and separated by the distance Δ.

(a) First of all, by Exercise 6-9 we can replace each convex curve K by a centrally symmetric convex curve K^* of the same diameter which bounds an area at least as great as that bounded by K. Hence we need only seek a centrally symmetric curve of diameter 1 enclosing a figure of maximum area. In a centrally symmetric convex figure of diameter 1, the distance of a point M from the center of symmetry O cannot exceed

---

[†] A careful examination of the proof justifies, in fact, the conclusion that the area of K is strictly less than the area of K^* if K and K^* are different (that is, if K has no center of symmetry).

the value $\frac{1}{2}$, otherwise the distance between M and its image M' under a reflection in O would exceed 1 (Diagram 274). Hence every such convex curve of diameter 1 can be enclosed in a circle of diameter 1 (Diagram 274) and therefore cannot enclose a greater area than does the circle.

Note. From the theorem just proved it is easily deduced that the circle is the (not necessarily convex) plane figure of diameter 1 which encloses the greatest area. In fact, for each nonconvex figure there is a convex figure of the same diameter having a greater area (see Diagram 44 a on page 32 and the corresponding text, further Exercise 1-7.)

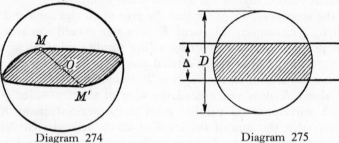

Diagram 274   Diagram 275

(b) Just as in Exercise 6-10 a, we can limit ourselves to the consideration of centrosymmetric convex curves. Any two parallel supporting lines of a centrosymmetric convex curve are symmetric with respect to the center of symmetry O. If the width of such a curve is $\varDelta$, then the curve has a pair of supporting lines, each of which is at a distance $\varDelta/2$ from O. Hence the curve lies entirely within a strip of width $\varDelta$ bounded by two parallel lines equidistant from O. On the other hand, a centrosymmetric curve of diameter D lies entirely inside a circle of diameter D whose center is the center of the curve (see the solution to Exercise 6-10 a). The intersection of the strip of width $\varDelta$ and the circle of diameter D (Diagram 275) is a centrally symmetric convex figure of width $\varDelta$, diameter D, and maximum area; each other such figure must belong entirely to this intersection.

Note. Exercise 6-10 a implies Exercise 6-10 b easily since 6-10 b is a generalization of 6-10 a.

6-11. (a) Prove that of all convex figures of diameter D and perimeter L ($L \leq \pi D$; cf. Exercise 7-17 a) the figure of greatest area is shown in Diagram 89 a (page 66). It consists of two equal circular segments with chord length D and arc length $L/2$. (b) Prove that of all convex figures of width $\varDelta$ and perimeter L ($L \leq \pi\varDelta$; see Exercise 7-18 a), the figure shown in Diagram 89 b has the greatest area. This figure is bounded by parallel and equal segments whose distance apart is $\varDelta$, and by two semicircles of diameter $\varDelta$.

(a) By Exercise 6-9 a, we need only find a centrally symmetric curve of Diameter D and length L that bounds a figure of maximum area. Let K be the desired curve; moreover let A and B be two points of the curve whose distance is the maximum value D. Since K is centrally symmetric, the segment AB must pass through the center of symmetry O and be bisected by it [if the chord AB of K did not pass through O, then the segment $A'B'$ symmetric to AB with respect to O would be a chord of K different from AB, and one of the diagonals AA' or BB' of the parallelogram $ABA'B'$ would be longer than AB (Diagram 276)].

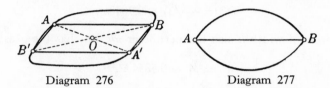

Diagram 276   Diagram 277

We consider the part of K lying on one side of the chord AB. Our problem is thus reduced to finding a convex curve consisting of the segment AB and a curve of length $L/2$ which bounds a figure of maximum area. By Exercise 5-11 a, such a curve is a circular segment; hence the desired curve K has the form shown in Diagram 277.

(b) As in the solution of Exercise 6-11 a, we can restrict ourselves to the study of centrosymmetric convex curves. A centrosymmetric convex curve of width $\varDelta$ has two parallel supporting lines l_1 and l_2, each at a distance $\varDelta/2$ from the center of symmetry. Let A and B be points of contact of the supporting lines l_1 and l_2 with the curve K which are symmetric points with respect to O. We consider the part of K lying on one side of the chord AB, so that our exercise is reduced to finding a convex curve of length $(L/2) + d$ that consists of the segment AB of length d, segments of the parallel lines l_1 and l_2 passing through A and B, and a curved piece which bounds a

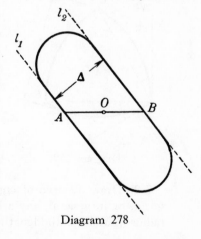

Diagram 278

figure of maximum area. This problem can be solved like the fundamental Exercise 5-11 (or Exercise 5-12). We obtain a curve consisting of the segment AB, segments of the lines l_1 and l_2, and a semicircle of diameter $\varDelta$ tangent to l_1 and l_2. The desired curve has the form shown in Diagram 278.

7-1. Calculate the perimeter of a Reuleaux triangle and its area. Which is greater, the area of a circle or the area of a Reuleaux triangle of equal width? Also determine the size of the interior angles at the corner points of a Reuleaux triangle.

If the width of a Reuleaux triangle (Diagram 279) is h, then each of the three arcs has length $2\pi h/6$, and the length of the entire curve is πh. The area of a Reuleaux triangle is the difference between the sum of the areas of the three circular sectors of radius h and central angle 60° and twice the area of the triangle ABC; that is, the area is

$$h^2/2 \, (\pi - \sqrt{3}) \approx 0.7048h^2.$$

A circle of width h also has perimeter πh, but has the greater area

$$\pi h^2/4 \approx 0.7854 \, h^2.$$

Each arc joining the vertices of the triangle corresponds to an angle of 60°. Hence the angle between the tangent AM and the chord AB is exadtly 30° (Diagram 279), and the angle MAN at the corner point A of the Reuleaux triangle is 120°.

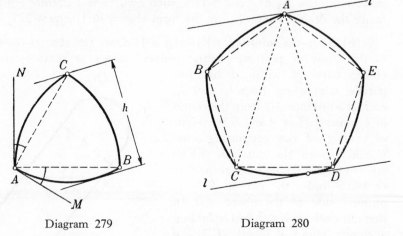

Diagram 279   Diagram 280

7-2. Draw a curve of constant width h which consists of five, seven, or in general, any arbitrary odd number of circular arcs of radius h. What is the length of each of these curves?

Let $ABCDE$ be a regular pentagon with greatest diagonal h. About each vertex of the pentagon draw an arc of radius h joining the two opposite vertices (Diagram 280). The resulting convex curve is of constant width, since any two parallel supporting lines are such that one of them passes through a vertex while the other is tangent to the opposite arc, and thus the distance between them is h. The angle CAD is $36°$; hence the length of each of the five arcs of the curve is $2\pi h/10$ and the total length of the curve is πh.

The same construction can be carried out for every regular polygon with an odd number of sides. (The polygon must have an odd number of sides, since for each vertex there must be two opposite vertices connected by an arc of radius h.) If we start with a regular polygon of $2n - 1$ sides, then the resulting curve has $2n - 1$ equal arcs of radius h; the central angle of each arc is $2\pi/2(2n - 1)$ and the total length of the curve is $(2n - 1) \cdot 2\pi h/2(2n - 1) = \pi h$.

We note that it is not necessary for this construction that the initial polygon with an odd number of sides be regular. All that is required is that each diagonal of the polygon which joins a vertex to one of the two opposite vertices (the number of such diagonals equals the number of vertices of the polygon) have length h while the remaining diagonals and all the sides of the polygon have length less than h. It is easy to show that many irregular polygons satisfy these conditions. About each vertex of such a polygon we draw an arc of radius h joining the two opposite vertices (Diagram 281). The resulting convex

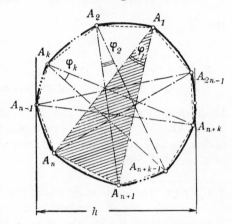

Diagram 281

curve is of constant width. Any pair of parallel supporting lines has the property that one of them passes through a vertex of the polygon and the other is tangent to the circular arc joining the two opposite vertices. Hence the distance between the lines is h.

We now prove that the length of the curve just constructed is also equal to πh. Denote the angle $A_{n+k-1}A_kA_{n+k}$ by ρ_k, where A_{n+k-1} and A_{n+k} are the vertices opposite to the vertex A_k (Diagram 281). Then the central angle corresponding to the arc joining A_{n+k-1} and A_{n+k} is ρ_k. Thus the curve to be studied consists of $2n - 1$ arcs of radius h forming a total arc to which the angle $\rho_1 + \rho_2 + ... + \rho_{2n-1}$ corresponds. If we can prove that

$$\rho_1 + \rho_2 + ... + \rho_{2n-1} = 180°,$$

then it will follow that the length of our curve is equal to the length of a semicircle of radius h, namely πh.

Consider the triangles with vertices A_k, A_{k+n-1}, and A_{k+n} (for the case $k = 1$, such a triangle is shaded in Diagram 281). There are $2n - 1$ such triangles. Hence the sum of the angles of these triangles is $(2n - 1) \cdot 180°$; that is, the sum of the angles of all these triangles is the sum of all angles of the polygon $A_1 A_2 \ldots A_{2n-1}$, where the angles ρ_1, ρ_2, ..., ρ_{2n-1} each appear three times. (Thus, for example, ρ_1 occurs in the sum of the angles of the triangles $A_1 A_n A_{n+1}$, $A_{n+1} A_1 A_2$, and $A_n A_1 A_{2n-1}$). Hence the sum of the angles of all the given triangles is equal to the sum of the angles of a polygon of $(2n - 1)$ sides plus twice the sum $\rho_1 + \rho_2 + \ldots + \rho_{2n-1}$.

Therefore

$$(2n - 1)\,180° = [(2n - 1) - 2]\,180° + 2(\rho_1 + \rho_2 + \ldots + \rho_{2n-1}),$$

that is

$$\rho_1 + \rho_2 + \ldots + \rho_{2n-1} = 180°.$$

7-3. Prove that the distance between two points of a curve of constant width h cannot exceed h.

If the length of a chord AB of a curve K of constant width h were greater than h, then the distance between the supporting lines perpendicular to AB would also be greater than h, contrary to the definition of a curve of constant width.

7-4. Prove that each supporting line has only one point in common with a curve of constant width h. In a curve of constant width, each chord joining the contact points of two parallel supporting lines is perpendicular to those lines and hence has length h.

See Exercise 1-6.

7-5. Prove that each chord of a curve of constant width whose length equals the width of the curve must be a diameter.

In view of Exercise 7-3, we can apply the result of Exercise 1-8.

7-6. Prove that any two diameters of a curve of constant width must intersect in the interior or on the curve. If they intersect on the curve, then their point of intersection A is a corner point of the curve, and the exterior angle of the curve at A is not less than the angle between the two diameters.

Suppose that the diameters AD and BC intersect in the exterior of the curve or are parallel (Diagram 282). Then they are sides of an inscribed quadrilateral $ABCD$. Since the sum of the angles of a quadrilateral is $360°$, at least one of the angles A, B, C, D is not less than $90°$; suppose it is D. Then the segment $AC > h$, since $AD = h$ and $AC > AD$ (for $\sphericalangle ADC > \sphericalangle ACD$). This contradicts the assertion of Exercise 7-3.

If two diameters AB and AC intersect at A on a curve of constant width (Diagram 283), then the lines l_1 and l_2 through A, and perpendicular to AB and AC respectivly, are supporting lines of the curve. Hence two supporting lines pass through A, and A is a corner point.

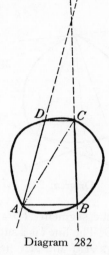

Diagram 282

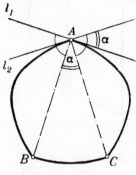

Diagram 283

If the angle BAC is α, then the angle between the lines l_1 and l_2 is α. The exterior angle at A is thus not less than α (and hence the interior angle at A is not greater than $180° - \alpha$).

7-7. Prove that the circle is the only curve of constant width with a center of symmetry.

Let K be a curve of constant width with center of symmetry O. It is easy to see that all diameters of K pass through O. In fact, if a diameter AB of K did not go through O, then the segment $A'B'$ symmetric to AB with repect to O (Diagram 284) would also be a diameter of K, by symmetry. Then the diameters AB and $A'B'$ would be parallel, contrary to Exercise 7-6.

Hence all diameters of K pass through O. Because of the symmetry of K, each diameter must be bisected by O. Thus K is a circle of radius $h/2$ and center O.

7-8. Prove that if a curve of constant width h has a corner point, then one of the arcs of the curve is a circular arc of radius h.

Conversely, if some arc of a curve of constant width h is an arc of a circle of radius h, then the curve has a corner point.

Let A be a corner point of a curve of constant width h, and let AM

and AN be the tangent rays to K at A (Diagram 285). Perpendicular to the rays AM and AN, we draw the segments AB and AC respectively, each of length h. Finally we draw an arc BC of radius h about the point A and prove that all points of the arc BC belong to the given curve of constant width.

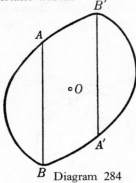

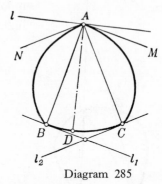

Diagram 284   Diagram 285

Let D be any point of arc BC. Draw the segment AD and let l denote the line through A perpendicular to AD. The line l is a supporting line of the given curve, since both of the rays AM and AN lie on one side of it. Since l is a supporting line, and A is its points of contact with the curve, the segment AD of length h must be a diameter of the curve (Exercise 7-4); thus the point D lies on the curve, and by the same argument, all of the arc BC belongs to the curve. If the exterior angle at the corner point A is α, then the arc BC corresponds to the central angle α.

Conversely, suppose that an arc BC of a curve of constant width h is a circular arc of radius h (Diagram 285) and center A. Draw the tangents l_1 and l_2 to the arc BC at B and C respectively. Then l_1 and l_2 are supporting lines of the curve with contact points B and C. The segments AB and AC are perpendicular to l_1 and l_2 and have length h; that is, AB and BC are diameters of the curve. Thus A is a corner point of the curve (see Exercise 7-6).

7-9. Prove that the interior angle at a corner point A of a curve of constant width cannot be less than $120°$. The only curve of constant width in which a corner has an interior angle of $120°$ is a Reuleaux triangle.

Let A be a corner point of a curve of constant width h. If the angle at the corner point A were less than $120°$, the exterior angle at A would be greater than $60°$. Then the curve of constant width would have an arc of radius h to which an angle of more than $60°$ corresponded (see the solution of Exercise 7-8). Hence the length of the chord joining the end points of this arc would be greater than h, and this, from Exercise 7-3, is impossible. Thus the interior angle at A cannot be less than 120°.

Now suppose that the interior angle at the point A of a curve of constant width h is 120°. Then the curve has an arc of radius h whose central angle BAC is 60° (Diagram 286), and the triangle ABC is

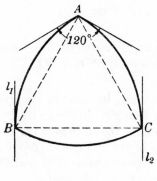

Diagram 286

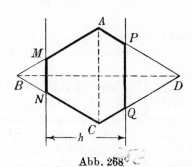

Abb. 288

Diagram 287

equilateral. Since $BC = h$, BC is a diameter. The lines l_1 and l_2 through B and C perpendicular to BC are supporting lines, since the distance between them is h. Since the diameters AB and BC meet at B, B is a corner point. This means that the arc BC of radius h about B and joining A and C belongs entirely to the curve. Likewise the arc of radius h joining A and B belongs to the curve. The three given points thus form a Reuleaux triangle.

7-10. Let $ABCD$ be a rhombus, and let MN and PQ be two line segments which are perpendicular to the diagonal BD and whose distance apart is h. (a) Prove that the perimeter of the hexagon $AMNCQP$ does not depend on the position of MN and PQ. (b) Prove that the area of the hexagon $AMNCQP$ assumes its maximum value when MN and PQ are at an equal distance $h/2$ from the diagonal AC of the rhombus; the area is a minimum when MN passes through the vertex B (or PQ passes through the vertex D) of the rhombus.

(**a**) Denote the perimeter of the rhombus $ABCD$ by p, the length of its diagonal BD by a, and the altitudes from the vertices B and D of triangles BMN and DPQ by h_1 and h_2 respectively. Then the perimeter of the hexagon $AMNCQP$ (Diagram 287) is

$$p - (BM + BN - MN) - (DP + DQ - PQ).$$

Since the triangles MNB and PQD are similar, we conclude that

$$(BM + BN - MN)/h_1 = (DP + DQ - PQ)/h_2.$$

Denote these fractions by k. Then the perimeter of $AMNCQP$ is

$$p - kh_1 - kh_2 = p - k(a - h),$$

since obviously $h_1 + h_2 = a - h$. However, the expression $p - k(a - h)$ does not depend on the position of the lines MN and PQ.

(b) The area of $AMNCQP$ differs from the area of the rhombus $ABCD$ by the sum of the areas of the triangles BMN and DPQ, and the areas of these triangles are proportional to the squares of the altitudes h_1 and h_2. Because the sum of the areas of the triangles is proportional to $h_1^2 + h_2^2$, we need only determine the positions of MN and PQ for which $h_1^2 + h_2^2$ has a maximum and minimum. The sum

$$h_1 + h_2 = a - h$$

does not depend on the position of MN and PQ. Since

$$h_1^2 + h_2^2 = \tfrac{1}{2} [(h_1 + h_2)^2 + (h_1 - h_2)^2]$$
$$= \tfrac{1}{2} [(a - h)^2 + (h_1 - h_2)^2],$$

the sum $h_1^2 + h_2^2$ has the least value when

$$h_1 - h_2 = 0, \qquad h_1 = h_2$$

(this corresponds to the position of MN and PQ at a distance $h/2$ from the center of the rhombus), and has the greatest value when $|h_1 - h_2| = a - h$; that is, $h_1 = 0$ or $h_2 = 0$ (in this case MN or PQ passes through a vertex of the rhombus).

Note. The line MN can pass through the vertex B of the rhombus only when PQ remains to the right of the diagonal AC (Diagram 287); that is, when the distance h between MN and PQ is at least half the diagonal BD. We shall encounter this case in the solution of Exercise 7-12. For $h < a/2$, the difference $|h_1 - h_2|$ is greatest (and hence the area of the hexagon is least), if MN or PQ coincides with the diagonal AC.

7-11. By examining equiangular polygons of 2^n-sides which are circumscribed about an arbitrary curve K of constant width h and also about a circle of diameter h, derive Barbier's Theorem: *All curves of constant width h have length πh.*

Let O be a circle of diameter h and let K be any curve of constant width h. We will prove that any two equiangular polygons with 2^n-sides circumscribed about O and K have the same perimeter. The proof is by induction on n. It is clear that two squares circumscribed about O and K have the same perimeter; these squares are, in fact, congruent.

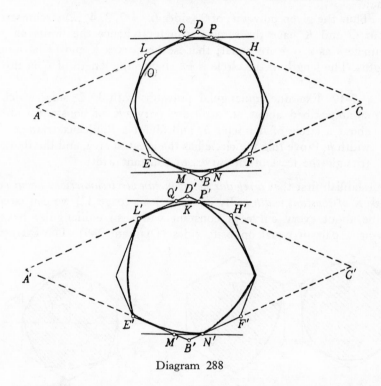

Diagram 288

Suppose it is known that all equiangular polygons of 2^n sides circumscribed about K and O have equal perimeters. Consider two sides, say BE and BF, of a polygon of 2^n sides which meet in a vertex and the two opposite sides DL and DH (Diagram 288); the extensions of these sides form a parallelogram $ABCD$ with equal altitudes; that is, a rhombus. We carry out this construction for both O and K. The resulting rhombuses $ABCD$ (circumscribed about O) and $A'B'C'D'$ (circumscribed about K) are congruent since they have equal angles and equal altitudes. We also draw supporting lines MN and PQ to the circle O perpendicular to the diagonal BD, and supporting lines

$M'N'$ and $P'Q'$ to the curve K perpendicular to $B'D'$. The distance between these supporting lines is obviously h. By Exercise 7-10 a, we can assert that the hexagons $AMNCPQ$ and $A'M'N'C'P'Q'$ have the same perimeter. Thus the polygons circumscribed about O and K which result from the polygons of 2^n sides by replacing BE, BF, DL, and DH by EM, MN, NF, LQ, QP, PH (and a like replacement of $B'E'$, etc.) have the same perimeter. Upon carrying out this construction for each pair of sides BE and BF which meet in a vertex, we obtain equiangular polygons of 2^{n+1} sides and prove that their perimeters are equal.

Thus the given polygons of 2^n sides ($n = 2, 3, 4, ...$) circumscribed about O and K have the same perimeters; hence the limits of these perimeters as $n \to \infty$ are equal; that is, the curves K and O have equal lengths. The length of the circle is πh; hence the length of K is also πh.

7-12. Examine equiangular polygons with $3 \cdot 2^n$ sides which are circumscribed about an arbitrary curve K of constant width h, about a circle of diameter h, and about a Reuleaux triangle T of width h. Prove that the circle has the greatest area, and the Reuleaux triangle the least of all curves of constant width.

We establish first that *a regular hexagon can be circumscribed about every curve K of constant width h*. By Exercise 3-4 a (page 32) we can circumscribe about every curve of constant width an equiangular hexagon having a pair of equal opposite sides (Diagram 289). The extensions

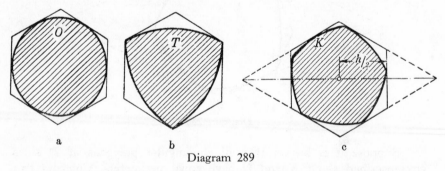

a   b   c
Diagram 289

of the other four sides of this hexagon form a parallelogram with an angle of 120°. Both of the altitudes of this parallelogram are of length h; that is, the parallelogram is a rhombus of altitude h. The two equal sides of the hexagon are perpendicular to the greater diagonal of the rhombus and intersect this diagonal at distance $h/2$ from the center of the rhombus (this follows from the equality of the sides). It is easy to see that this implies that the hexagon in question is regular and that the radius of its inscribed circle is $h/2$.

We now circumscribe a regular hexagon about each of the following: a circle O of diameter h, a Reuleaux triangle T of width h, and any curve K of constant width h (Diagram 289). We note that three vertices of the regular hexagon circumscribed about the Reuleaux triangle T coincide with the corner points of the curve T (Diagram 289 b). Just as in the solution of Exercise 7-11, we double the number of sides of

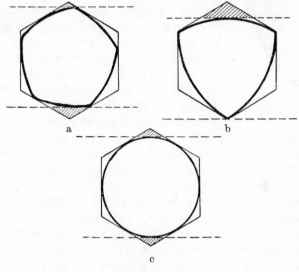

a   b

c

Diagram 290

the polygons circumscribed about T, O, and K; that is, we pass from circumscribed hexagons to circumscribed polygons of twelve sides, then to those of 24 sides, etc.

Consider the resulting equiangular polygons of $3 \cdot 2^n$ sides circumscribed about O, T, and K. We will prove that for every n, the area of the polygon of $3 \cdot 2^n$ sides circumscribed about the circle O cannot be less than, and the area of the polygon of $3 \cdot 2^n$ sides circumscribes T cannot exceed, the area of the polygon of $3 \cdot 2^n$ sides circumscribed about K. The proof is by induction. Suppose that this theorem has already been proved for polygons of $3 \cdot 2^n$ sides. We will then show that it also holds for polygons of $3 \cdot 2^{n+1}$ sides. For $n = 1$, our assertion is correct, since the hexagons circumscribed about O, T, and K are all equal (and, in fact, are regular hexagons with incircles of radius $h/2$).

The area of the polygon with $3 \cdot 2^{n+1}$ sides is obtained from the area of a polygon of $3 \cdot 2^n$ sides by subtracting from the latter the areas of the pairs of triangles cut off from the polygon of $3 \cdot 2^n$ sides by pairs of parallel supporting lines of the curve (Diagram 290). For the circle O, the polygon of $3 \cdot 2^n$ sides is regular, and we draw in each case secants equidistant from the center of the polygon of $3 \cdot 2^n$ sides (since the circle is centrosymmetric). We now show that for the Reuleaux triangle T, one of the secants always goes through a vertex of the polygon of $3 \cdot 2^n$ sides. One of two parallel supporting lines of a Reuleaux triangle must, in fact, pass through a corner point (Diagram 91 b). Since all corner points of the Reuleaux triangle are vertices of the circumscribed hexagon, upon construction of the circumscribed equiangular polygon of 12 sides, one line in each of the three pairs of parallel supporting lines goes through a vertex of the hexagon. The equiangular polygon of 12 sides circumscribed about the Reuleaux triangle T is thus in reality only 9 sided; that is, three of its sides are of length zero (see the definition of the circumscribed polygon, Section 1, page 14) so that all three corner points of the Reuleaux triangle are vertices of the 9-sided polygon (Diagram 291). Similarly, for each equiangular polygon of $3 \cdot 2^n$ sides circumscribed about the Reuleaux triangle T, all three corner points of the Reuleaux triangle are vertices of the polygon of $3 \cdot 2^n$ sides (actually each of these polygons has fewer than $3 \cdot 2^n$ sides). Hence in each pair of parallel supporting lines which we draw to the Reuleaux triangle in constructing the polygon of $3 \cdot 2^{n+1}$ sides, there is always one passing through a vertex of the polygon of $3 \cdot 2^n$ sides.

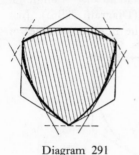

Diagram 291

In the polygons of $3 \cdot 2^n$ sides circumscribed about O, T, and K, we now consider the rhombuses which are formed by two adjacent sides l_1 and l_2 and by the sides l_3 and l_4 parallel to l_1 and l_2 respectively. All three of these rhombuses have altitude h and the same angles (equal to the angles of the regular polygon of $3 \cdot 2^n$ sides; that is, $180° (3 \cdot 2^n - 2)/(3 \cdot 2^n)$; therefore they are congruent. From Exercise 7-10 b, in the case of the circle the sum of the areas of the triangles cut off from the given rhombus by a pair of parallel sides of the circumscribed polygon of $3 \cdot 2^{n+1}$ sides is not greater, and for the Reuleaux triangle is not less, than that for the curve K (for the circle these lines are symmetric with respect to the center of the rhombus, while for the Reuleaux triangle one of them passes through a vertex of the rhombus). Therefore the area of the polygon of $3 \cdot 2^n$ sides circumscribed about the circle O is not less than the area of the polygon of $3 \cdot 2^n$ sides circumscribed about the curve K, while the area of the polygon of $3 \cdot 2^n$ sides circumscribed about the Reuleaux triangle T is not greater than the area of the polygon of $3 \cdot 2^n$ sides circumscribed about the curve K. By passing to the limit, we prove that the circle O bounds an area not less than the area bounded by K, while the Reuleaux triangle T bounds an area not greater than K does.

In fact, we can assert that a curve K which is not a circle encloses a smaller area than O does, and not merely an area which is not greater than that enclosed by O. Similarly, K bounds a greater area than T does if K is not a Reuleaux triangle. Every time we draw pairs of parallel supporting lines to O and to K, we cut off a pair of triangles from the polygon about K whose area is not less than the area of the pair of triangles that are cut off from the polygon about O. Hence the areas obtained by passing to the limit can be equal only if each time, in both cases, we cut off pairs of triangles of equal area. This is possible only if each pair of parallel supporting lines to K drawn in constructing a polygon of $3 \cdot 2^{n+1}$ sides is symmetric with respect to the center of the rhombus formed by adjacent sides of the polygon of $3 \cdot 2^n$ sides. If this occurs, then all polygons of $3 \cdot 2^n$ sides circumscribed about K are centrally symmetric (with the center of symmetry at the center of the regular hexagon circumscribed about the curve K). Hence K itself must have a center of symmetry and is thus a circle (see Exercise 7-7).[†]

It is still easier to prove that if the curve K is different from the Reuleaux triangle T, then it bounds a greater area than T does. The curve K encloses an area equal to that bounded by T only if under our construction, the pairs of parallel supporting lines of K and T cut off triangles of equal area from the polygons each time. However, the first pair of parallel supporting lines of K drawn in this construction need not cut off from the hexagon circumscribed about K an area of the same size as that which the pair of parallel supporting lines of the Reuleaux triangle T cuts off from the regular hexagon circumscribed about the curve T. This occurs only if one of the two parallel supporting lines of K passes through a vertex of the regular hexagon circumscribed about K, which in turn is possible only if the corresponding vertex of the hexagon belongs to K and occurs only if K has an angle of 120°; that is, if K is a Reuleaux triangle (*cf.* Exercise 7-9).

Thus, if K is any curve of constant width h and area S, then

$$0.7048h^2 \approx \tfrac{1}{2} h^2(\pi - \sqrt{3}) \leq S \leq \tfrac{1}{4}\pi h^2 \approx 0.7854h^2.$$

The areas of curves of constant width thus lie between rather narrow bounds.

7-13. Given any convex curve K of constant width, prove that the circle inscribed in K and that circumscribed about K must be concentric, and that the sum of their radii equals the width of the curve.

[†] From Exercises 5-7 and 5-8 it also follows, using Barbier's Theorem (Exercise 7-11), that a curve of constant width which is not a circle bounds a smaller area than the circle O of equal width.

Let K be any curve of constant width h and let O be a circle of radius r which does not extend outside K; also let O' be a circle of radius $h - r$ concentric with O (Diagram 292). We will prove that O' contains K; that is, that every point of O' lies on or outside K.

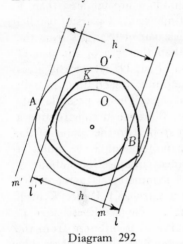

Diagram 292

Let A be any point of O', m' the tangent to O' at A, and the tangent to O parallel to m' and at a distance h from m'. Denote by B the point at which m is tangent to O. Also let l and l' be the supporting lines of K parallel to m and m'. The distance between l and l' is h, the same as that between m and m'. Since B lies in the interior of K (or belongs to K), the line m does not lie outside the strip formed by the lines l and l'. Thus m', at distance h from m, does not lie between l and l'. Hence the point A on m' is not inside K, as we wished to show. If O' is a circle of radius R enclosing the curve K and if O is a circle concentric with O' and with radius $h - R$, then we prove analogously that O does not extend beyond K.

Now let O_c be the circumcircle and O_i an incircle of K. Let R and r, respectively, be their radii. Then R cannot be greater than $h - r$, since the circle of radius $h - r$ concentric with O_i encloses K and the circumcircle has the least radius of all circles enclosing K. Also O_c cannot have a radius smaller than $h - r$, since otherwise a circle of radius $h - R$ concentric with O_c would lie inside K and would have a radius greater than r. Hence $R + r = h$.

Assume now that O_c and O_i are not concentric. Then the circle O' of radius R and concentric with O_i encloses K, and we thus have two circles O_c and O' of equal radius R enclosing K (Diagram 293). Then a circle can be constructed with radius less than R which contains K. The center of this circle lies at the midpoint of the join of the centers of O_i and O', and the circle passes through the two points of intersection of these circles. This contradicts the hypothesis that O_c is the circumcircle.

7-14. Prove that the Reuleaux triangle is the curve of constant width h with the greatest circumradius (and hence with the least in-radius; see Exercise 7-13). The circle, on the other hand, has the smallest circumradius (and the greatest in-radius).

It is easy to see that the radius of the circumcircle of the Reuleaux triangle of constant width h is $h\sqrt{3}/3$ (Diagram 294). All curves of constant width h have diameter h (*cf.* Exercises 7-3 and 7-4), and by Jung's Theorem (Exercise 2-4 and Exercise 6-1), the radius of a circle circumscribed about a curve of diameter h does not exceed $h\sqrt{3}/3$.

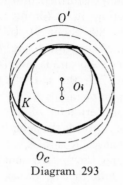

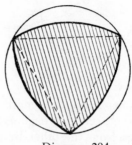

Diagram 293   Diagram 294

If a curve K of constant width h is not a Reuleaux triangle, then it is easy to show that the radius of the circumcircle of K is less than $h\sqrt{3}/3$ (and not merely not greater than $h\sqrt{3}/3$). The radius of the circumcircle of a plane figure of diameter h can attain the maximum value $h\sqrt{3}/3$ only if the circumscribed circle contains three points of the figure forming an equilateral triangle of side h (see Exercise 6-1). If a curve K of constant width h has three points forming an equilateral triangle of side h, then the sides of this equilateral triangle are diameters of K, and K is clearly a *Reuleaux* triangle.

The second part of the exercise is completely obvious, since the circumcircle of a circle is the circle itself; that is, it has the same diameter, and the diameter of the circumcircle of a general curve K of constant width cannot be less than the diameter of K. If a curve K of constant width h is not a circle, then the diameter of the circumcircle of K is obviously greater than h.

Thus we see that for all curves of constant width h, the radius R of a circumcircle and the radius r of an incircle lie between the following rather narrow bounds:

$$0.5h = h/2 \leq R \leq h\sqrt{3}/3 \approx 0.58h,$$
$$0.42h \approx h(3 - \sqrt{3})/3 \leq r \leq h/2 = 0.5h.$$

7-15. Prove that the sum of an arbitrary curve of constant width h with the same curve turned through 180° is a circle of radius h. Obtain from this theorem a new proof of Barbier's Theorem.

Let K be a curve of constant width h and let K' be the curve obtained from K by a rotation of 180° about the origin O (K' is symmetric to

K with respect to O); let $K^* = K + K'$ (Diagram 295). It follows at once from Exercise 4-11 that K^* is a curve of constant width $2h$. Also,

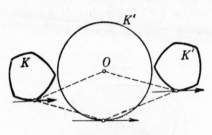

K^* is a centrosymmetric curve with center of symmetry O; that is, K^* is transformed into itself by a reflection in O (or by rotation through 180° about O). In such a rotation K goes into K', K' into K, and hence the sum is invariant. By Exercise 7-7, the curve K^* must be a circle of radius h.

Diagram 295

The perimeter of K^* is $2\pi h$. On the other hand, the length of K^* is the sum of the lengths of K and K' (see Section 4, page 46). Since the curves K and K' are equal (one arises from the other by rotation through 180°), their lengths are also equal. Thus twice the length of K is $2\pi h$; that is, K has length πh (Barbier's Theorem).

7-16. If the sum of a curve K with the curve K' obtained by rotating K through 180° is a circle, then K is a curve of constant width.

Let K be a convex curve with the property that if K' is obtained from K by reflection in any point O (by rotation through 180° about the point O), then the sum $K^* = K + K'$ is a circle of radius h. If the width of K in some direction is l, then the width of K' in this direction is

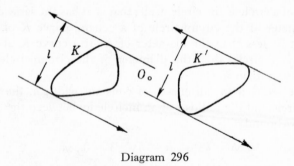

Diagram 296

also l (Diagram 296) and, by Exercise 4-11, the width of $K^* = K + K'$ is $2l$. Since K^* is a circle of radius h, its width in every direction is $2h$; thus $2l = 2h$ and hence $l = h$. That is, the width of K in every direction is h.

7-17. (a) Prove that of all convex curves of diameter 1, curves of constant width 1 have the greatest length. (b) In a curve $\overline{K}$ of constant width D, let AB and PQ be two parallel chords such that the diagonals AQ and BP of the trapezoid $ABQP$ are diameters of the curve. We denote the distance between the lines AB and PQ by Δ. Prove that the curve K, formed from the arcs AP and BQ of $\overline{K}$ and the chords AB and PQ, has the greatest length of all convex curves of diameter D and width Δ.

(a) Let K be a convex curve of diameter 1; let K' be the curve obtained by reflecting K in some point, and let $K^* = K + K'$. Obviously K^* is a centrally symmetric convex curve with diameter 2 and length twice that of K (see Exercises 6-9 a, b, and c; we note that the curve denoted by K^* in Exercise 6-9 is similar to the curve K^* of the present exercise, with ratio of similarity $\frac{1}{2}$). The distance of a point of K^* from the center of symmetry O of K^* cannot exceed 1, since otherwise the diameter of K^* would exceed 2. Hence the curve K^* is contained in a circle of radius 1. The length of K^* (and hence also the length of K which equals $\frac{1}{2}$ the length of K^*) is largest when K^* is a circle of radius 1; that is, when K is a curve of constant width 1 (see Exercise 7-16).

(b) Let K be any convex curve of diameter D and width Δ and let K' be obtained from K by reflection in some point. Then the curve $K^* = K + K'$ is a centrally symmetric convex curve of diameter $2D$ and width 2Δ; the length of K^* is twice that of K (see Exercise 6-9 a, b, and c). Since its width is 2Δ, K^* can be enclosed in a strip formed by two parallel lines whose distance apart is 2Δ. Because K^* is centrally symmetric, these two lines at minimum distance are supporting lines of K^* and are equidistant from the center of symmetry O of K^*. On the other hand, since the diameter of K^* is $2D$, K^* is contained in a circle of radius D about the center of symmetry O (see the solution of Exercise 7-17 a). Hence K^* lies within the curve heavily outlined in Diagram 297; thus K^* (and therefore K also) has the greatest length when K^* coincides with this curve.

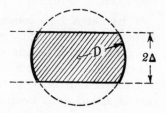

Diagram 297

For the curve K described in the statement of the exercise, $K + K'$ coincides with the heavily outlined curve in Diagram 297. In fact, $\overline{K} + \overline{K}'$ is a circle of radius D. The points A', B', P', Q' of the curve $\overline{K}'$, which arise from the points A, B, P, Q of K by rotation of $\overline{K}$ through $180°$ about O, correspond (in the sense of Exercise 4-5) to the points B, A, Q, P of $\overline{K}$. The sums of corresponding points of arcs AQ and

$B'P'$ thus form a circular arc of radius D; the same holds for the arc $A'Q'$ and BQ. The assertion of the exercise follows from this.

If the sum of K and K' is the curve shown in Diagram 297, then it is easy to see that K must coincide with the curve described in the statement of the exercise (*cf.* Exercise 4-9 and 7-16).

7-18. (a) Prove that curves of constant width 1 have the least length of all convex curves of width 1. (b) Let AB and CD be two diameters of a curve $\overline{K}$ of constant width $\varDelta$; let l_1 and l_2 be two supporting lines of $\overline{K}$ perpendicular to AB, and let l_3 and l_4 be supporting lines perpendicular to CD. Denote by P the intersection of l_1 and l_3, and by Q the intersection of l_2 and l_4. Let D be the distance between the points P and Q. Prove that the curve K formed from the segments AP, PD, BQ, QC and the arcs AC and BD of $\overline{K}$ has the smallest length of all curves of width $\varDelta$ and diameter D.

(a) Let K be any convex curve of width 1, and let K' be obtained from K by reflection in some point O. Then $K^* = K + K'$ is a centrosymmetric curve of width 2 whose length is twice that of K (see Exercises 6-9 a, b, and c).

Since its width is 2, the curve K^* must contain the circle of radius 1 about O, the center of symmetry of K^*. If there were some point A of K^* inside this circle, then the distance between the supporting line of K^* through A and the supporting line obtained by reflecting the first line in O would be less than 2.

Thus we see that K^* has the smallest length if it coincides with the circle of radius 1. It follows that K must be a curve of constant width 1 (see Exercise 7-16).

(b) Let K be a convex curve of width $\varDelta$ and diameter D, and let K' be obtained from K by reflection in some point O; then $K^* = K + K'$ is a centrosymmetric curve of width $2\varDelta$ and diameter $2D$ whose length is twice that of K (see Exercises 6-9 a, b, and c).

Let A and B denote two points of K^* at distance $2D$. It is evident that A and B must be symmetric with respect to the center O of K^*

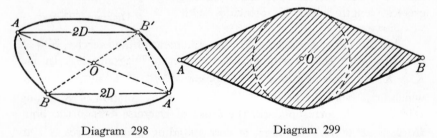

Diagram 298   Diagram 299

(otherwise reflection of A, B in O would yield points A', B' such that one of the chords AA' or BB' would be greater than $2D$; Diagram 298). On the other hand, since K^* has width 2Δ, it contains the circle of radius Δ about O (see the solution of Exercise 7-18 a). Thus K^* (and therefore K) has the least possible length if K^* consists of two arcs of a circle of radius Δ about O and the four sections of the tangents from the points A and B to this circle (Diagram 299). Hence by Exercises 7-16 and 7-18, the curve K has the form shown in Diagram 99 (page 76).

7-19. Obtain a new proof of Barbier's Theorem from the Approximation Theorem.

First we prove that a curve K_0 of constant width h which consists only of circular arcs of radius h has length πh (the construction of such a curve in the neighborhood of any preassigned curve of constant width h is described in the text). Consider any single arc AB of K_0 and draw diameters of K_0 through A and B. If these diameters intersect in a point C on the curve, then C is the center of the arc AB (Diagram 300 a),

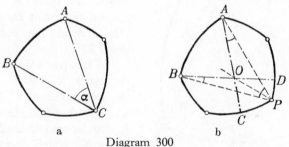

Diagram 300

and the length of arc AB is the product of the angle α between these diameters and the width of K_0. If the diameters AC and BD of K_0 intersect in the interior of the curve, then by the construction of K_0 (*cf.* pages 77-80), the center P of the circular arc AB is the intersection of circular arcs CP and DP with centers at A and B respectively (Diagram 300 b). The sum of the lengths of the arcs AB, CP, and PD is equal to the product of the angle between diameters AC and BD and the width h of K_0. In fact, the arc $AB = h \cdot (\sphericalangle APB)$, arc $CP = h \cdot (\sphericalangle CAP)$, arc $PD = h \cdot (\sphericalangle PBD)$ and the sum of the angles APB, CAP, and PBD is, as is known, equal to the angle between AC and BD. (If O is the intersection of AC and BD, then the sums $\sphericalangle APO + \sphericalangle PAC$ and $\sphericalangle BPO + \sphericalangle PBD$ are each equal to one of the two parts into which the line PO divides $\sphericalangle AOB$.)

If we add the lengths of all parts of K_0 which are included between diameters passing through neighboring corner points of the curve, then we can easily show that the total length of K_0 is πh.

Now consider any curve K of constant width h. Construct a sequence of curves $K_1, K_2, ..., K_n, ...$, each of constant width h and formed entirely of circular arcs of radius h, such that K is the limit of this sequence. By the above proof, the length of each of the curves $K_1, K_2, ..., K_n, ...$ is πh. Hence the length of K is likewise πh, since its length is the limit of the lengths of $K_1, K_2, ..., K_n, ...$ (see Section 4, page 50).

7-20. From the Approximation Theorem, obtain a new proof that of all figures of constant width h, the Reuleaux triangle bounds the smallest area.

First we consider curves of constant width h consisting only of circular arcs of radius h. Let K_0 be such a curve; let AC and BD be two of its diameters passing respectively through two neighboring corners A

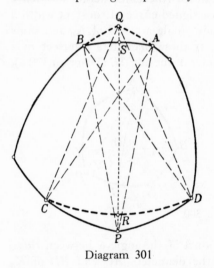

Diagram 301

and B of K_0. The part of K_0 included between the diameters AC and BD, which intersect inside the curve, consists of the arc CP about the point A, the arc DP around the point B, and the arc AB around the point P (Diagram 301).

The arcs AB, CP, and PD of the curve K_0 can be replaced by the arcs AQ about C, QB about D, and CD about Q. Hence the curve K_0 can be transformed into a new curve K_0', which also has constant width h (Diagram 30.).

We now prove that *if the chord CD is greater than the chord AB,* then the area bounded by K_0' is less than that bounded by K_0. We must show that the area $S(CPD)$ of the curvilinear triangle CPD is greater than the area $S(ABQ)$ of the curvilinear triangle ABQ. Draw the segments CA, CQ, DB, DQ, AP, and BP, each of length h, and also connect the points P and Q. We have supposed that $CD > AB$; hence we have $\overset{\frown}{CD} > \overset{\frown}{AB}$ also, since these arcs have the same radius h. The intersections of the segment PQ with arcs CD and AB are denoted by R and S respectively. Then $RP = SQ$ (for $PS = RQ$, since these segments are radii of the arcs AB and CD respectively).

The area of the curvilinear triangle CPD is the sum of the areas $S(CPR)$ and $S(PDR)$ of the curvilinear triangles CPR and PDR; likewise $S(ABQ) = S(ASQ) + S(BSQ)$. Since $\overset{\frown}{CD} > \overset{\frown}{AB}$, if $\overset{\frown}{CR} \geq \overset{\frown}{SA}$ and $\overset{\frown}{DR} \geq \overset{\frown}{SB}$, then both equalities cannot hold, and the corresponding relations $S(CPR) \geq S(SAQ)$ and $S(PDR) \geq S(BSQ)$ then imply $S(CPD) > S(AQB)$. If, for example, $\widehat{CR} \geq \widehat{SA}$, then by placing the curvilinear triangle SQA on the curvilinear triangle CPR, so that PR coincides with QS and the arc SA falls on arc RC, it can be shown that A lies between C and R (Diagram 302). Then the curvilinear triangle SAQ is contained in the triangle RCP (all the circular arcs have the same radius), and hence $S(CPR) \geq S(SAQ)$.

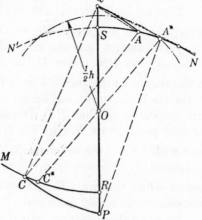

Diagram 302   Diagram 303

Thus when $\widehat{CR} \geq \widehat{SA}$ and $\widehat{DR} \geq \widehat{SB}$, the relation $S(CPD) > S(ABQ)$ holds. There is still the case to consider in which one of the two arcs DR and CR is greater and the other less than the arc SB and the arc SA respectively. Suppose that $\widehat{CR} > \widehat{SA}$ and $\widehat{DR} < \widehat{SB}$. Since $\widehat{CD} > \widehat{AB}$, we have

$$\widehat{CR} - \widehat{SA} > \widehat{SB} - \widehat{DR}.$$

From the last inequality we must still prove the analogous inequality for areas, namely

$$S(CPR) - S(SAQ) > S(SBQ) - S(PDR).$$

From this we can obtain

$$S(CPR) + S(PDR) > S(SAQ) + S(SBQ),$$

that is,

$$S(CPD) > S(ABQ).$$

This unsettled question of the area inequality can also be formulated as follows: Let PQ be a segment greater than h; let R and S be points of this segment for which $RQ = PS = h$ (and therefore $PR = SQ$); let $\widehat{RM}$ and $\widehat{SN}$ be circular arcs of radius h about the points Q and P respectively (Diagram 303). Finally, let C and A be points of $\widehat{RM}$

and $\overset{\frown}{SN}$ respectively such that $AC = h$; let $\overset{\frown}{AQ}$ and $\overset{\frown}{CP}$ be circular arcs of radius h joining A with Q and C with P (C and A are obviously the respective centers for these arcs). Then we assert that as the difference between the arcs CR and AS (for $\overset{\frown}{CR} > \overset{\frown}{AS}$) increases, the difference of the areas of the curvilinear triangles CPR and AQS also increases.

First we establish that $\overset{\frown}{AS} = \overset{\frown}{CR}$ holds only for a definite position of the point A. Assuming $\overset{\frown}{AS} = \overset{\frown}{CR}$, the points R, A, S, C are vertices of a parallelogram, and the diagonal AC passes through the center O of the segment RS. Hence $OA = OC = \frac{1}{2} h$. There is only one point on the arc $\overset{\frown}{SN}$ at distance $\frac{1}{2} h$ from O (all told there are two such points on the circle; however, one lies on the arc SN' symmetric to the arc SN with respect to the line RS). Denote this point by $A*$ and the corresponding point of arc RM by $C*$. If A coincides with $A*$, then C coincides with $C*$ and the difference $\overset{\frown}{CR} - \overset{\frown}{AS}$ vanishes. As A moves from $A*$ toward S, C moves from $C*$ toward M, and the arc AS becomes smaller while the arc CR increases. Hence the difference $\overset{\frown}{CR} - \overset{\frown}{CS}$ increases continuously from zero.

To prove this assertion, join the points P and $A*$. In triangle $PA*Q$ we then have $OA* = \frac{1}{2}h$ and $PQ > h$; the median $OA*$ is thus less than half the corresponding side PQ. Hence $\sphericalangle PA*Q$ is obtuse, so $A*$ is the first point of intersection of the line $QA*$ with the arc SN. Hence as A moves from $A*$ toward S, $\sphericalangle PQA$ becomes smaller and smaller.

The point C is thus a vertex of the isosceles triangle QAC with base QA and legs of length h. As A moves from $A*$ toward S, the segment QA becomes smaller, and therefore the base angle CQA increases. Since $\sphericalangle PQA$ decreases, $\sphericalangle CQP$ must obviously increase and the point C moves from $C*$ toward M.

Hence an increase in the difference $\overset{\frown}{CR} - \overset{\frown}{AS}$ is equivalent to a decrease in the arc AS; that is, the point A is displaced from $A*$ toward S. Then the difference $S(CPR) - S(ASQ)$ obviously increases since the curvilinear triangle CPR increases (for C moves away from R), but the triangle SAQ becomes smaller (A approaches S). Thus the required relation is proved.

We now prove that *every curve K of constant width h which consists solely of four or more circular arcs of radius h bounds an area greater than that of a Reuleaux triangle of width h*. We use the theorem just proved and change the curve K so that it always remains a curve of constant width h and yet the area bounded by it becomes smaller and smaller. The number of arcs composing the curve will become less and less until we finally obtain a Reuleaux triangle.

Let AB be the smallest (or one of the smallest) of the arcs that constitute the curve K. The end points A and B of this arc are corner points of K and hence are the centers of certain arcs of the curve (see the solution of Exercise 7-8). The intersection P of the arcs CP and PD with centers at A and B is the center for the arc AB (Diagram 304); C and D are corner points of K. Since the total number of arcs forming the curve is, by hypothesis, at least four, C cannot coincide with B and D with A simultaneously. Thus K has at least one arc about C or D different from the arcs AB, CP, and PD.

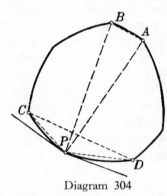
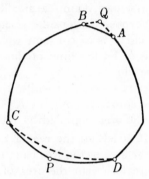

Diagram 304   Diagram 305

We claim that $AB < CD$. The arc CP is less than 60° (otherwise the chord CP would not be less than the width h of the curve, and hence would equal h, so that the curve would be a Reuleaux triangle; see the solution of Exercise 7-8). Therefore the tangent to the arc PC at the point P forms with the chord PC an angle less than 30°, and the angle APC between the radius AP and the chord PC is greater than 90° − 30° = 60°; likewise $\angle BPD$ is greater than 60°. Since, however, $\angle APB$ (as the central angle of arc AB) is less than 60°, we have

$$\angle CPD = \angle APC + \angle BPD - \angle APB > 60° + 60° - 60° = 60°.$$

Hence the chord CD is greater than at least one of the chords CP and PD (in triangle CPD the angle CPD cannot be the smallest angle). By our choice of the arc AB, the chord AB cannot exceed the chords CP and PD. Thus we conclude that chord AB is smaller than chord CD.

Now we replace the arcs AB, CP, and PD of K by the arcs AQ about C, QB about D, and CD about Q (Diagram 305). By the result in the first part of the proof, the area bounded by K becomes smaller under this replacement. The total number of arcs forming K also becomes smaller, for the two arcs CP and PD are replaced by a single arc CD, while the arc AB is replaced by the arcs AQ and QB, and at least one of these is an extension of an adjacent arc (since arc AQ has the center C and arc QB has the center D, and K already has an arc about C or an arc about D).

Continuing this process, we finally obtain a curve of constant width consisting of only three circular arcs. Evidently this curve can only be a Reuleaux triangle. In fact, at least one of the arcs must be equal to or greater than 60°; this arc corresponds to a corner of the curve whose angle is equal to or less than 120°; *cf.* Exercise 7-9 for further details.

It is easy to see from the foregoing that no curve K of constant width h can bound a smaller area than the Reuleaux triangle. For this purpose we consider a sequence of curves $K_1, K_2, ..., K_n, ...,$ where each curve is of constant width h and consists only of circular arcs of radius h; let the limit of this sequence be K. By the above proof, each of the curves $K_1, K_2, ..., K_n, ...$ bounds a greater area than that of a Reuleaux triangle of width h. Hence the area bounded by K, the limit of the curves $K_1, K_2, ..., K_n, ...$ (*cf.* Section 4, page 50), cannot be less than the area bounded by the Reuleaux triangle of width h.

It is left to the reader to prove, by completing these arguments, that the area of the Reuleaux triangle is actually smaller (and not merely not greater) than the area of every other curve of the same constant width.

8-1. (a) Let a circle whose radius equals the altitude of an equilateral triangle roll along one side of such a triangle. Prove that the arc cut out of the circle by the sides of the triangle always equals 60°. Prove also that the "lens" formed by reflection of these arcs in their corresponding chords always remains within the triangle. In what follows we shall call the boundary curve of this lens a *Δ-biangle*. The *Δ*-biangle is a *Δ*-curve.

Compute the length of a *Δ*-biangle of height h and also the area that it bounds. Which is greater, the area of a circle of radius $\frac{1}{3} h$ or the area of a *Δ*-biangle of height h? (b) At each contact point of an equilateral triangle with an inscribed *Δ*-biangle, a line is constructed perpendicular to the side of the triangle. Prove that these three perpendiculars intersect in a point. In addition, find the locus described by the point of intersection of these perpendiculars when the *Δ*-biangle rotates inside the equilateral triangle and also the locus of this point when the equilateral triangle rotates so that it remains circumscribed about the *Δ*-biangle when the latter is stationary.

(a) Let ABC be the given equilateral triangle, and let $AB'C'$ be the symmetric triangle with respect to A. Let BC be tangent to a circle whose radius equals the altitude of the triangle and whose center in a certain position is O. Let K be the point of contact of BC with the circle.

The sides AC and AB determine an arc MKN of the circle (Diagram 306). The line OA is parallel to BC and is therefore an axis of symmetry of the figure. Hence the sides AB' and AC' determine an arc $M'N'$ equal to the arc MKN. The angle at A, equal to 60°, is measured by $\frac{1}{2}(\widehat{MN} + \widehat{M'N'})$; hence each of these arcs is 60°.

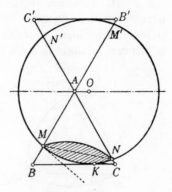

The angle between the chord MN and the tangent to the circle at M or N is thus 30°. Consequently, to prove that the biangle shaded in the diagram is always inside the triangle ABC, we must show that the angles AMN and ANM are never less than 30°. As the

Diagram 306

circle moves these angles vary from 30° to 90°. Thus the biangle is a $\varDelta$-curve.

The length of the $\varDelta$-biangle is one-third the perimeter of the circle of radius h, that is, $2\pi h/3$. The area bounded by the curve is twice the area of a circular segment of radius h and arc 60°, that is, $h^2 \cdot (2\pi - 3\sqrt{3})/6 \approx 0.18\, h^2$. The incircle of an equilateral triangle of altitude h (a circle of radius $\frac{1}{3}h$) also has length $2\pi h/3$, but its area is $h^2\pi/9 \approx 0.34\, h^2$ and is thus greater than the area of the $\varDelta$-biangle.

(b) Let P be the intersection of the perpendiculars to the sides of

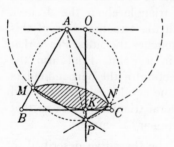

Diagram 307

the triangle erected at M and N (Diagram 307). Obviously the quadrilateral $AMPN$ can be inscribed in a circle. The center O of arc MKN of the $\varDelta$-biangle tangent to the side BC lies on this circle. This follows from the fact that $\sphericalangle MON = \sphericalangle MAN = 60°$. The segment AP is a diameter of this circle since both $\sphericalangle AMP$ and $\sphericalangle ANP$ are 90°. Hence $\sphericalangle AOP = 90°$; that is, the segment OP is perpendicular to AO and hence also to BC. The line OP passes through the point of contact K of the $\varDelta$-biangle and BC. Hence the perpendiculars to the sides of the triangle at M, N, and K intersect in the point P.

We now obtain the locus of P. The size of the diameter AP of the circle $MPNOA$ does not depend on the position of the $\varDelta$-biangle in the equilateral triangle. The chord MN of constant length (the chord of the biangle) spans an arc of 120° in this circle. It is evident that the diameter of this circle equals a side of triangle ABC. In fact, if OP

passes through C, then P coincides with C and AP with AC. Hence $AP = AC$. In other words, the distance from P to the vertex of the triangle on the opposite side of MN must always equal the side of the triangle. The locus described by P when the $\varDelta$-biangle rotates in the equilateral triangle is shown in Diagram 308 a.[†]

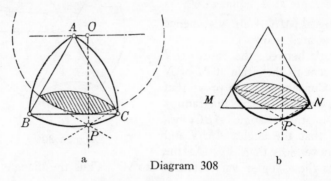

a   Diagram 308   b

Obviously $\sphericalangle MPN = 180° - \sphericalangle MAN = 120°$ (Diagram 307). Hence the locus of P when the equilateral triangle rotates and remains circumscribed about the fixed $\varDelta$-biangle has the form shown in Diagram 308 b.

8-2. About the vertices of a square of side h we draw four circles of radius h. Prove that the boundary curve of the figure resulting from the intersection of these circles is a $\varDelta$-curve of height h. Compute the length of this curve and the area bounded by it. (b) Circumscribe an equilateral triangle about the $\varDelta$-curve given in Exercise 8-2 a; erect perpendiculars to the sides of this triangle at the points where the curve touches the sides. Prove that these three perpendiculars intersect in a point. Find also the locus described by this point of intersection of the perpendiculars when the given $\varDelta$-curve rotates inside the equilateral triangle, and the locus it describes when the equilateral triangle rotates so that it remains circumscribed about the stationary $\varDelta$-curve.

(a) Let $ABCD$ be a square and let $MNPQ$ be the curve described in the statement of the Exercise (Diagram 309). Triangle CDM is equilateral by construction; hence $\sphericalangle MDC = 60°$, $\sphericalangle MDA = 30°$. Triangle AMD is isosceles, so that

$$\sphericalangle DAM = \frac{180° - 30}{2} = 75°, \qquad \sphericalangle BAM = 15°;$$

likewise $\sphericalangle DAQ = 15°$ and we have

$$\sphericalangle MAQ = 90° - 15° - 15° = 60°.$$

[†] It is easy to see that this locus is a Reuleaux triangle. (See Section 7, page 71.)

Since the triangle ADM is congruent to the triangle ABQ, we have $AM = AQ$. Triangle AMQ is therefore equilateral as are the triangles BNM, CPN, and DQP.

Let RST be an equilateral triangle in which two sides pass through M and Q, while the third is tangent to the arc PN at H. Then $\measuredangle MAQ = 60^\circ = \measuredangle MRQ$, so the points A, R, M, Q lie on a circle. Then we have

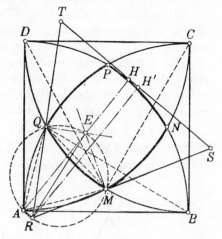

Diagram 309

$$\measuredangle ARM = 180^\circ - \measuredangle AQM = 120^\circ;$$

hence the segment AR is parallel to the side ST of the triangle (since $\measuredangle ARS + \measuredangle RST = 180^\circ$). Hence the altitude RH' of the triangle RST is equal to the segment AH and is therefore equal to the side of the original square.

Triangle RST also contains the curve $MNPQ$. Each of the arcs MN, NP, PQ, and QM measures 30° ($\measuredangle MDA = \measuredangle NDC = \measuredangle MDN = 30^\circ$); hence, for example, the tangents at the points N and P to the arc NP form angles of 15° with the chord NP. Each of the angles NMS and PQT lies between 15° and 45° ($\measuredangle NMS = 15^\circ$ if H coincides with P and the altitude of the triangle RST has the direction of AP; $\measuredangle NMS = 45^\circ$ if H coincides with N). The arcs MN and PQ (and also NP) lie inside the triangle RST. The arc MQ also lies in this triangle since $\measuredangle MQR$ and $\measuredangle QMP$ lie between 45° and 75° ($\measuredangle MQR = 45^\circ$ if H coincides with P; $\measuredangle MQR = 75^\circ$ if H coincides with N).

Finally we note that, considering equilateral triangles in which two sides pass through adjacent corner points of the curve $MNPQ$ while the third is tangent to the opposite arc, we obtain equilateral triangles whose sides are arbitrarily directed and which are circumscribed about the curve $MNPQ$—in fact we obtain all circumscribed equilateral triangles. The altitude of each of these triangles equals the side of the square, that is, h.

Thus $MNPQ$ is a $\varDelta$-curve. It consists of four circular arcs of 30° and radius h. The length of the curve is $2\pi h/3$ (hence it equals the length of the incircle of the triangle and also the length of the $\varDelta$-biangle of height h). It is easy to show that the area bounded by the curve is $[(\pi/3)+1 - \sqrt{3})] h^2 \approx 0.31\, h^2$. This is a value between the area of the incircle and the area of the $\varDelta$-biangle of height h (see Exercise 8-1 a).

(b) Denote by E the second intersection of the segment AH with the circle through the points A, R, M, and Q (Diagram 309). Then ER is a diameter of this circle, since $\angle EAR = 90°$ (EA is perpendicular to ST and AR is parallel to ST). Hence $\angle EMR = 90° = \angle EQR$; that is, the perpendiculars to the sides of the triangle RST erected at the points M, Q, and H intersect at E.

We will now determine the locus of all such points E. The diameter RE of the circle $MRAQE$ does not depend on the position of the curve in the triangle: the chord MQ of constant length in this circle subtends an arc of 120°. It can be proved that the length of the segment RE is equal to $2\sqrt{2 - \sqrt{3}}\, h$, where h is the side of the square (the altitude of the triangle RST). The locus of E when the given $\varDelta$-curve is rotated within the equilateral triangle is shown in Diagram 310 a.

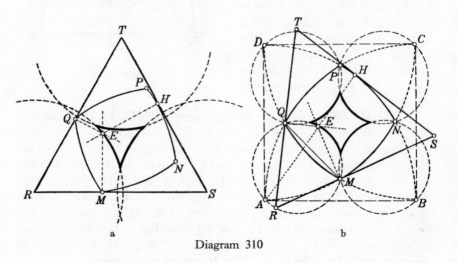

Diagram 310

It is obvious that $\angle MEQ = 180° - \angle MRQ = 120°$. Hence the locus of E when the equilateral triangle rotates and remains circumscribed about the fixed curve $MNPQ$ has the form shown in Diagram 310 b.

8-3. Let K be a $\varDelta$-curve and let T be an equilateral triangle circumscribed about K whose sides touch K at the points A, B, C. Prove that the side of each equilateral triangle circumscribed about triangle ABC is not greater than the side of T.

Let K be any $\varDelta$-curve; let T be an equilateral triangle circumscribed about it, and let A, B, and C be the points of intersection of the sides of the triangle T with the curve K (Diagram 311). Further let T_1 be any equilateral triangle whose sides pass through A, B, and C. We must show that the altitude of the triangle T_1 does not exceed that of the triangle T.

Let T_1' be a triangle circumscribed about K whose sides are parallel and similarly directed to those of T_1. Triangle T_1' contains the triangle T_1 (since the points A, B, and C belong to the curve and hence must be inside T_1' or on its boundary). Therefore the altitude of T_1 does not exceed the altitude of T_1', but from the definition of a Δ-curve, the altitude of T_1' is equal to the altitude of triangle T.

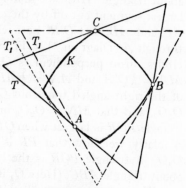

Diagram 311

8-4. Prove that the perpendiculars to the sides of an equilateral triangle circumscribed about a Δ-curve K intersect in a point if the perpendiculars pass through the points of contact of the triangle with K.

We begin by solving the following auxiliary problem: *To circumscribe about a given triangle ABC as large an equilateral triangle as possible.*

The solution of this problem is not difficult. First of all we draw circular arcs of 240° outside the given triangle ABC and about its sides (Diagram 312). In order to construct any equilateral triangle circum-

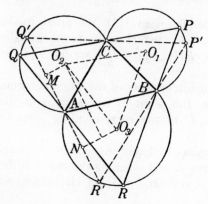

Diagram 312

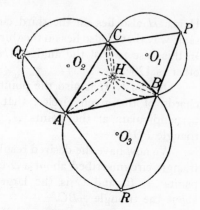

Diagram 313

scribed about the triangle ABC, we need only draw a segment $Q'R'$ through the point A whose end points lie on the arcs constructed on the sides AC and AB. The lines $Q'C$ and $R'B$ intersect in the point P' of the third arc and form an equilateral triangle $P'Q'R'$ circumscribed about triangle ABC.

To construct the *largest* of all the equilateral triangles circumscribed about triangle ABC, we merely need to find on a line through A the largest segment cut off by the circular arcs constructed on the segments AC and AB. Let $Q'R'$ be such a segment cut out by these two arcs through A (Diagram 312). From the centers O_2 and O_3 of the two given circles, drop perpendiculars O_2M and O_3N onto the line $Q'R'$. Then $MA = \frac{1}{2}Q'A$ and $AN = \frac{1}{2}AR'$; thus $MN = \frac{1}{2}Q'R'$. By examination of the right-angled trapezoid O_2O_3NM, it is easily shown that $MN \leq O_2O_3$, and that $MN = O_2O_3$ only if $Q'R'$ is parallel to O_2O_3. Thus the triangle PQR is largest when QR is parallel to O_2O_3; then $QR = 2O_2O_3$. Similarly we show that PR is parallel to O_1O_3 and PQ is parallel to O_1O_2, if triangle PQR is the largest equilateral triangle circumscribed about triangle ABC. (Here O_1 is the center of the circle with chord BC.)

We now point out that if triangle PQR is the largest equilateral triangle circumscribed about the triangle ABC, then the perpendiculars to the sides of triangle PQR at the points A, B, C intersect in a point. Our construction shows, in fact, that these perpendiculars are nothing but the common chords of pairs of the circles about the points O_1, O_2, O_3. It is easy to show that these circles intersect in a point. For this purpose we denote by H the intersection of the two circles constructed on the segments AB and BC. If H lies inside the triangle ABC, then $\sphericalangle AHB = \sphericalangle BHC = 120°$ and thus

$$\sphericalangle AHC = 360° - 120° - 120° = 120°.$$

Hence H also lies on the third circle (Diagram 313). We prove in the same way that H also lies on the third circle when H is outside the triangle. In this case two of the angles AHB, BHC, and CHA are 60° and the other is 120°.

Obviously H is also the point of intersection of the three common chords of the given circles, that is, the point of intersection of the perpendiculars at the points A, B, C to the corresponding sides of triangle PQR.

We now have the desired result, since by Exercise 8-3 the equilateral triangle circumscribed about a $\varDelta$-curve K and touching the curve at the points A, B, and C is the largest equilateral triangle circumscribed about the triangle ABC.

8-5. Prove that each supporting line of a $\varDelta$-curve can have only one point in common with the curve.

Assume that some arc PQ of a $\varDelta$-curve K is a linear segment, and let T be an equilateral triangle circumscribed about K, one of whose for B. Thus A and B move along the sides of T while the third side of T is tangent to an arc AB of K (if the points A and B move on the sides RQ and RS of T (Diagram 317), then the arc of K which lies on the same side of the segment AB as the vertex R of triangle T remains inside T, since the one-sided tangents at the points A and B form with the chord AB angles that do not exceed 30º).

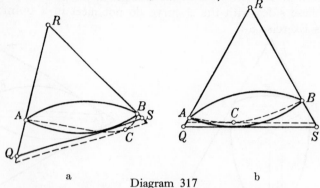

a   b

Diagram 317

Draw a $\varDelta$-biangle D whose end points coincide with the points A and B. If any point C of K is outside D, then an equilateral triangle can be drawn about K whose altitude exceeds the segment AB (Diagram 317 a; note that the altitude of an equilateral triangle circumscribed about the $\varDelta$-curve D must be AB). If any point C of K is within D, then an equilateral triangle can be circumscribed about K with altitude less than AB (Diagram 317 b). Both of these cases contradict the definition of a $\varDelta$-curve. Hence the $\varDelta$-curve K must coincide with D.

8-7. Prove that a $\varDelta$-curve has no corner with an interior angle of less than 60º. The only $\varDelta$-curve with an interior angle equal to 60º is a $\varDelta$-biangle.

If the angle at A of a $\varDelta$-curve K does not exceed 60º, then there is an equilateral triangle T circumscribed about K, one of whose vertices is A (Diagram 316 a). If B is a point of contact of the opposite side of T with the $\varDelta$-curve K, then the distance from A to B cannot be less than the altitude h of T. By Exercise 8-6 it follows that $AB = h$ and that K is a $\varDelta$-biangle.

8-8. Prove that the circle is the only $\varDelta$-curve that is carried into itself by a rotation of 120º about some point.

To prove this assertion, we need the following theorem. Let T be an equilateral triangle; let h be its altitude, let O be any interior point, and let h_1, h_2, h_3 be the lengths of the perpendiculars let fall from O onto the sides of the triangle. Then $h = h_1 + h_2 + h_3$.

sides has the segment PQ in common with K (Diagram 314). Let
two other sides of T touch K at the points A and B, and let O be
point of intersection of the perpendiculars to the sides of the trian
at A and B. Drop a perpendicular OH onto the third side of the trian
Let C be any point of the segment PQ except H. Then the three
pendiculars drawn to the sides of the triangle at the contact points
B, C, of these sides with the Δ-curve do not meet in a point, w
contradicts Exercise 8-4.

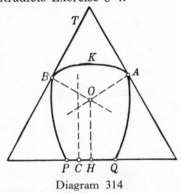
Diagram 314

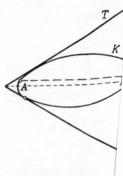
Diagram 315

8-6. Prove that the diameter of a Δ-curve K of height h
exceed h. If the diameter is equal to h, then K is a Δ-biang

Let A and B be two points of a Δ-curve K, and let T be an e
triangle circumscribed about K so that an altitude of the t
parallel to the segment AB (Diagram 315). Obviously AB
exceed the altitude of T, and is therefore not greater than t
h of the Δ-curve.

Now suppose that the distance from A to B is h (Diagra

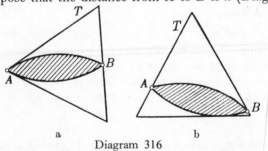
a
Diagram 316
b

Then A must coincide with a vertex of T, so that the ang
not exceed 60° (more exactly, the angle between each one-
at A—see page 0—and the line AB cannot exceed 30°
readily that when K is displaced within T, the point A
move along the sides of the triangle (Diagram 316 b); th

To show this, join O to the vertices of T (Diagram 318). Then T is divided into three triangles T_1, T_2, T_3 of areas $\frac{1}{2}ah_1$, $\frac{1}{2}ah_2$, $\frac{1}{2}ah_3$ respectively, where a is the length of the sides of T. Since

$$\tfrac{1}{2}ah_1 + \tfrac{1}{2}ah_2 + \tfrac{1}{2}ah_3 = \tfrac{1}{2}ah,$$

we have

$$h_1 + h_2 + h_3 = h.$$

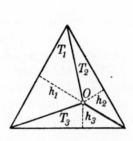

Diagram 318

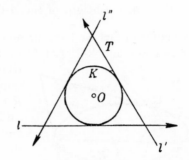

Diagram 319

Now let K be any $\varDelta$-curve of height h which is carried into itself by a rotation of 120° about any interior point (obviously no convex curve can be carried into itself by a rotation about an exterior point), and let l be any supporting line of K. Circumscribe about K an equilateral triangle T one of whose sides lies on l (Diagram 319). When K is carried into itself by a rotation of 120° about O, the equilateral triangle circumscribed about K is transformed into an equilateral triangle circumscribed about K whose sides have the same direction as the sides of T (a rotation of 120° does not change the directions of the sides of an equilateral triangle); that is, T is transformed into itself. Let l' and l'' denote the other two sides of T. A rotation of 120° carries l into l' and l' into l''. We showed above that the sum of the distances of O from l, l', l'' equals the altitude, h, of T. Since l, l', l'' are carried into each other by a rotation of 120° about O, they must be equidistant from O; that is, the distance of each of these lines from O is $\frac{1}{3}h$. But l is any supporting line of K. Hence all supporting lines of K are at a distance $\frac{1}{3}h$ from O.

From this it is easy to see that K must be a circle of radius $\frac{1}{3}h$ and center O. If any point A of K lies within this circle, the distance of O from the supporting line of K through A is less than $\frac{1}{3}h$ (Diagram 320 a). If on the other hand a point A lies outside this

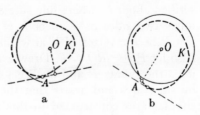

Diagram 320

circle, then the distance from O to the supporting line of K perpendicular to OA exceeds $\frac{1}{3}h$ (Diagram 320 b).

8-9. Let A, B, C be the points of intersection of a Δ-curve K with the sides of an equilateral triangle T circumscribed about K; moreover let O be the vertex outside the triangle ABC of the equilateral triangle ABO constructed on the side AB. Prove that $OC = h$, the height of the Δ-curve K.

As a matter of fact we have already used this theorem in the solution of Exercises 8-1 and 8-2. Let O be a point which forms an equilateral triangle with A and B and lies on the same side of the line AB as the vertex R of the triangle T (R is the point of intersection of the sides through A and B). Let P be the intersection of the perpendiculars erected to the sides of T at the points A, B, and C (Diagram 321; see Exercise 8-4). Then $\measuredangle AOB = 60^\circ = \measuredangle ARB$ and $\measuredangle APB = 120^\circ$. The points A, O, R, B, and P therefore lie on a circle, from which it follows that $\measuredangle ORB = 120^\circ$, so that the line OR is parallel to side l of T through C. The line RP is then a diameter of the circle in question. Hence OP is perpendicular to OR and also to l. Thus it follows that C lies on OP extended. We thus see that OP is parallel to the altitude of T through the vertex R, and the length of OC equals the length h of the altitude of T.

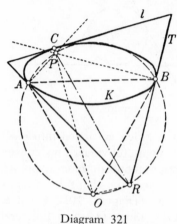

Diagram 321

8-10. Construct a Δ-curve of height h consisting of five or seven or, in general, any number not divisible by three, circular arcs of radius h. Find the length of the curve constructed.

Let L be a regular polygon of n sides, where n is not divisible by three. Let PQ be one of its sides and let T be an equilateral triangle circumscribed about L, where one side of T contains the segment PQ. Let the other two sides of T meet L at the points A and B (Diagram 322). Let R be the vertex of T at which the sides through A and B intersect. Also let $PR = RQ = h$. Draw a circular arc of radius h about R which joins the points P and Q. We join each pair of adjacent vertices of L by such arcs and assert that the convex curve K consisting of the n circular arcs constructed in this fashion is a Δ-curve of height h. We will prove this.

Let SUV be an equilateral triangle whose sides SU and SV pass through the points A and B, while the third side UV meets the arc PQ at a point H (Diagram 322). Obviously the four points A, B, S, and R lie on a circle, since $\angle ARB = \angle ASB = 60°$. Hence $\angle RSB = \angle RSA + \angle ASB = 120°$, and the lines RS and UV are parallel ($\angle RSV +$

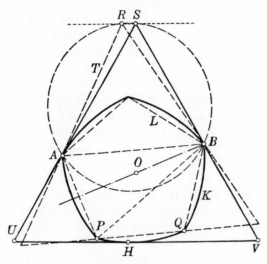

Diagram 322

$\angle SVU = 180°$). Thus the altitude of the triangle SUV is $RH = h$, as we wished to show.

Triangle SUV also contains the curve K. To prove this, we show that the triangle ABP must be isosceles. If $n = 3m + 1$, then between A and B there are exactly m sides of the regular polygon L. The same is true between A and P and between B and Q. If $n = 3m + 2$, then between A and B and also between B and P there are $m + 1$ sides of L, while between A and P there are exactly m sides. (We note that here we use the hypothesis that n is not divisible by three, for if n were equal to $3m$, then the triangle ABP would not be isosceles.) If H coincides with P or with Q then the triangle SUV is tangent not only to arc PQ but also to a circular arc with end point A or B. In Diagram 322, for example, $n = 5 = 3 \cdot 1 + 2$; if now H coincides with P, then the triangle SUV is symmetric with respect to AB and in this position SU touches an arc of K through A.

We conclude that for any position of H on the arc PQ, the arcs of K with A and B as end points, and lying on the same side of the line AB as does vertex S of triangle SUV, remain inside triangle SUV. It is even easier to establish that the two other arcs of K having A and B as end points always remain in the interior of the triangle SUV.

Thus for any position of H on the arc PQ, the entire curve K is contained in the triangle SUV.

If we examine all triangles with two sides passing through corner points of K while the third is tangent to one of the circular arcs, then we obtain all equilateral triangles circumscribed about the curve K. Since the altitude of each such triangle is h, K must be a Δ-curve. For $n = 4$, we obtain the curve described in Exercise 8-2. We can also establish that for $n = 2$, the construction leads to a Δ-biangle (in this case instead of starting from a regular n-sided polygon L, we must begin with a segment).

We can show that there is no Δ-curve consisting of $n = 3m$ circular arcs of radius h constructed on the sides of a regular n-sided polygon. We leave it to the reader to carry out the proof.

We note further that it is not necessary for our construction to require that the polygon L be regular. The polygon L of n sides (where n is not divisible by three) need only have a property which can be described as follows: Let T be a regular triangle circumscribed about L, one of whose sides contains the side PQ of the polygon, while the two other sides contain the vertices A and B respectively. Denote by R the vertex of the equilateral triangle constructed on the segment AB and lying on the other side of the line AB from the points P and Q (Diagram 323). In order that the construction described above be possible, the segments RP and RQ must be equal no matter what side PQ of L is selected. Furthermore, the length of these equal segments (we denote it by h) must be independent of the choice of the side PQ of L. It is easy to see that this condition is satisfied by some irregular polygons. If every two adjacent vertices of such a polygon L are joined by a circular arc of radius h, we assert that the curve thus obtained is a Δ-curve of altitude h.

The proof of this theorem resembles the proof given above when L was regular. The first part of the proof does not in any way depend on the regularity of L and is derived in our more general case exactly as before. To prove that K is always contained in the equilateral triangle T (two of whose sides pass through the corner points A and B of K while the third side touches a circular arc PQ at some point O), we previously used the equality of two sides of the triangle ABP (or the triangle ABQ) which, however, does not occur if L is not regular. Hence we must recast this part of the proof. We present it briefly.

It is readily apparent that the three perpendiculars to the sides of the equilateral triangle T at the points A, B, and P intersect in a point O when two sides of T pass through A and B and the third side meets the circular arc PQ at P. (For the proof of this fact the irregularity of the polygon L has no significance. It is important, however, that the points A, O_1, R, B, and O (Diagram 324) lie on a circle.) Let AD and BF be two sides of L such that the points F, B, D, A, P, and Q (D may coincide with B, Q with F) occur on the polygon L in cyclic order (Diagram 324). We choose the smaller of the two angles RAD and SBF, say SBF. Then it is obvious that the equilateral triangle T_1, one of whose sides contains the segment BF and whose other two sides pass through A and P respectively, is circumscribed about the polygon L.

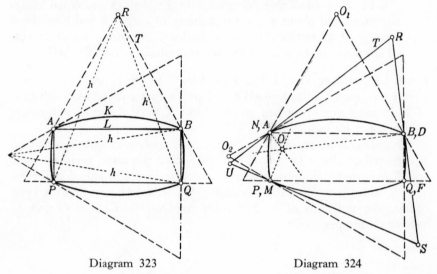

Diagram 323   Diagram 324

We examine the equilateral triangle T', two sides of which pass through A and P while the third is tangent to the arc BF (of radius h) at the point B. Since the line BO passes through O_2 (Diagram 324), the triangle T' coincides with T. In case the point of contact H of the side of T with arc PQ coincides with P, then T touches not only the arc PQ but also the arc BF. Hence for any position of H on arc PQ, the arc BF lies inside the triangle T. Similarly we can conclude from the position of T when H and Q coincide that the arcs MA and NB of K (the vertices, B, N, A, M, P, and Q of L appear in cyclic order) lie inside the triangle T for any position of H on the arc PQ.

Thus the triangle T includes the entire curve K for any position of H on the arc PQ of K. But examination of all equilateral triangles, two sides of which pass through the corner points of K while the third touches an arc of this curve, shows that these are all the equilateral triangles circumscribed about K. Since all these triangles have altitude h, K must be a $\varDelta$-curve.

To calculate the length of this curve, we observe that if the central angle α corresponds to PQ, then the triangle T rotates through the angle α when the point H is displaced from Q toward P. When the equilateral circumscribed triangle is rotated through 120°, the triangle assumes its original position, except that its vertices exchange places; the point A, at which one side of the triangle touches an arc of K, runs over the entire curve K under such a rotation. The sum of the central angles of all circular arcs of radius h constituting K is therefore $120°$, and the length of the curve K is $2\pi h/3$.

8-11. By considering polygons with $3 \cdot 2^n$ sides and equal angles circumscribed about a general $\varDelta$-curve of height h and also about a circle O of radius $\frac{1}{3}h$, prove Barbier's Theorem for $\varDelta$-curves: all $\varDelta$-curves of height h have the same length, namely $2h/3$.

Let K be any $\varDelta$-curve of height h, and let O be the incircle of an equilateral triangle of altitude h. We will prove that equiangular polygons of $3 \cdot 2^n$ sides circumscribed about O and K have the same perimeter. The proof is by induction.

Equilateral triangles (that is, equiangular polygons with $3 \cdot 2^0$ sides) circumscribed about O and K not only have the same perimeter but are all congruent. Suppose that the circumscribed equilateral polygons of $3 \cdot 2^n$ sides have the same perimeter. We wish to prove that then the equiangular polygons of $3 \cdot 2^{n+1}$ sides circumscribed about O and K have the same perimeter.

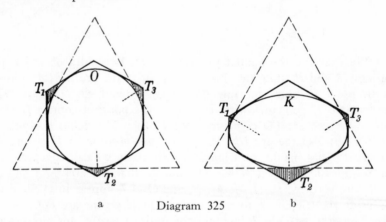

a   Diagram 325   b

Draw equilateral triangles T about the curves O and K, each triangle having a side perpendicular to one of the angle bisectors of the polygon of $3 \cdot 2^n$ sides (Diagram 325). These triangles cut off from each polygon of $3 \cdot 2^n$ sides three similar triangles T_1, T_2, and T_3. We now prove that the sum of the altitudes of T_1, T_2, and T_3 for both K and O is the same.

To show this, we extend the sides of the polygon of $3 \cdot 2^n$ sides which intersect T and obtain two circumscribed equilateral triangles T' and T'' which intersect T (Diagram 326 a). The points of intersection of the sides of T' and T'' which are vertices of triangles T_1, T_2, and T_3

are denoted by A, B, and C. We draw a triangle T^* whose sides are parallel to those of triangle T and which passes through A, B, and C. By the construction of the triangle T, the sides of T^* are bisectors of the acute angles formed by the sides of T' and T'' through A, B, and C (Diagram 326 b). Finally, we erect perpendiculars at A, B, and C to the sides of T^* (bisectors of the obtuse angles formed by the sides of T' and T'').

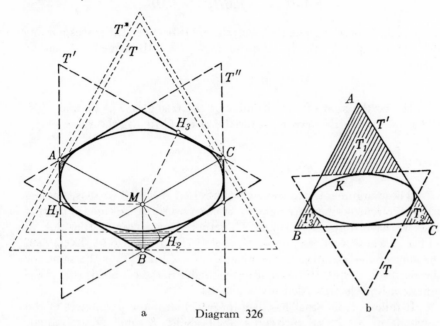

a Diagram 326 b

It is easy to see that these perpendiculars intersect in a point M. In fact, let M be the intersection of the perpendiculars to T^* at A and B. Then AM is the locus of all points equidistant from the sides of T' and T'' through A. The segment BM is the locus of all points equidistant from the sides of T' and T'' through B. Since the triangles T' and T'' circumscribed about K and O are congruent, the sum of the distances of any point which is an interior point of T' and T'' from the three sides of T' equals the sum of the distances of the same point from the three sides of T'' (see the theorem at the beginning of the solution of Exercise 8-8). From this we infer that the point M (the intersection of the lines AM and BM) is also equidistant from the sides of triangles T' and T'' through C. Thus MC is a perpendicular to the side of T^* through C.

The sum $AM + BM + CM$ is, on the one hand, equal to the altitude of triangle T^* and, on the other hand, is equal to the altitude h of T plus the sum of the altitudes of triangles T_1, T_2, and T_3. The altitude of triangle T is the same for K and O. In fact, if MH_1, MH_2, and MH_3 are perpendiculars to the sides of triangle T' (the sum $MH_1 + MH_2 + MH_3$ is equal to the altitude h of triangle T), then we have

$$MH_1 = MA \cdot \cos \sphericalangle AMH_1, \qquad MH_2 = MB \cdot \cos \sphericalangle BMH_2,$$
$$MH_3 = MC \cdot \cos \sphericalangle CMH_3.$$

However

$$\sphericalangle AMH_1 = \sphericalangle BMH_2 = \sphericalangle CMH_3,$$

since each of these angles equals half the angle between the corresponding sides of triangles T' and T'', and this angle, 2α, is the same for K and O. Hence

$$MA + MB + MC = h/\cos \alpha.$$

Hence the sum of the altitudes of the triangles T_1, T_2, and T_3 is the same for the Δ-curve K as for the circle O (it has the value

$$\frac{h}{\cos \alpha} - h = h \cdot \frac{1 - \cos \alpha}{\cos \alpha}\Big).$$

These arguments are somewhat different if $n = 0$ (that is, passing from a circumscribed triangle to a circumscribed hexagon). In that case we have only one triangle T', rather than a pair of triangles T' and T'', whose vertices are A, B, and C (Diagram 326 b). Even then the sum of the altitudes of the triangles T_1, T_2, and T_3 is the same for the curves K and O. We leave it to the reader to establish this (the proof differs very little from that given above).

It follows from what has been proved that if the perimeters of the polygons of $3 \cdot 2^n$ sides circumscribed about K and O are equal, then the perimeters are also equal for the two polygons obtained from these polygons of $3 \cdot 2^n$ sides by removal of the triangles T_1, T_2, and T_3 (cf. the solution of Exercise 7-11). If at each vertex of the equiangular polygon of $3 \cdot 2^n$ sides a triangle is removed, we obtain a polygon of $3 \cdot 2^{n+1}$ sides. Thus, if the equiangular circumscribed polygons of $3 \cdot 2^n$ sides of K and O have the same perimeter, the equiangular polygons of $3 \cdot 2^{n+1}$ sides also have the same perimeter. This completes the proof by induction.

By passing to the limit, we infer that K and O have the same length $2\pi h/3$ (see the solution of Exercise 7-11).

8-12. By considering equiangular polygons with $3 \cdot 2^n$ sides circumscribed about any Δ-curve K of height h, about a circle O of radius $\frac{1}{3}h$, and about a Δ-biangle D of height h, prove that among all Δ-curves of height h, the circle encloses the greatest area and the Δ-biangle the least area.

Let K be any Δ-curve, D a Δ-biangle, and O a circle, all of height h. Circumscribe an equiangular hexagon about the circle O (it is necessarily regular; Diagram 327 a). Circumscribe about D a rhombus with angles of 60° and 120° whose vertices at the acute angles are at the vertices of D (Diagram 327 b). We regard the rhombus about D as an equiangular

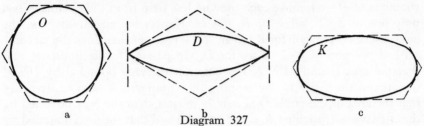

a   b   c
Diagram 327

hexagon with two opposite sides of length zero. We assert that an equiangular hexagon can always be circumscribed about K whose area is no greater than the area of the regular hexagon about O and no less than the area of the rhombus about D (Diagram 327 c). The proof of this assertion is the most difficult part of our solution of the exercise. We postpone it to the end and meanwhile will use the assertion without proof.

About O we circumscribe a regular hexagon, about D a rhombus, and about K an equiangular hexagon with area between that of the regular hexagon and that of the rhombus. We shall double in turn the number of sides of the equilateral polygons circumscribed about K, D, and O, beginning with the circumscribed hexagons and proceeding as in the solution of Exercise 8-11. For this purpose, we remove each time from the polygons circumscribed about K, D, and O three mutually similar triangles, the sum of whose altitudes is the same in all three cases (see the solution of the previous exercise). The sum of the areas of these three removed triangles is proportional to the sum of the squares of their altitudes. However if $h_1 + h_2 + h_3$ is constant, then $h_1^2 + h_2^2 + h_3^2$ has the smallest value if $h_1 = h_2 = h_3$ and the largest value if $h_1 = h_2 = O$.[†]

It is obvious that the first possibility is realized when the Δ-curve is a circle O (this follows from the fact that a circle is transformed into itself by a rotation of 120° about its center; then T_1 goes into T_2, and T_2 into T_3). The second possibility is realized when the Δ-curve is a Δ-biangle (every equilateral triangle circumscribed about a Δ-biangle passes through the two corner points, which for $n = 1$ are vertices of

[†] The truth of this can be seen immediately from the equalities
$$h_1^2 + h_2^2 + h_3^2 = \tfrac{1}{2}[(h_1 + h_2 + h_3)^2 + (h_1 - h_2)^2 + (h_1 - h_3)^2 + (h_2 - h_3)^2],$$
$$h_1^2 + h_3^2 + h_2^2 = (h_1 + h_2 + h_3)^2 - 2h_1h_2 - 2h_1h_3 - 2h_2h_3.$$

all polygons of $3 \cdot 2^n$ sides circumscribed about the Δ-biangle). That is, two of the cut-out triangles reduce to points.

From the circumscribed polygon of $3 \cdot 2^n$ sides for the circle we therefore remove each time no more than from the circumscribed polygon of $3 \cdot 2^n$ sides for the curves K and D; from the circumscribed rhombus of D we remove each time no less than from the circumscribed polygons of $3 \cdot 2^n$ sides for K and O. Hence, for all values of n, the circumscribed polygon for K has an area no greater than does the circumscribed polygon of $3 \cdot 2^n$ sides for D. On passing to the limit, we find that the area bounded by K lies between the area bounded by D and the area of the circle O. By refining the argument, we can easily prove that the area of the circle O is strictly greater than the area bounded by the Δ-curve K (provided K is not a circle) and that the area bounded by the Δ-biangle D is strictly less than the area bounded by the Δ-curve K (provided K is not a Δ-biangle). The proof is very similar to the arguments at the end of the solution to Exercise 7-12; Exercises 8-7 and 8-8 must be used. We leave it to the reader to complete the proof.

We must show finally that *an equiangular hexagon can be circumscribed about every Δ-curve K whose area lies between that of the equiangular circumscribed hexagon for the circle O and that of the rhombus with $60°$ and $120°$ angles circumscribed about the Δ-biangle D* (we suppose that the Δ-curves D, O, and K all have height h).

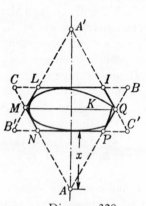

Diagram 328

We circumscribe about K an equilateral hexagon $ILMNPQ$ with an axis of symmetry through the midpoints of the opposite sides IL and NP (Diagram 328; the existence of such a circumscribed hexagon was proved in Exercise 3-4 b). We wish to compute the area of this hexagon. If we extend its sides until they meet, we obtain two equilateral triangles ABC and $A'B'C'$ with altitude h circumscribed about the Δ-curve K. The axis of symmetry of the hexagon is perpendicular to the bases BC and $B'C'$ of the triangles and passes through the vertices A and A'.

The distance of the vertex A from the side NP is denoted by x, where $0 \leq x \leq h$. If S is the area of the triangle ABC, then the area of the triangle ANP is $(x^2/h^2)\,S$, and the area of the triangle AMQ is $[(h + x)^2/4h^2)]S$ (the distance from A to A' is $h + x$ and that from A to MQ is $(h + x)/2$). The area of the trapezoid $MNPQ$ is thus

$$\left[\frac{(h + x)^2}{4h^2} - \frac{x^2}{h^2} \right] S = \frac{h^2 + 2hx - 3x^2}{4h^2}\, S.$$

The area of the hexagon $ILMNPQ$ is therefore

$$\frac{h^2 + 2hx - 3x^2}{2h^2} S.$$

If we put this expression into the form

$$\frac{h^2 + 2hx - 3x^2}{2h^2} S = \frac{(4h^2/3) - [(h/\sqrt{3}) - \sqrt{3}\, x]^2}{2h^2} S,$$

we can see that the area is greatest when $h/\sqrt{3} = \sqrt{3}\, x$ or $x = h/3$. In this case $ILMNPQ$ is regular. We infer that no equiangular hexagon which is circumscribed about a convex curve K and which has an axis of symmetry through the midpoints of parallel sides has a greater area than the regular hexagon circumscribed about the circle O.[†]

Since the rhombus circumscribed about D (Diagram 327 b) corresponds to the value $x = 0$, the area of the hexagon $ILMNPQ$ is not less than the area of this rhombus if

$$\left| \frac{h}{\sqrt{3}} - \sqrt{3}\, x \right| \leq \left| \frac{h}{\sqrt{3}} \right|, \quad \text{that is,} \quad \frac{h}{\sqrt{3}} - \sqrt{3}\, x \geq - \frac{h}{\sqrt{3}}$$

and

$$x \leq \tfrac{2}{3}\, h,$$

and it is actually less than that of the rhombus if $x > \tfrac{2}{3} h$.

If $x \leq \tfrac{2}{3} h$, the hexagon in question already satisfies our requirement, since its area is not greater than that of the circumscribed regular hexagon of the circle O and not less than that of the circumscribed rhombus of the curve D.

Thus there remains only the case in which a symmetric equiangular hexagon for which $x > \tfrac{2}{3} h$ can be circumscribed about K. We will show in this case that still another symmetric equiangular hexagon with a corresponding value of $x < \tfrac{2}{3} h$ can be circumscribed about K.

Let $ILMNPQ$ be a hexagon such that $x > \tfrac{2}{3} h$ (Diagram 329); let I', L', M', N', P', Q' denote the points of contact of the sides IL, LM, MN, NP, PQ, QI, respectively, with the curve K. Now consider a symmetrical hexagon circumscribed about K whose axis of symmetry forms an angle of not more than 60° with the line MQ (the existence of such a hexagon follows from the note after the solution of Exercise 3-4 b). We assert that the distance between the sides of this hexagon which are perpendicular to the axis of symmetry is greater than $h/3$; this implies that there corresponds to this hexagon a value $x < \tfrac{2}{3} h$; the

[†] It is easy to see that no equiangular hexagon circumscribed about the curve K (even if it has no axis of symmetry) has a greater area than a regular hexagon circumscribed about the circle O.

area of the hexagon in question is thus not less than the area of the rhombus circumscribed about D.

Suppose that the axis of the given hexagon forms an angle $\alpha \leq 30^{\circ}$ with the line MQ; then the sides of the hexagon perpendicular to the axis form the same angle $\alpha \leq 30^{\circ}$ with the axis of $ILMNPQ$ and touch the arcs $L'M'$ and $P'Q'$ of K (Diagram 329 a). The distance between

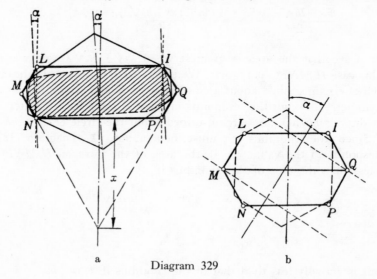

Diagram 329

these sides merely decreases if they are displaced so that they pass through the vertices I and N (or through the vertices L and P). The distance between parallel lines through I and N lying inside the angles PIQ and LMN respectively (for example, the lines parallel to the given sides of the hexagon) is smallest if these lines coincide with the lines LN and PI. In this limiting case, the distance between the lines is IL; that is, is greater than $\frac{2}{3}h$ (since the inequality $x > \frac{2}{3}h$ holds for the hexagon $ILMNPQ$).

Next, suppose that the axis of the hexagon in question forms an angle α with the line MQ such that $30^{\circ} \leq \alpha \leq 60^{\circ}$. The sides of this hexagon perpendicular to the axis form the same angle α with the axis of $ILMNPQ$ and therefore touch the arcs $I'L'$ and $N'P'$ (or $Q'I'$ and $M'N'$) of K (Diagram 329 b). Hence the distance between these sides merely decreases if they are displaced parallel to themselves so that they pass through Q or M. Clearly, the distance between the displaced lines is least if they form an angle of 60° with the axis of the hexagon $ILMNPQ$. In this limiting case, the distance between the lines is MQ; that is, is greater than $\frac{1}{3}h$, since $MQ > \frac{2}{3}h$ (this follows from the fact that the inequality $x > \frac{2}{3}h$ holds for the hexagon $ILMNPQ$). Thus we have completely proved the assertion stated at the beginning of the solution.

8-13. If K is any Δ-curve, and K' and K'' are curves obtained by rotating K through 120° and 240° respectively, prove that the sum $K + K' + K''$ is a circle. Obtain from this fact a new proof of Barbier's Theorem for Δ-curves.

Let K be any Δ-curve and let K' and K'' be the curves obtained by rotating K through 120° and 240° respectively about some point O. Also let T be any equilateral triangle circumscribed about K. The rotations carry T into triangles T' and T'' circumscribed about K' and K'' respectively (Diagram 330).

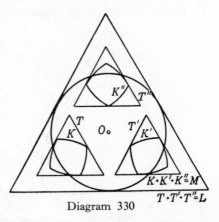

Diagram 330

The altitudes of T' and T'' are equal to h, and the sides of these triangles are parallel to the sides of T. Thus $T + T' + T''$ is an equilateral triangle of altitude $3h$ whose sides have the same directions as those of T (see Exercise 4-7). By Exercise 4-8, the triangle $L = T + T' + T''$ is circumscribed about the curve $M = K + K' + K''$. Thus each equilateral triangle circumscribed about M has the altitude $3h$; that is, M is a Δ-curve of height $3h$. But M is carried into itself by a 120° rotation about O (K goes into K', K' into K'', and K'' into K; and $M = K + K' + K''$ is invariant). Hence M is a circle of radius h (see Exercise 8-8).

Since the length of M ($= 2\pi h$) is the sum of the lengths of K, K', and K'' (see Exercise 4-7) and is therefore three times the length of K, the length of K is $2\pi h/3$ (the Barbier's Theorem for Δ-curves).

8-14. Prove that if the rotation of a curve K through 120° and 240° produces curves K' and K'' respectively such that $K + K' + K''$ is a circle, then K is a Δ-curve.

Let K be a convex curve, let K' and K'' be obtained from K by rotations of 120° and 240° respectively about some point O, and suppose that $M = K + K' + K''$ is a circle of radius h. Let L be an equilateral triangle circumscribed about M, and let T, T', T'' be equilateral triangles circumscribed about the curves K, K', K'' respectively whose sides have the same directions as those of L. The triangles T' and T'' are obtained by rotations of T about O of 120° and 240° respectively; hence $L = T + T' + T''$ (see Exercise 4-8). The altitude of L is $3h$, since it is circumscribed about a circle of radius h. The triangle T is circumscribed about K and its altitude is $\frac{1}{3}$ that of the triangle L, that is $\frac{1}{3}(3h) = h$. Hence K is a Δ-curve of altitude h.

8-15. Prove that the greatest height H and the least height h of a convex curve K satisfy the inequality

$$h \leq H \leq 2h$$

and that $H = h$ if and only if K is a Δ-curve. Prove also that $H = 2h$ if and only if K is an equilateral triangle.

It is obvious, of course, that curves of constant width are characterized by the equation $H = h$ (Δ-curves). If K' and K'' are obtained from K

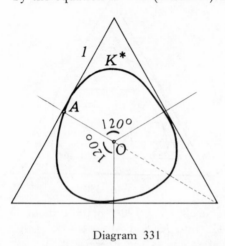

Diagram 331

by rotating K through 120° and 240° respectively, it follows from Exercises 4-7 and 4-8 (*cf.* the solution of Exercise 6-9 b) that $K^* = K + K' + K''$ has in every direction a height three times the greatest height of K; in particular, the greatest and least heights of K^* are $3H$ and $3h$ respectively. Also, K^* has a center of symmetry O of the third order (that is, it is transformed into itself by a rotation of 120° around point O), and the length of K^* is three times that of K (*cf.* the solution of Exercises 6-9 a and b). The distance of any point A of K^* from O cannot exceed H, since otherwise the supporting line l of K^* perpendicular to OA would be at a distance greater than H from O, and the height of K^* in the direction perpendicular to l would be greater than $3H$ (Diagram 331). Hence K^* lies entirely inside the circle S of radius H and center O. On the other hand, K^* is inscribed in an equilateral triangle T of altitude $3H$ with center O, that is, a triangle circumscribed about the circle S. Therefore K^* is circumscribed about the equilateral triangle t whose vertices are the points of contact of T and S. The least height of K^* (and hence the least height of K also) will have the least possible value if K^* coincides with t; then, as is easily seen, $3h = 3H/2$, and K is an equilateral triangle of altitude h (*cf.* Exercise 4-9).

8-16. Prove that: (a) Of all convex curves of given greatest height H, the curves of constant height H (that is, Δ-curves) have the greatest length, and the equilateral triangle of altitude $H/2$ has the least length; (b) Of all convex curves of given height h, the Δ-curves of height h have the least length, and the equilateral triangle of altitude h has the greatest length; (c) Of all convex curves of given greatest height H and given least height h, the greatest length is possessed by the curves that consist of three segments of the sides of an equilateral triangle of altitude h and three arcs of a Δ-curve of height H; the least length is possessed by the curves that consist of three arcs of a Δ-curve of height h and of six segments, which lie respectively on the lines of support at the ends of these arcs, and which intersect by pairs in the vertices of a triangle of greatest height H.

(**a**) Since $K^* = K + K' + K''$ lies entirely inside the circle S of radius H (see the solution of Exercise 8-15), the length of K^* is greatest if K^* coincides with S; K is then a Δ-curve of height H (see Exercise 8-14). Since K^* entirely encloses the equilateral triangle t of altitude $3H/2$ (see solution of Exercise 8-15), the lengths of K^* and K will be least if K coincides with t, and then K is an equilateral triangle of altitude $H/2$.

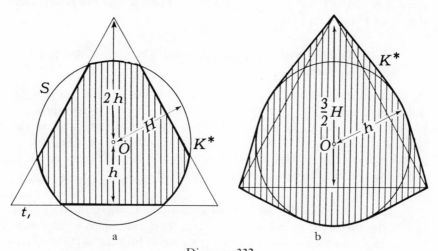

Diagram 332

(**b**) Since a convex curve K of height h must be contained in some equilateral triangle t of altitude h, its length cannot exceed the perimeter of t. The length of K is maximal and is equal to the perimeter of t only if K coincides with t.

Note further that the distance of any point of $K^* = K + K' + K''$ from the center of symmetry O of third order (see solution of Exercise 8-15) cannot be less than h; in fact if $OA < h$, where A is a point of K^*, then the supporting line l through A has a distance from O less than h, and the height of K^* in the direction perpendicular to l is less than $3h$, contrary to the fact that the least height of K^* is $3h$. Hence K^* contains the circle ρ of radius h and center O. The lengths of K^*

and K will be least if K^* coincides with the circle ρ. Then K is a $\varDelta$-curve of height h (see Exercise 8-14).

(c) The curve $K^* = K + K' + K''$ lies entirely in the circle S of radius H with center at O, the center of symmetry of third order of this curve (see the solution of Exercise 8-15). Since the least height of K^* is $3h$, K^* is contained in an equilateral triangle t_1 of altitude $3h$ (with center at the center O of K^*). The lengths of K^* and K are greatest if K^* coincides with the curve (heavily outlined in Diagram 332 a) obtained from the intersection of S and t_1. Then K will have the form shown in Diagram 117 a (page 89).

Moreover, K^* is circumscribed about an equilateral triangle of altitude $3H/2$ (see solution of Exercise 8-15) and lies entirely outside the circle ρ of radius h (see solution to Exercise 8-16 b; the center is the center of the triangle t). Hence K^* has greatest length if it is bounded by segments of the tangents from the vertices of t to the circle ρ and by three arcs of the circle ρ (Diagram 332 b). Then K has the appearance shown in Diagram 117 b.

8-17. Obtain from the Approximation Theorem a new proof of Barbier's Theorem for $\varDelta$-curves.

At the end of the solution to Exercise 8-10 it was established that all $\varDelta$-curves of height h consisting of circular arcs of radius h have the same length, $2\pi h/3$. Since the length of any $\varDelta$-curve K of height h is the limit of the lengths of $\varDelta$-curves of height h consisting of circular arcs of radius h, and since the limit of these curves is K itself (see Section 4, page 50), every $\varDelta$-curve of height h has length $2\pi h/3$.

8-18. Let the altitudes of an equilateral triangle be continued beyond the corresponding vertices; on these extensions let segments be laid off equal to the sides of the triangle. Join the vertices of the triangle by circular arcs circumscribed about the end points of the extended altitudes. Prove that all rectangles circumscribed about the convex curve formed from the three circular arcs have the same perimeter. Compute the length of this curve and the area it bounds if the perimeter of a rectangle circumscribed about the curve is $4l$.

Given an equilateral triangle ABC, let P, Q, and R be the centers of the arcs mentioned in the statement of the exercise, and let K be the curve formed by these arcs (Diagram 333). We shall determine the angles of this curve at the corner points A, B, and C. Draw the altitude CH of the triangle and the segments AP and BP, where P is the center of the arc AB. Then $\sphericalangle APC = \frac{1}{2} \sphericalangle ACH$ (the triangle ACP is isosceles).

Hence $\sphericalangle APC = 15° = \sphericalangle PAC$ and $\sphericalangle APB = 30°$. Thus AP is a tangent to arc AC (the angle between the segment AC and the tangent to the arc AC at A is 15°). The angle at A between the tangents AP and AR to the arcs AC and AB is 90°. Hence all three vertices of K lie on the boundary of each rectangle circumscribed about K, for three sides of the circumscribed rectangle pass through A, B, and C, and the fourth side touches one of the circular arcs.

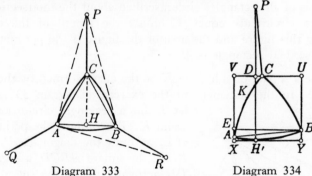

Diagram 333 Diagram 334

Now let $UVXY$ be a rectangle circumscribed about K such that XY touches the arc AB of K at H' (Diagram 334). We draw the segment $H'P$ (P is the center for arc AB) which intersects the side UV of the rectangle at the point D. Finally we draw BE parallel to XY and UV. Then the right triangles ABE and CPD are congruent (hypotenuse and angle equal hypotenuse and angle); hence $DP = BE = XY$. Thus

$$PH' = PD + DH' = XY + YU.$$

This expression is the semiperimeter of the rectangle $UVXY$. Thus the perimeter of every rectangle circumscribed about K is $2PA$.

If the perimeter of the circumscribed rectangle is $4l$, then the radii of the arcs forming K is $2l$ and the central angle of each arc is 30° (see above). Thus the length of K is one-fourth the circumference of a circle of radius $2l$, that is, πl.

In order to compute the area bounded by K, let a denote the common length of the sides of triangle ABC. Then we have (Diagram 333)

$$PH = a + \frac{a\sqrt{3}}{2} = a\left(\frac{2+\sqrt{3}}{2}\right),$$

$$PA = \sqrt{PH^2 + AH^2} = a\sqrt{2+\sqrt{3}} = 2l.$$

$$a = \frac{2l}{\sqrt{2+\sqrt{3}}} = 2l\sqrt{2-\sqrt{3}}.$$

The area bounded by K is the sum of the areas of the three circular segments, whose chords have length a, and the area of triangle ABC; that is

$$l^2(\pi - 3) + l^2\sqrt{3}\,(2 - \sqrt{3}) = l^2(\pi + 2\sqrt{3} - 6) \approx 0.60l^2.$$

8-19. Two circles are drawn about the opposite vertices of a square with radii equal to the side of the square. Prove that the perimeters of all rectangles circumscribed about the intersection of these two circles are equal. Compute the length of the curve bounding this figure and the area of the figure if the perimeter of a circumscribed rectangle is $4l$.

Let $ABCD$ be a square of side l, let K be the curve formed by the two arcs BD given in the statement of the exercise (Diagram 335), and

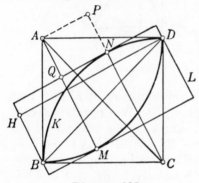

Diagram 335

let L be a rectangle circumscribed about K. To compute the perimeter of L, we draw the diagonals AC and BD of the square $ABCD$, a segment DH perpendicular to the side of the rectangle through D, and the segments AM and CN, where M and N are the points of contact of the sides of L with the arcs of K (M lies on the arc about A, and N lies on the arc about C). Let AM intersect the side of L through N in the point Q. Finally we draw the segment AP perpendicular to the line CN at P.

From the congruence of right triangles CAP and BDH (hypotenuse and angle equal), we conclude that $DH = CP$. The perimeter of L is

$$2(DH + QM) = 2(CP + QM).$$

It is evident that

$$QM = AM - AQ, \qquad CP = CN + NP = AM + AQ,$$
$$CP + QM = 2AM,$$

so the perimeter of L equals $4AM$ and also equals $4l$.

The length of K equals πl. The area bounded by K is the difference between the sum of the areas of the two circular sectors of radius l and central angle 90° and the area of the square $ABCD$, that is,

$$\frac{\pi l^2}{2} - l^2 = l^2\left(\frac{\pi}{2} - 1\right) \approx 0.57l^2.$$

8-20. If all the rectangles circumscribed about a convex curve K have perimeter $4l$, then the length of K is πl.

Let $ABCD$ and $A'B'C'D'$ be two rectangles circumscribed about a curve K, each with perimeter $4l$. The eight sides of these rectangles form an octagon circumscribed about K. Let $MNPQ$ be a rectangle circumscribed about K with a side perpendicular to the bisector of one of the angles of the octagon (Diagram 336). The rectangle $MNPQ$ cuts off from the octagon four similar triangles T_1, T_2, T_3 and T_4 (shaded in the diagram). We now show that the sum of the

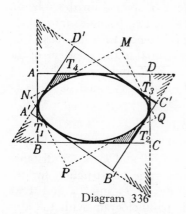

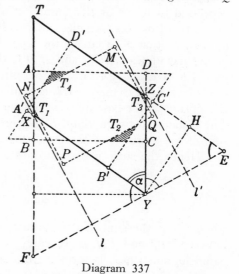

Diagram 336   Diagram 337

altitudes of th se triangles depends only on l and the angle formed by corresponding sides of the rectangles $ABCD$ and $A'B'C'D'$.

To prove this, we consider the parallelogram formed by the lines $A'B'$, AB, $C'D'$, and CD and the parallelogram formed by $B'C'$, BC, $A'D'$, and AD. As can be seen from Diagram 336, each side from a pair of adjacent sides of one of the rectangles is an altitude of one of the parallelograms; hence the sum of the four altitudes of the two parallelograms is $4l$. The sides of the first parallelogram are intersected by the lines MN and PQ, the sides of the second by the lines NP and MQ (Diagram 336). The sum of the distances between MN and PQ and between MQ and NP (the semiperimeter of the rectangle $MNPQ$) is $2l$.

Now we consider the parallelogram $XYZT$ and its sides intersecting the lines MQ and NP. By construction, these lines are parallel to the bisectors of the opposite angles of the parallelogram (Diagram 337). Through the vertices X and Z of the parallelogram, which are also respective vertices of the triangles T_1 and T_3 cut off from $XYZT$, we draw lines l and l' parallel to PN and MQ. The sum of the altitudes of

T_1 and T_3 is obviously equal to the difference of the distance between the lines l and l' and the distance between the lines PN and MQ. Through the vertex Y, we draw a line perpendicular to l and l' which meets the extensions of TZ and TX at the points E and F respectively. The sum of the altitudes constructed on the sides of the two similar isosceles triangles YZE and YXF equals the sum of the altitudes of the parallelogram $XYZT$. The sum of the bases YE and FY of the triangles (that is, twice the distance between l and l') can easily be expressed in terms of this sum. Let α denote the known vertex angle of the two isosceles triangles YZE and YXF (this angle equals $\sphericalangle XYZ$ of $XYZT$; that is, it equals the angle between the sides $A'B'$ and DC of the rectangles $ABCD$ and $A'B'C'D'$). Then the angle between the base YE of triangle YZE and the altitude YH erected on the side ZE is $\alpha/2$ (the right triangle YHE is similar to the two triangles into which the altitude to the base divides triangle YZE); hence $YE = YH/\cos(\alpha/2)$. The distance between l and l' is therefore equal to the quotient of the sum of the altitudes of the parallelogram $XYZT$ and $2\cos\alpha/2$.

Hence the sum of the altitudes of T_1 and T_2 is equal to

$$\frac{H_1}{2\cos\alpha/2} - h_1,$$

where H_1 is the sum of the altitudes of $XYZT$ and h_1 is the distance between MQ and PN. If we carry out the same construction for the parallelogram which is formed from the sides of T_2 and T_4, and if we note that the sum of the altitudes of this parallelogram with the altitudes of $XYZT$ is $4l$ and that the distance between MN and PQ plus the distance between PN and MQ is $2l$, we see that the sum of the altitudes of the four triangles T_1, T_2, T_3, and T_4 is equal to

$$2l\left(\frac{1}{\cos\alpha/2} - 1\right) = \frac{2l(1 - \cos\alpha/2)}{\cos\alpha/2}.$$

Now let O be a circle of radius $\frac{1}{2}l$. The perimeter of any square circumscribed about O is $4l$. We circumscribe rectangles about K and O; the perimeters of these rectangles are equal. We also consider new rectangles circumscribed about O and K whose sides are perpendicular to the bisectors of the angles of the original rectangles. The sum of the altitudes of the triangles cut off from the original rectangle is the same for O and K, and the resulting octagons have the same perimeter. (We leave it to the reader to carry out the argument for himself; the argument is somewhat simpler than that given above.) The perimeters of equiangular polygons of 2^n sides circumscribed about O and K are equal for all $n = 2, 3, \ldots$. This is proved by induction. Suppose that the perimeters of equiangular polygons of 2^{n-1} sides circumscribed about

K and O are equal. We can then show that the perimeters of equiangular polygons of 2^n sides circumscribed about O and K are equal (cf. the solution of Exercise 7-11).

Then, using limits, it is easy to deduce that K and O have the same length, namely, πl.

8-21. If the perimeters of all rectangles circumscribed about a convex curve K are equal, then $K + K'$ is a curve of constant width if K' is obtained from K by a 90° rotation; conversely, if $K + K'$ is a curve of constant width, and K' is obtained from K by a 90° rotation, then the perimeters of all rectangles that are circumscribed about the convex curve K are equal. Obtain from this statement of a new proof of the generalization of Barbier's Theorem. What is $K + K'$ if K is the curve of Exercise 8-18 or the curve of Exercise 8-19?

Let K_1 be a curve such that all of its circumscribed rectangles have perimeter $4l$. Let K_1' be obtained from K by a 90° rotation about a certain point O. Also, let K be the sum of K_1 and K_1', and let L be any rectangle circumscribed about K (Diagram 338). Consider the rectangles L_1 and L_1' whose sides are parallel to those of L and which are circumscribed about K_1 and K_1' respectively.

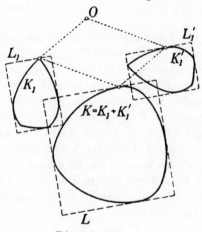

Diagram 338

Obviously L_1' is obtained from L_1 by rotation through 90° about O; the perimeter of L_1 is $4l$, in view of the property of K_1. It follows from the definition of the addition of polygons (see Exercise 4-7) that $L_1 + L_1'$ is a square of side $2l$. By Exercise 4-8 we have $L = L_1 + L_1'$. Thus we see that every rectangle L circumscribed about K is a square of side $2l$; hence K is a curve of constant width $2l$.

Conversely, let $K = K_1 + K_1'$, where K_1' is obtained from K_1 by rotation through 90° about some point O, and suppose that K is a curve of constant width $2l$. Let L_1 be any rectangle circumscribed about K_1. When L_1 is rotated through 90° about O, a rectangle L_1' is obtained which is circumscribed about K_1'. Obviously the sides of L_1 and L_1' have the same directions. Hence by Exercise 4-8, $L = L_1 + L_1'$ is a rectangle circumscribed about K. Since K has constant width, L must be a square of side $2l$. The perimeter of the square L is equal to the sum of the perimeters of the rectangles L_1 and L_1' (see Exercise 4-7), and since L_1 and L_1' are congruent (L_1' is obtained from L by a 90° rotation about O), the perimeter of L is twice that of L_1. Thus all rectangles L_1 circumscribed about K_1 have the same perimeter; that is, $4 \cdot 2l/2 = 4l$.

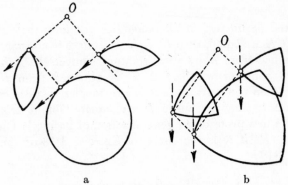

Diagram 339

From this result and from Barbier's Theorem for curves of constant width (see Exercise 7-11; also the proof of Barbier's Theorem contained in Exercise 7-15), the generalization of Barbier's Theorem follows directly. Congruent curves K_1 and K_1' whose sum K is a curve of constant width have, of course, the same length. By Barbier's Theorem, the length of K equals $2\pi l$, and the sum of the lengths of K_1 and K_1' equals the length of K (see Section 4, page 46). Therefore twice the length of K_1 is $2\pi l$ and the length of K_1 is πl.

We leave it to the reader to show that $K_1 + K_1'$ must be a circle if K_1 is the curve in Exercise 8-19 (Diagram 339 a), and that if K_1 is the curve in Exercise 8-18) then $K_1 + K_1'$ is a Reuleaux triangle (Diagram 339 b).

BIBLIOGRAPHY

Aleksandrov, A. D.: *Die innere Geometrie der konvexen Flächen* (The interior geometry of convex surfaces). Akademie-Verlag, Berlin, 1955.

Aleksandrov, A. D.: *Vypuklye Mnogogrannika* (Convex polyhedra). Gostehizdat, Moscow-Leningrad, 1950.

Aleksandrov, P. S.: *Kombinatornaya Topologiya* (Combinatorial topology). Gostehizdat, Moscow-Leningrad, 1947.

Blaschke, W.: *Kreis und Kugel* (Circle and sphere). W. de Gruyter, Berlin, 1956.

Bonnesen, T. and Fenchel, W.: *Theorie der konvexen Körper* (Theory of convex bodies). Ergebnisse der Mathematik und ihrer Grenzgebiete 3, Berlin, 1934.

Courant, R. and Robbins, H.: *What Is Mathematics?* Oxford University Press, New York, 1941.

Delone, B. N. and Žitomirskiĭ, O. K.: *Zadačnika po Geometrii* (Collection of exercises in geometry). Moscow-Leningrad, 1950.

Dukor, I. G.: "K teoreme Helli o sovokupnosti vypuklyh tel c obščimi točkami" (On Helly's Theorem about the set of convex bodies with common points). Uspehi mat. nauk, vol. X, 1944.

Filippov, A. F.: "Èlementarnoe dokazateľstvo teoremy Žordana" (An elementary proof of the Jordan Curve Theorem). Uspehi mat. nauk, vol. V, 5, 1950.

Helly, E.: "Über die Menge konvexer Körper mit gemeinsamen Punkten" (On the set of convex bodies with common points). Jahresberichte der Deutschen Mathematiker-Vereinigung, vol. 32, 1923.

Kamenetskiĭ, I. M.: "Rešenie geometričeskoĭ zadači L. Lyusternika" (The solution of a geometrical problem of L. Lyusternik). Uspehi mat. nauk, vol II, 2, 1947.

Kryžanovskiĭ, D. A.: *Izoperimetry* (Isoperimetry). Moscow-Leningrad, 1938.

Lyusternik, L. A.: *Vypuklye tela* (Convex bodies). Moscow-Leningrad, 1941.

Rademacher, H. and Schoenberg, I. J.: "Helly's Theorems on Convex Domains and Tschebyscheff's Approximation Problem." *Canadian Journal of Mathematics*, vol. 2, 1950.

Rademacher, H. and Toeplitz, O.: *The Enjoyment of Mathematics* (translated by H. S. Zuckerman). Princeton University Press, 1957.

Radon, J.: "Mengen konvexer Körper, die einen gemeinsamen Punkt enthalten" (Sets of convex bodies which have a common point). *Annals of Mathematics*, vol. 83, 1921.

Šklyarskiĭ, D. O. et al.: "Izbrannye zadači i teoremy èlementarnoĭ matematiki" (Selected problems and theorems of elementary mathematics), vol. 1, Gostehizdat, Moscow-Leningrad, 1950.

Šnirel'man, L. G.: "O ravnomernyh približeniyah" (On uniform approximations). Izvestiya nauk (mathematical series), vol. 2, 1938.

Šnirel'man, L. G.: "O nekotoryh geometričeskih svoĭstvah zamknutyh krivyh" (On some geometric properties of closed curves). Uspehi mat. nauk, vol. X, 1944.

Scholanter, M.: "On Certain Minimum Problems in the Theory of Convex Curves." *Transactions of the American Mathematical Society*, vol. 73, no. 1, 1952.

Vol'pert, È. I.: "Èlementarnoe dokazateľstvo teoremy Žordana" (An elementary proof of the Jordan Curve Theorem). Uspehi mat. nauk, vol. V, 5, 1950.

INDEX

INDEX